A GUIDE
TO THE LITERATURE
OF CHEMISTRY

SECOND EDITION

A GUIDE
TO THE LITERATURE
OF CHEMISTRY

E. J. CRANE
Director and Editor
The Chemical Abstracts Service

AUSTIN M. PATTERSON
Formerly Professor of Chemistry
Antioch College, Ohio

ELEANOR B. MARR
Assistant Professor of Chemistry
Hunter College, New York

New York · **JOHN WILEY & SONS, Inc.**
London · **CHAPMAN & HALL, Ltd.**

Dedicated to

AUSTIN M. PATTERSON

FOREWORD

This edition is primarily the work of Dr. Eleanor B. Marr, who consented to do the work when the authors of the first edition gave up hope of finding time for this big task.

Miss Marr, who teaches a course in chemical literature at Hunter College in New York City, had built up extensive files of information in the field of this book. This information, brought up to date and extended, makes the second edition a fuller record by far than was the first edition.

The completed manuscript was edited with some revision by the original authors so that, while Miss Marr is now the principal author, the authors of the first edition, with appreciation of her work, have contributed enough from their wide experience with chemical literature to make this in a restricted sense a three-author product.

When time for a third edition comes, the book will be completely Miss Marr's. Before his death, Austin M. Patterson spoke warmly of his appreciation of her thorough work and I am sure that he would join me now in such an expression. The book is moving into good hands.

E. J. CRANE

February, 1957

PREFACE
TO SECOND EDITION

The first edition of *A Guide to the Literature of Chemistry* was the first comprehensive book to appear in its field. Dr. Crane and Dr. Patterson performed a great service for the profession of chemistry when they prepared this scholarly work in 1927. I consider it an honor to have been asked to join them in writing the second edition. I gratefully acknowledge the assistance given me by Dr. Crane and Dr. Patterson.

Before I comment on the second edition, I wish to call attention to the preface to the first edition, which is reprinted in part, and the foreword to the second edition.

Points that cannot be overemphasized are the vital role that the literature plays in the development of chemistry, the advantages of consulting the literature to obtain the answers to many questions and to put research on a firm foundation, and the importance of learning the nature of the literature and how to use it by students majoring in chemistry.

The great abundance and variety of recorded chemical information and the accelerated rate at which the literature is growing make use of the literature difficult. Many have pointed out the need for a comprehensive and up-to-date guide to the literature.

The second edition of the *Guide* is intended to be used both as a reference work and as a textbook. Its coverage of the field of chemical literature is comprehensive and I have endeavored to document and index it thoroughly. Some changes were made in the galley proof to have the book as up to date as possible when it comes off the press.

The textbook features include discussions of basic principles and topics, emphasis on how to use each form of chemical literature, and an introduction to the art of literature searching.

The method of organizing the material that was used in the first edition has been retained for the most part in the second edition. The material in the appendixes has been treated in a different way to save space. The entire book was rewritten and two chapters were added, one on trade literature and the other on government publications of interest to chemists and chemical industry. Material retained from the first edition was brought up to date.

To keep the length of the new edition within reasonable limits many topics have been treated in a condensed fashion. This edition of the *Guide* (1) contains the most frequently used information, (2) gives sources where additional information can be found, (3) gives sources of less frequently used information, and (4) points out methods whereby one can keep up to date on the literature and on methods of using it.

Enumeration of all the differences between two editions that have a thirty-year time interval between them would take too much space. However, a few other differences will be considered briefly.

The book list in Chapter 2 is not as comprehensive as the one that appeared as Appendix 8 of the first edition was when it was compiled in 1927. To publish a bibliography of such scope today would require an entire book. Several comprehensive bibliographies on chemistry and science have appeared in recent years and means for locating books have improved. Accordingly, only a sufficient number of books have been listed in Chapter 2 to show the general nature of the books available today and to provide basic reference material for the use of students and of those who are not specialists in a given field of chemistry. The books listed were selected from a file that I have maintained for some time by use of one or more of the following criteria: (1) books generally considered to be standard reference works, (2) my personal knowledge of the content of the book, (3) purchase by outstanding chemical libraries in New York City, and (4) reviews.

The descriptions of the journals of greatest chemical interest listed in Chapter 3 are much briefer, with the exception of the major abstract journals, than descriptions were in the first edition. The large number of journals that were added to the list in the second edition made brief comments necessary. However, particular attention was given to listing collective indexes and to giving the changes that have occurred in the names of important journals throughout most of their existence.

Chapter 8, "Procedure in Literature Searches," is very different and, in my experience, should be much more useful for initiating chemists into the art of literature searching than the chapter on the same subject in the first edition has been.

ELEANOR B. MARR

February, 1957

PREFACE
TO FIRST EDITION

The literature of chemistry is like a great, inspiring mountain with a core of rich ore. It is inspiring because the work of great men, of many earnest investigators, is recorded there. To obtain anything like full profit in its use one must learn how to climb this mountain and must know where and how to dig for the ore he needs. With the help of the many successful chemists who have generously contributed the results of their experience, we have attempted in this book to point the way. Experience in editing *Chemical Abstracts* has aided us. The various sources of chemical information have been classified, discussed generally and described specifically, and methods of use have been outlined. Certain types of information have been put in appendixes in a form which it is hoped will serve for convenient reference.

It has been our thought that the information on chemical literature, as here assembled and arranged, should be useful not alone to the student in college who is endeavoring to acquire proficiency in the chemical library as well as in the laboratory, but also to the chemist of wider experience. The literature has been produced for the service of others, for much greater use than it receives. Improved efficiency of an individual in making searches saves time, adds resource, and makes for the bigger kind of progress which results from scientific advances, along with the personal gain made.

The literature of chemistry is international. It has been treated so. In certain spots, however, as in the libraries described, it has seemed unavoidable and not altogether unfitting that the book should have an American leaning.

The reader is asked to excuse the rather frequent reference to *Chemical Abstracts*. From its nature it is the American publication most intimately associated with chemical literature searches and the one best known to us and probably also to most of those who may use this book; it has therefore been easiest and perhaps most effective to draw on it now and then for examples to illustrate points discussed.

E. J. CRANE
AUSTIN M. PATTERSON

March 12, 1927

CONTENTS

CHAPTER 1

THE PROBLEM
AND OBJECTIVES

INTRODUCTION

Since the human mind is capable of storing only a limited amount of information it is preeminently desirable that a part of it consist of a thorough knowledge of how to obtain recorded information when needed. The greatest genius cannot afford to neglect taking advantage of all that is already known in his field. A worker can now know intimately only a small part of even his own branch of chemistry. Acquaintance with the sources of information, intimate in the case of publications of the greatest interest and value to the individual, and a good knowledge of methods of searching are invaluable attainments. Skill in the library has not had as much emphasis as skill in the laboratory, but it is just as worthy of effort. In recent years there has been a distinct awakening as to this situation, accompanied by renewed and extensive efforts more effectively to solve the problems presented.

Human progress is made by cooperation, and a great factor for progress in this scientific and industrial age is research. Cooperation in research is effected chiefly by means of the literature. A notably fine spirit of cooperation and service among men of science and industry prompts the publication of the results and conclusions from their experiments and experiences for the benefit of all.

Although the spirit of laboratory research ought never to be discouraged, there is need for more great minds to be devoted to the correlation, interpretation, and application of recorded facts. The production of chemical literature has run ahead of use; we fall far short of full assimilation and interpretation of available records.

1

Scientific literature grows approximately in proportion to the increase in scientific and technical research. Generated in part by the problems of World War II and in part by the dependence of the modern economy and its way of life on scientific knowledge, there has been a tremendous surge in research activities during the past dozen years. Research expenditures have increased at least five-fold in ten years. Along with this growth has come a much stronger realization of the need to record and key the rapidly accumulating information in such a way as to keep it available and useful. Respect has increased for those who help in this recording, information organization, and utilization. Such workers, in industry, in government, in universities, and in the more generally useful publishing field, have responded actively. They have increased their own research to find new and more effective methods, as well as to improve existing abstracting, indexing, and like services. The problem is being attacked in various ways.

Many American universities are giving courses in the use of chemical literature. A survey of Johoda [1] shows that often chemical students are required to take these courses. It can be added that for the individual who likes chemistry at a desk as contrasted with chemistry in the laboratory good careers in chemical literature work are now available.

A great deal of attention is being paid to the development of scientific aids for literature searching; these include a variety of machines and other devices. The mechanical aids save time in certain types of searches, particularly for limited fields searched most effectively by the builders of specific mechanized systems, but they do not replace the human mind.

The Division of Chemical Literature of the American Chemical Society, formed in 1949, presents many valuable papers at the meetings of the Society; most of these are published and are very helpful to those who work with chemical literature.

The improvement of the abstracting and indexing of scientific literature to aid in its utilization is also receiving much attention. UNESCO is serving in various ways, as by helping to standardize practices, to provide translating aids, and to assist backward or handicapped countries by supporting the development of title lists and other guiding means for locating and acquiring published material. The UNESCO International Conference on Science Abstracting held in Paris, June 20–25, 1949, did much to stimulate thinking and planning. The final report of this conference was published by the Columbia University Press, New York, in 1951. UNESCO is not in a position to obtain or publish abstracts.

The International Abstracting Board (IAB) organized in 1949 by the International Council of Scientific Unions on a recommendation by UNESCO, first to aid in the field of physics, was expanded to cover chemistry in 1954.[2] This board does not prepare abstracts, but aids member abstracting journals in various other ways. *Chemical Abstracts* is the IAB representative of chemistry for the English language.

The First International Congress on Documentation of Applied Chemistry was held in London, England, on November 22–25, 1955, with active participation by American chemists.

The documentation societies and institutes, which exist in many countries, devote a large proportion of their work to improving the methods of recording, publishing, disseminating, and retrieving scientific information from the records and literature; to improving the abstracting and indexing of scientific literature; and to organizing scientific information so it can be used more effectively. Many of these societies publish journals that are useful in keeping up with their work; some information about these periodicals is given on page 330.

The American Documentation Institute was organized in 1937 by a chemist, Watson Davis, and many chemists have participated in its considerable accomplishments.

The International Federation for Documentation (FID) is the organization through which the documentation societies and institutes in the various countries cooperate and work on problems of mutual concern. FID also devotes a considerable amount of its work to improving science documentation and to making scientific information more accessible and consequently more useful. Some of FID's most valuable activities are the maintenance of a card file of current abstracting and indexing services and the abstract and indexing periodicals that they publish. *Index Bibliographicus*, 3rd ed., published jointly by FID and UNESCO, is a guide to the current abstract and indexing periodicals; Volume I is devoted to the sciences. The American Documentation Institute is the adhering body to FID for the United States.

Science documentation centers have been established in many European countries; some of them are organized on a national basis and provide very extensive services to scientists, including the publication of abstract journals and indexing periodicals. Some European countries have limited funds for laboratories and experimental research, and all place a very high value on the scientific literature to find the solutions to their problems. Walter Southern, in a paper entitled *European Chemical Documentation Services*,[3] gives an excellent summary of, and a considerable amount of detailed information about, the work and services of the documentation centers in nearly all of the countries of Europe.

Science documentation centers have also been established in several countries in Asia, Africa, and South America with the help of UNESCO. For the most part these centers are in countries where funds for laboratory research are decidedly limited, and a concerted effort is being made to utilize the scientific literature to the fullest degree. Among these centers are the Mexican Scientific and Technical Documentation Center, which is now publishing a science indexing periodical in the Spanish language (see page 280), and the national center for India.

Still another sign and accomplishment in the picture of modern effort for better chemical documentation is to be found in the much wider interest and activity of the past dozen years in chemical nomenclature development. Such activity has been especially strong in the United States and international cooperation has increased.

While *Chemical Abstracts* has always done research work from time to time to improve its methods, this investigational activity was markedly increased in 1954 and still more in 1956 after entry into the new *Chemical Abstracts* building completed on The Ohio State University campus in the fall of 1955. Space for a separate research department is provided in this building.

A partial solution of the problem of the utilization of the chemical literature is specialization. There is a growing tendency for research groups to include one or more chemists who devote themselves exclusively to literature searching and to making recorded information more readily available to their colleagues. Individual industrial concerns have also discovered that their own records need improvement to prevent waste from inadequate utilization of the information accumulated and kept within their own doors.

PURPOSES OF SEARCHES

A good knowledge of the literature and of how to use it is worth while for many reasons.

The immediate reason for a literature search is likely to be to gain information for a more or less definite specific purpose if someone else has discovered and published what is needed. Lack of a supply of information as complete as the records will provide is likely to result in (1) the use of inferior apparatus and experimental methods, (2) poorly planned investigations, and (3) useless duplication. The literature is the foundation of every scientific inquiry of importance. Most scientific workers are glad to aid in the advancement of science and realize that there is a direct connection between knowledge of the literature and scientific progress. Stature as a scientist is at stake in the use or neglect of the library.

The literature is not solely a storehouse of facts. It supplies new ideas, new viewpoints, and a broader vision. Most of it is the product of earnest research workers. Great men have usually found time to write. Familiarity with the literature of one's subject is the only way possible of acquiring the proper historical perspective.

OBSTACLES

Aside from the question of personal skill in making searches of the literature there are several obstacles that stand in the way of the greatest efficiency.

In the first place the **state of the literature** is none too good. A satisfactory information service in any science should enable the individual to obtain all of the available information needed with a minimum expenditure of time and effort, and it should make it possible for him to keep in touch with general developments in his field. This service should include (1) journals devoted to full papers, (2) a complete abstract journal that is scientifically and adequately indexed, (3) periodic surveys and reviews, and (4) summaries in convenient form for reference purposes (reference books, handbooks, tables). Chemistry is better equipped with facilities of this sort than are other sciences, but there are omissions and faults, as will be pointed out later. The patent literature is classed with journals publishing original papers in chemistry, and the abstract journal must cover patents to be complete.

The heterogeneous character of the literature affects the efficiency of searches. The different kinds of printed sources might be considered to include:

(a) Original articles
(b) Patents
(c) Abstracts
(d) Treatises
(e) Bibliographies

(f) Reviews
(g) Indexes
(h) Dictionaries
(i) Tables
(j) Trade catalogs, bulletins, and advertisements

These may be issued in various forms—as books, journals, pamphlets, cards, microcards, microfilm, or motion pictures. Some may be published in large numbers and widely distributed; others, such as dissertations, may be comparatively inaccessible. Each kind will be discussed separately in succeeding chapters.

The great abundance of recorded information makes chemical literature searching difficult, and the quantity of this literature is growing at an accelerated rate. Except for World War periods, this growth has continued during many years. A measure of chemical literature growth is pictured in the accompanying graph, based on the numbers of abstracts of papers published annually by *Chemical Abstracts* since its beginning in 1907. It will be noted that in approximately half a century the literature of chemistry has increased about ten-fold. *Chemical Abstracts* has always endeavored to cover the chemical literature completely.

In 1954 *Chemical Abstracts* published 67,606 abstracts of papers

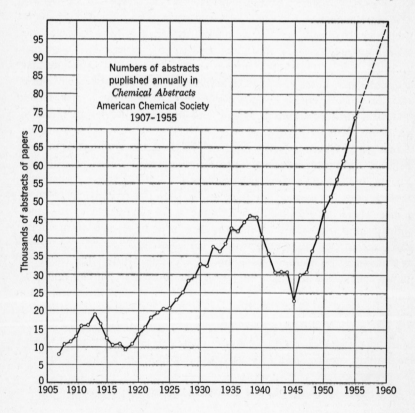

and 11,083 abstracts of patents; it announced 1,926 new books.
Those interested in the numbers of abstracts for other specific years
or in the distribution of abstracts by the classifying sections can
obtain this information from the annual reports of the editor of
Chemical Abstracts (in the Proceedings of the American Chemical
Society during the earlier years, and in *Chemical and Engineering
News,* usually a February number, since 1938).

For the abstracting of all of the papers containing new information
of chemical interest, *Chemical Abstracts* systematically examines over
7,000 scientific, technical, and trade periodicals at the present time.

When one considers these facts it is difficult to avoid a "swamped"
feeling unless he knows pretty thoroughly how to select and to use
the parts of the literature that may be needed.

Distribution of the chemical literature is a great problem. Research activity has been spreading rapidly during the last decade or
two with resulting inauguration and growth of chemical publication
in parts of the world formerly inactive or relatively so. *Chemical
Abstracts* now covers publications that originate in 87 different countries. For the most part chemists must rely on libraries and documentation centers to store and share published information. Abstract
journals and indexing periodicals direct attention to this rapidly
accumulating literature, and photocopying by libraries and other
agencies is a great help in distributing it. Providing still better
facilities for connecting producer and consumer constitutes one of
the great needs of science.

Language limitations present big obstacles. Something like forty
different languages are used in the publication of chemical papers.
No one individual can be expected to read all of them. American
chemists are not as good linguists as the chemists of some other parts
of the world, as Europe. Fortunately for Americans and for their
colleagues in the British Commonwealth, a large proportion of chemical publication is now appearing in the English language. As shown
in statistics by Crane,[4] something more than a third of the chemical
papers published are now appearing in America with enough additional papers appearing in the British Commonwealth to carry the
figure to over one-half. In addition there is a strong tendency for
Scandinavian and Japanese chemists to publish in English. Papers
in English appear scattered in other places, as in Swiss journals.
Books and other forms of chemical literature are also published in
many languages.

The leading position of the English language in chemical publications is of comparatively recent origin. Up to about 1930, the German language was the predominate one.

Probably four-fifths of the world's original chemical publication is now emanating from the United States, the British Commonwealth, Germany, France, Japan, and Russia. This means that English, German, French, Japanese, and Russian are the languages it is most important for chemists to know. Italian, Dutch, and Spanish would follow these. Japanese and Russian present special difficulties, as is well known. Americans rarely learn to read Japanese, but a good many Americans are learning to read Russian. Of course, in dealing with chemical literature it is helpful to be a good linguist, but the modern tendency is to depend more and more on the help of others to a reasonable degree instead of learning numerous languages. Every literature searcher should at least know English, German, and French; and, if possible, Russian. The USSR periodicals use only Russian; the former practice of using French or German has ended.

Language obstacles present themselves even if a translation can be obtained. If a translation is involved, there are at least four chances for the final user to get the wrong meaning: (1) the original writer may not express himself properly, (2) the translator may make an error, at least as to some finer shade of meaning, (3) the translator may express himself poorly, and (4) the final user may misinterpret some part of the translation.

The foreign language difficulty is not the only language obstacle in the dissemination of knowledge. Individuals in varying degrees are limited in their abilities to express ideas and facts in any language. Some scientists, careful as experimenters, are careless in choice of words and in phraseology in reporting their results. Exactly obtained results are inexactly described and discussed. Even though a writer may be a very careful one, the language which he uses will have limitations of expression. Words change in meaning with time and place. Occasionally, as in patents, self-interest affects truthfulness of expression, or legal phraseology obscures meaning for the scientist. The intricacies of chemical nomenclature make exactness difficult in chemical papers. Nomenclature is discussed in Chapter 8, Indexes.

DIRECT COMMUNICATION

Although the published record is of necessity the most prolific source of information, this general preliminary discussion would be incomplete if mention were not made of direct communication with other workers either verbally or by correspondence. This common practice of the early days is naturally diminishing in proportion to other methods of communication; it is justified in special circumstances. It constitutes one of the great advantages of attending scientific meetings; there is time for such discussions then—discussions usually of mutual value. To discuss a subject with a specialist for an hour may be worth as much as reading about it for days. Also, there are certain types of information that are obtainable only by direct communication. The more formal discussions, during meetings, of papers read is an analogous method of benefit to all assembled, but unfortunately crowded meeting programs are causing this good practice to diminish.

Lectures, exhibitions, motion pictures, television, and radio also serve in the dissemination of chemical information, particularly to the general public.

KINDS OF SEARCHES

The reasons that prompt chemical literature searches are many. Needs and points of view may vary greatly. Searches by the research chemist, the chemical literature specialist, the student, the writer, the bibliographer, the manufacturer, and the patent investigator are likely to differ considerably. The object of the search may be a specific bit of information, as the boiling point of benzene, or it may be an extensive one on the present state of knowledge of a more or less general topic. Chemical manufacturers may require a great variety of business and legal information in addition to chemical information. No hard and fast rule of procedure in searching can be laid down. This subject is taken up more fully in Chapter 10, Procedure in Literature Searches.

PLAN OF THIS BOOK

The three important points of view in considering the literature of chemistry are those of production, distribution, and use.

Use receives the main emphasis in this book. Some consideration of production and distribution is included because these affect use. The various kinds of sources of chemical information are analyzed. The important journals, books, and other publications are described and classified. Ways of keeping up to date on the various sources of information are given. Libraries and indexes are discussed in relation to literature searches. The Appendixes are intended to supply information to answer many little questions that arise in literature searches. Methods of searching the literature are emphasized.

The authors hope this information will not only be of help in searches, but will also create a greater appreciation of chemical literature searching as an art and will aid in the mastering of it. Practice and experience will be necessary.

LITERATURE CITED

(1) Johoda, Gerald, "University Instruction in Chemical Literature," *J. Chem. Educ.* **30,** 245–246 (1953).
(2) Crane, E. J., *Chem. Eng. News* **33,** 995 (1955).
(3) Southern, Walter, *Library Quarterly* **25,** 235–242 (1955).
(4) Crane, E. J., *Chem. Eng. News* **29,** 4251 (1951); **31,** 864 (1953).

CHAPTER 2

BOOKS

THE USES OF CHEMICAL BOOKS

Chemical books have most important uses. They introduce the novice to the general field of the science or of some part of it, explain new theories in the light of already known facts, and help to coordinate and systematize knowledge. They furnish information, exhaustive or not, in a form adapted for quick reference, and guide the searcher back to the original source by means of citations. Historical works record the development of the science, popular books initiate the public into its mysteries and elicit interest and support, and treatises on the various fields of chemistry give the reader the benefit of the long experience or combined researches of many workers. Who shall say that the chemist can depend on journals alone? The mere fact that nearly two thousand new books of chemical interest are published annually proves the demand for them.

Books offer convenient **starting points** in many literature searches. If the subject is new to the searcher, he will naturally read a general discussion of the topic, if such exists, then turn to the more detailed treatises, and finally find his way into the journal literature.

On the other hand, if he is looking for some definite fact, a book may give exactly what he wants and his search ends.

The general advantage of books as starting points are convenience of reference and, in most cases, more or less logical classification of the subject. Their disadvantage is that they are out of date by the time they are printed and hence must be supplemented by the more recent journals. This is notably true for any subject that is undergo-

11

ing a rapid development, as, for example, the chemistry related to atomic energy or polymerization and plastics.

Ultimately the chemist depends on the original published sources for his information, and he will go back to these in every search of any magnitude. Usually the original source is a journal article or a patent, but it may be a thesis, bulletin, or some other form of separate publication. Occasionally it may be a book. New contributions of either theory or fact are rarely published in book form by authors at present. **Most books are secondary sources of information.**

In this chapter special emphasis is placed on the books that serve as **guides to the original articles** and thus immensely facilitate literature searches. A reference book that does not cite its authorities fully should be regarded as incomplete.

In the following discussions we will consider the types of chemical books and their reference value in this order: encyclopedic works, treatises of broad scope, indexes, formula lexicons, general books (including textbooks), monographs, dictionaries and glossaries, books of constants and tabular compilations, pocketbooks, publisher's series, formularies, and trade catalogs.

In considering each type, the examples given are those of general chemical interest that are most useful. Then, classified lists of the most generally useful books for the various fields of chemistry follow. Older reference books are included because they are often useful in patent searches and in locating information before the abstract journals covered the literature so thoroughly. The system of classification for these reference books is that used for the abstracts in *Chemical Abstracts*, with the exception that general chemistry is separated from physical chemistry. The final section of this chapter deals with obtaining information about old and new books, and with the purchase of books.

ENCYCLOPEDIC WORKS

Encyclopedic works that cover all of chemistry are seldom attempted now. Our knowledge is so extensive that it is practically impossible to cover all of it in one reference work, even by using the relatively short summaries that are characteristic of an encyclopedia.

Most of the recent and current ones either limit their coverage to selected topics about which information is most frequently needed or to specific fields of chemistry. The names of these reference works are frequently misleading—they are often called dictionaries. Perhaps this custom arose because the topics are usually entered in alphabetical order. The encyclopedias are particularly useful if a relatively short summary of a topic is needed; those that include references and bibliographies are valuable in more extensive searches.

Current and Recent

Thorpe's Dictionary of Applied Chemistry. (4th ed., 12 vols., London, Longmans, Green, 1937–1954.) This edition is wider in scope than the previous ones and is a general reference work for the various branches of chemistry and chemical industry. It is no longer limited to applied chemistry. After Volume 5, much more emphasis is placed on the physical chemistry of applied chemistry, and the physico-chemical articles that should have been included in Volumes 1–5 are included in later volumes under modified titles as much as possible. Only the first four volumes of this edition had been issued when it was interrupted by World War II. The first five volumes were edited by Sir Jocelyn Thorpe and Martha Whiteley, the rest by Whiteley and A. J. E. Welch, with the assistance of an editorial board (I. M. Heilbron, H. J. Emeleus, H. W. Melville, and A. R. Todd). The entries, which are alphabetically arranged, vary in length from a few lines to a number of pages, and include numerous references to the journal articles. This edition has a collective index. It is the most comprehensive chemical encyclopedia and an indispensable reference work.

The first edition of Thorpe's *Dictionary of Applied Chemistry* appeared in 1890 in 3 volumes, the second in 5 volumes, and the third (1921–1927) in 7 volumes. The third edition had a supplement of 2 volumes (1934–1936). Editions 1–3 were edited by Sir Edward Thorpe.

Dizionario di chimica generale e industriale, by M. Giua and C. Giua-Lollini (2nd ed., 3 vols., Turin, Unione Tipografico, 1948–1950) is a useful encyclopedia which gives references to the literature.

Villavecchia's Dizionario di merceologia e di chimica applicata (5th ed., 4 vols., Milan, Hoepli, 1949) covers applied chemistry and the natural sciences, including chemistry.

Kingzett's Chemical Encyclopedia, 8th ed. edited by R. Strong (Princeton, Van Nostrand, 1952, 1186 pp.), gives brief digests of topics in chemistry and applied chemistry. It does not include many references to the journal literature, and is more like a dictionary than an encyclopedia.

Older Encyclopedias

Fehling's Neues Handwörterbuch der Chemie (10 vols., Braunschweig, Vieweg, 1871–1930) is a continuation of Liebig, Poggendorff, and Wöhler (see below). The bibliographies are good and it contains much information not easily found elsewhere.

Frémy's Encyclopédie chimique (10 tomes or 94 vols., Paris, Dunod, 1882–1887, with an index in 1899) is a very comprehensive work for all fields of chemistry and covers practically all that was known at the time it was issued. It contains thousands of illustrations.

Ladenburg's Handwörterbuch der Chemie (13 vols., Breslau, Trewendt, 1882–1896) has many references to the literature.

Liebig, Poggendorff, and Wöhler's Handwörterbuch der reinen und angewandten Chemie (1st ed., 1837 and 2nd ed., 9 vols., Fehling (ed.), 1856–1865, Braunschweig, Vieweg) was continued in Fehling's work (see above).

Nicholson's Dictionary of Chemistry (London, R. Phillips, 1795–1808) is the earliest of these encyclopedias.

Ure's Dictionary of Chemistry (6th ed., 4 vols., London, Longmans, Green, 1867–1878) was based on Nicholson's work of 1808 and was a standard reference in its day in England.

Watt's Dictionary of Chemistry (1st ed., 6 vols., 1872–1874, and 2nd ed., 4 vols., rewritten by Morley and Muir, London, Longmans, Green, 1888–1894) gives many references to the literature.

Wurtz's Dictionnaire de chimie pure et appliquée (5 vols. and 2 supplements, making 14 vols. in all, Paris, Hachett, 1874–1908) was the standard French work of its day.

Treatises or "Handbücher"

This type of publication, which treats a subject systematically and gives numerous references to the journal literature, exists in many fields of chemistry. The German treatises are frequently called "Handbücher." Treatises are exceedingly valuable source books in reference work because they assemble large quantities of information. One disadvantage with the very large and comprehensive ones, as, for example, Beilstein's *Handbuch der organischen Chemie*, is that it is practically impossible to keep them anywhere nearly up to date. Another drawback to large treatises that appear in parts over a long period of time is that the first parts issued are outdated before the work is completed.

However, treatises are often in effect a system of monographs; the parts should be so regarded and their dates taken into consideration. To determine the actual date when a part of a treatise is issued and the period of time that it covers, it is usually necessary to examine the preface carefully, particularly in the case of reprints.

Another point to consider in relation to a treatise with which the searcher is unfamiliar is the need to study its method of organization before he uses it. Some treatises have an index for every volume, while others do not, and the quality of the indexes varies widely. Usually, the method of organization, the abbreviations used, and the scope of the work are given in the preface or the introduction.

There is no treatise that covers chemistry as a whole. The most important ones in each field will be given later.

INDEXES IN THE FORM OF BOOKS

This type of publication is rather rare in chemistry because the abstract journals and the index serials are the most useful guides to the literature. There are several valuable indexes of general chemical interest discussed in Chapter 8, Indexes. A few others have been issued to meet a specific need, as, for example, *The Ring Index* (Patterson and Capell) for organic chemistry, *The Color Index* (Rowe) for dyes, and several formula lexicons. These will be considered later.

Formula Lexicons

These are books in which chemical compounds are arranged according to their empirical formulas by a simple system, so that the name and a description of the compound can be turned to at once. In the case of some organic formulas, the same empirical formula represents a considerable number of compounds; then it is necessary to know something about nomenclature. This is the weakness of formula indexes. If a chemist wishes to get information about a certain compound from a treatise or an abstract journal, he must know the name that is used for it, and this constitutes a difficulty in consulting them. Chemical nomenclature has been improving gradually ever since Guyton de Morveau and his associates introduced the first system of nomenclature in 1787, but there is still a diversity of names for compounds, especially organic ones, and names are often different in different languages. On the other hand, chemical formulas correspond exactly to compositions and are international.

Three formula lexicons were issued between 1884 and 1926, but none appeared after 1926 because the need for them as separate publications ended after abstract journals published formula indexes. Two of these lexicons are for organic compounds (Richter and Stelzner), and the other (Hoffmann) is for inorganic compounds.

Max Moritz **Richter's Lexikon der Kohlenstoffverbindungen** covers organic compounds. The first edition appeared in 1884; the third edition is in four volumes and brings the literature down through 1909 (Leipzig, Voss, 1910–1912). It gives references to the third edition of Beilstein's *Handbuch der organischen Chemie* and to the literature that was not covered by Beilstein; it is coextensive with the main series of the fourth edition of Beilstein as to the period covered. The system of arranging formulas in Richter's *Lexikon*, given in the preface in four languages, has been used in the formula indexes of a number of journals and reference works since then.

Robert **Stelzner's Literatur-Register der organischen Chemie** (5 vols., Berlin, Verlag Chemie, 1913–1926) covers the period 1910–1921 for organic compounds. It uses the Richter system for entering the formulas; it gives the names of, and considerable data about, the compounds and full references to the literature; but it does not give references to Beilstein. Stelzner's *Literatur-Register* is coextensive with the first supplement to the fourth edition of Beilstein's *Handbuch der organischen Chemie*.

Richter's *Lexikon* and Stelzner's *Literatur-Register* between them give the formulas of all organic compounds that were known through 1921. The first formula index that has ever been issued for Beilstein's *Handbuch der organischen Chemie* by its publishers appeared in the fourth edition, and it gives the formulas for all the compounds in the main series and its first supplement; it covers the literature through 1919. However, Richter and Stelzner are still useful because they include compounds in division IV of the fourth edition of Beilstein that are not covered by its own index, and for their references to *Chemisches Zentralblatt*, to which, in a sense, they serve as a formula index for organic compounds through 1921.

M. K. **Hoffmann's Lexikon der anorganischen Verbindungen** (3 vols. bound as 4, Leipzig, Barth, 1912–1919) gives the formulas for all analytical and synthetic inorganic compounds known to 1910 and covers the literature to April 1909. This work does not use Richter's system for entering formulas but has one of its own that is explained in the introduction to Volume 1, Part I. It contains references to the 7th edition of the *Gmelin-Kraut Handbuch der an-*

organischen Chemie (see page 26) and, in a sense, is a formula index to it.

Chemical Abstracts started its formula index for both organic and inorganic compounds in 1920, and *Chemisches Zentralblatt* started its organic formula index in 1925. For the period 1910–1920 there is no systematic compilation of inorganic compounds by formulas.

General Books (Including Textbooks)

In addition to the giant treatises there is a great host of books on chemistry in all of its aspects. Some are reference works on a smaller scale, some are textbooks, and some are practical manuals; historical and popular works also belong to the group. The more important of those now in use will be found in the classified list in this chapter. No clear-cut line of demarcation can be drawn between reference works and many of the advanced textbooks that treat a subject thoroughly and give numerous citations to the journal literature.

Monographs

The monograph is a rather full treatise on a special topic. Owing to its limited range it can give the detailed information that is demanded by the research worker and yet be of manageable size and be issued as a whole instead of in parts. As compared with a large treatise on a subject, a series of monographs offers a more flexible framework. The continuity of the whole is not injured by the addition of new volumes or the revision of old ones to any extent desired. An example of a series of monographs on a given subject is *Die chemische Analyse,* published by Enke, Stuttgart (1907–   ) ; there are over 45 monographs by various authors in this series, many of which are now in the third edition.

The monographs on chemistry sponsored by the American Chemical Society and published by Reinhold, New York, are excellent examples of what a monograph should be; they give valuable summaries of existing knowledge on a given subject and include many references to the journal and patent literature. Two fairly recent titles in the American Chemical Society series are *The Furans,* by A. P. Dunlop and F. N. Peters (1953), and *Copper,* edited by Allison Butts (1954).

Dictionaries and Glossaries

A chemical dictionary is a word book that defines chemical terms and gives their usage. A work dealing with subjects arranged in alphabetical order is an encyclopedia. Unfortunately this distinction has not been observed in naming many chemical works; the terms dictionary and encyclopedia have been used interchangeably and one must see the publication to know which it is. *The Bibliography of Monolingual Scientific and Technical Glossaries* (Paris, UNESCO, 1955–   , available from Columbia Univ. Press, New York) is classified by subjects, lists glossaries published in many countries and many languages, and covers all branches of pure and applied science for which such works exist; a large number of chemical dictionaries are included. This bibliography will be published in several volumes. Volume 1 (1955) is devoted to National Standards.

Some of the most useful dictionaries are:

Bennet, Harry, *Concise Chemical and Technical Dictionary*, New York, Chemical Pub. Co., 1947, 1055 pp.

Gardner's *Chemical Synonyms and Trade Names*, 5th ed. revised by E. I. Cook, London, Technical Press, 1948, 558 pp.

Hackh and Grant's *Chemical Dictionary*, 3rd ed., Philadelphia, Blakiston, 1944, 925 pp.

Hayes, William, *Chemical Trade Names and Commercial Synonyms*, 2nd ed., New York, Van Nostrand, 1955, 466 pp.

Henderson's *Dictionary of Scientific Terms*, 5th ed., J. H. Kenneth (ed.), Edinburgh, Oliver & Boyd, 1953, 506 pp.

Miall, S., and Miall, L. M. (eds.), *A New Dictionary of Chemistry*, 2nd ed., London, Longmans, Green, 1949, 589 pp.

Römpp, H., *Chemie-Lexikon*, 2nd ed., 2 vols., Stuttgart, Franckh'sche Verlag, 1950–1951, 2105 pp.

Rose, E. G. (ed.), *The Condensed Chemical Dictionary*, 5th ed., New York, Reinhold, 1956, 1220 pp.

The Van Nostrand Chemist's Dictionary, Honig, Jacobs, Lewin, Minrath, and Murphy (eds.), New York, Van Nostrand, 1953, 761 pp.

Books of Constants

Chemists frequently need to use numerical data relative to the physical and chemical properties of substances as well as other kinds of numerical data in their work. A large amount of this factual material has been compiled in books, usually in tabular form. These compilations should be consulted first to see if the desired information has been included because searching the journal literature for this type of information is apt to be time consuming.

The problem of compiling these data and keeping the work up to date is a complex one. Taylor [1] summarized the problems in relation to continuous publications of *Tables Annuelles* (see below) in 1938 when he was the Chairman of a Committee of the National Research Council (US) and his discussion is still essentially true. The International Commission (Commission affiliée des Tables de Constantes), which is maintained jointly by the International Union of Pure and Applied Chemistry and the International Council of Scientific Unions, is still compiling tables of constants and numerical data, but it has not published a volume that includes all of these data for a year since 1939.

The Division of Chemistry and Chemical Technology of the National Research Council (USA) has a committee on Physical Constants. This committee [2] is preparing a directory of sources of data of physical constants, and is reviewing proposals for revision of the *International Critical Tables* (see below). Maizell [3] describes a number of sources of data on physical constants of chemicals and discusses methods of collecting and of judging the reliability of the data.

The best source of information on the future of both the *International Critical Tables* and *Tables Annuelles* is the Division of Chemistry and Chemical Technology of the National Research Council, Washington, D. C. This Division is the adhering organization to the International Union of Pure and Applied Chemistry.

The three most comprehensive works are:

1. **The International Critical Tables,** E. W. Washburn (ed.), 7 vols. and index, New York, McGraw-Hill, 1926–1933. This publication was under the auspices of the National Research Council of the United States. The literature was examined up to 1924 and much previously unpublished information was included. The data were examined critically before inclusion and references are given to the journals so one can learn, if needed, how a constant was determined. The tables cover chemistry, physics, and technology.

2. **Landolt-Börnstein's Zahlenwerte und Funktionen aus Physik, Chemie, Astronomie, Geophysik, Technik** (6th ed. of Landolt-Börnstein's *Physikalisch-chemische Tabellen*, Berlin, Springer). This edition started publication in 1950 under the editorship of A. Eucken. Four volumes, each volume to be in several parts, were announced and about half of the volumes were issued by 1956. Landolt-Börnstein (6th ed.) is not as comprehensive in some respects as the *International Critical Tables*, but it is the most up to date, and references are given to the original literature. The 5th edition (2

vols.) was published in 1923, and supplements (3 vols. in 6 parts) were issued, 1927–1936. The data in the 6th edition of *Landolt-Börnstein* have been examined more critically before inclusion than those in previous editions, but the evaluation of data is still less critical than it was in the *International Critical Tables*.

3. **Tables annuelles de constantes et données numériques de chimie, de physique, de biologie et de technologie,** C. Marie (ed.), 12 vols., Paris, Gauthier-Villars, 1912–1939. There are indexes for Vols. 1–5 and Vols. 6–10. These tables, which cover data for the period 1910–1936, are not critical; the principle object being to make as complete a collection as possible of numerical data. The continuation of this comprehensive work is doubtful. The International Commission (see p. 19) which is responsible for it is currently issuing tables separately in selected fields under the title, **Tables de constantes et données numériques, constantes selectionées** (Paris, Hermann, 1947–).

There are a number of specialized compilations and smaller works. Only three which are of general chemical interest are given here.

Forsythe, W. E. (ed.), *Smithsonian Physical Tables*, 9th ed., Washington, D. C., Smithsonian Institution, 1954, 827 pp.
Kaye, G. W. C., and Laby, T. H., *Tables of Physical and Chemical Constants*, 11th ed., London, Longmans, Green, 1955, 210 pp.
Seidell, A. (ed.), *Solubilities of Organic and Inorganic Compounds*, 3rd ed., 2 vols., New York, Van Nostrand, 1940–1942. Supplement 1952. This work includes data through 1949 and gives references to the literature.

Pocketbooks (Handbooks)

This is a rather well-defined class of books that contains miscellaneous information in handy form for the use of technical men. Pocketbooks contain physical constants and a variety of other material, and seldom give references to the literature. Each editor selects information thought to be of the most general interest so their coverage varies considerably. Several of the generally useful ones are given here; there are many others that cover the various fields of chemistry and industry, and some of them are given in the classified book list further on in this chapter.

The Chemists Yearbook (1951 edition), E. Hope (ed.), is revised frequently and is widely used in England (Tempirley, England, St. Ann's Press).

The Handbook of Chemistry and Physics, C. D. Hodgman (ed.), Cleveland, the Chemical Rubber Co., is very frequently revised and is widely used in the United States.

The Handbook of Chemistry, N. A. Lange (ed.), Sandusky, Ohio, Handbook Publishers, is revised frequently and widely used in the United States.

A new German work that contains a greater variety of physical data than most books of this type is Waldemar **Koglin's Kurzes Handbuch der Chemie,** Göttingen, Vandenhoeck und Ruprecht (1951–). Five volumes were announced and four have been issued; it has an alphabetical arrangement. This work was probably intended to be a small encyclopedia, but it is most useful as a handbook.

Publisher's Series

Scientific books are frequently issued as members of a series, all of which are on the same general subject. Such series are usually arranged by publishers, but may be the result of a joint arrangement between the publisher and some scientific organization. Many of them are edited by well-known individuals. If a book belongs to a series sponsored by a scientific society or to a series that has a scientist of high standing as editor, the quality of the work is assured.

The American Chemical Society Monograph Series, which is published for the Society by Reinhold, New York, is an outstanding example of such a series. Another is the *National Nuclear Energy Series,* which is being published by McGraw-Hill, New York; it was arranged through the War Department and the United States Atomic Energy Commission.

There is a wide range in the type of books published in these chemical book series; some are composed of monographs only, others of textbooks only, and others of laboratory manuals only. Still others are miscellaneous collections that indicate that a publisher who does not specialize in scientific or technical books is issuing some of them.

It is not necessary to know the name of a series to ascertain the existence of a book in it because each book is issued separately under its own title and author by the publisher in the usual way. Occasionally time is saved in locating a monograph on a given topic by glancing through a list of a publisher's series and then referring to the appropriate catalogue to see if it is a member of a certain series.

Formularies

Formularies are receipt books; they are intended primarily for those who have little technical training; but they have their uses and occasionally provide information on certain aspects of applied chemistry that is difficult to locate in other ways. Two of the most useful ones are:

Bennett, H. (ed.), *The Chemical Formulary*, 10 vols., New York, Chemical Publishing Co., 1934–1956.
Hopkins, A. A. (ed.), *Standard American Encyclopedia of Formulas*, New York, Grosset & Dunlap, 1953.

Trade Catalogs

The value of catalogs as sources of information is discussed in connection with trade literature. See page 201.

CLASSIFIED LIST OF REFERENCE BOOKS

This section is not intended to include all of the reference books in each field of chemistry, but to indicate the nature of the reference material available and to list works of most general interest. For more comprehensive book lists, see the last section of this chapter, Sources of Information about Books, pages 56–62.

1. Apparatus, Plant Equipment, Unit Operations

There are no comprehensive encyclopedias or large treatises in this field. Most of the books are devoted to specific unit operations or types of equipment. Some of the general works are:

Coleman, H. S. (ed.), *Laboratory Design*, New York, Reinhold, 1951, 360 pp. This was prepared at the direction of the National Research Council and is the only up-to-date work in its field.
Brown, G. G., and associates, *Unit Operations*, New York, Wiley, 1950, 611 pp.
Elliot, A., and Dickson, J. H., *Laboratory Instruments*, London, Chapman & Hall, 1951, 416 pp.
Jones, E. B., *Instrument Technology*, London, Butterworth, 1953– . Several volumes announced. Two vols. have appeared.
Lauer, B. E., and Heckman, R. F., *Chemical Engineering Techniques*, New York, Reinhold, 1952, 450 pp.
Riegel, R., *Chemical Process Machinery*, 2nd ed., New York, Reinhold, 1953, 735 pp.
Wittenberger, W., *Maschinen und Apparate in Chemiebetrieb*, Berlin, Springer, 1949, 348 pp.

2. Physical Chemistry

The works of general chemical interest that are in group two of the *Chemical Abstracts* classification have already been considered. There are no very comprehensive treatises for physical chemistry as there are for organic and inorganic chemistry, but, it must be remembered, a considerable amount of physical chemistry is involved in the chemistry of the elements and their compounds. Works on inorganic and organic chemistry and Thorpe's *Dictionary of Applied Chemistry* will yield considerable quantities of information on physical chemistry. Most of the books on physical chemistry are general textbooks or monographs on a portion of the field, as, for example, colloids, catalysis, and thermodynamics. There are several treatises and advanced textbooks of quite comprehensive nature.

Emschwiller, Guy, *Chimie physique*, 3 vols., Paris, Presses Univ. de France, 1951–1953.
Euken, Arnold, *Lehrbuch der chemischen Physik*, 3rd ed., 2 vols. in 3 parts, Leipzig, Akademische Verlagsgesellschaft, 1948–1949.
Jellinek, Karl, *Lehrbuch der physikalischen Chemie*, 2nd ed., 5 vols., Stuttgart, Enke, 1928–1938.
Partington, J. R., *An Advanced Treatise on Physical Chemistry*, 5 vols. London, Longmans, Green, 1949–1954.
Pascal, P. V. H., *Chimie générale*, 4 vols., Paris, Masson, 1949–1952. A treatise on physical chemistry.
Rutgers, A. J., *Physical Chemistry*, New York, Interscience, 1954, 824 pp.
Taylor, H. S., and Glasstone, S. (eds.), *A Treatise on Physical Chemistry*, 3rd ed., New York, Van Nostrand, 1946– . Five vols. announced, of which two appeared by 1956.
Taylor, H. S. (ed.), *A Treatise on Physical Chemistry*, 2nd ed., New York, Van Nostrand, 1931.

LABORATORY

Daniels, Farrington, and associates, *Experimental Physical Chemistry*, 5th ed., New York, McGraw-Hill, 1956, 568 pp.
Reilly, Joseph, and Rae, W. N., *Physico-Chemical Methods*, 5th ed., 3 vols., New York, Van Nostrand, 1954.

3. Electronic Phenomena and Spectra

Apparently there is no comprehensive discussion of this field except that found in the treatises on physical chemistry. Treatises on physics also discuss many phases of it. The following books, which cover some parts of the subject of electronic phenomena and spectra, are useful:

Crowther, J. A., *Ions, Electrons and Ionizing Radiations*, London, Arnold, 1949, 322 pp. A textbook.
Finkelnburg, W., *Atomic Physics*, New York, McGraw-Hill, 1950, 498 pp.
Massey, H. S. W., and Burhop, E. H., *Electronic and Ionic Impact Phenomena*, Oxford, Clarendon Press, 1952, 669 pp.
Sommerfeld, A., *Atombau und Spektrallinien*, 2 vols., Braunschweig, Vieweg, 1951.

24   BOOKS

3a. Nuclear Phenomena

Apparently comprehensive discussions of nuclear phenomena are to be found only in treatises on physical chemistry or on physics. It is difficult to make useful suggestions in this rapidly changing field.

GROUP I

These books will help those who are not specialists in this field to gain some knowledge of it.

Cooke, J. B., and Duncan, J. F., *Modern Radiochemical Practice,* London, Oxford Univ. Press, 1952, 24 pp.
Fermi, Enrico, *Nuclear Energy,* Chicago, Univ. of Chicago Press, 1950, 246 pp.
Finkelnburg, W., *Atomic Physics,* New York, McGraw-Hill, 1950, 498 pp. A translation of the first edition of the German work. It is an excellent survey of the field.
Finkelnburg, W., *Einführung in die Atom-Physik,* 2nd ed., Berlin, Springer, 1951. (First ed. in 1948, see above for translation.)
Friedlander, G., and Kennedy, J. W., *Nuclear and Radiochemistry,* New York, Wiley, 1955, 468 pp. This is a good textbook.
Gamov, G., and Critchfield, C. L., *Theory of Atomic Nucleus and Nuclear Energy Sources,* 3rd ed., New York, Oxford Univ. Press, 1949, 344 pp.
Stephens, W. E. (ed.), *Nuclear Fission and Atomic Energy,* Lancaster, Pa., Science Press, 1949, 294 pp. This gives an excellent summary of the work up to 1946 and includes very comprehensive references to the literature.
Williams, R. R., *Principles of Nuclear Chemistry,* New York, Van Nostrand, 1950, 307 pp. A good elementary text.

GROUP II

These are of more interest as reference works:

An International Bibliography of Atomic Energy (1925–1949), 2 vols., New York, Columbia Univ. Press, 1950–1951. This is a United Nations publication. A supplement appeared in 1952, and additional ones may be issued.
Goodman, Clark (ed.), *The Science and Engineering of Nuclear Power,* 2 vols., Cambridge, Mass., Addison-Wesley, 1949–1951.
National Atomic Energy Series. This is being published for the United States Atomic Energy Commission by McGraw-Hill, New York, 1948–   .
The titles of all of the books in this series are different. There will be about 60 volumes that will cover chemistry, physics, biological applications, and other topics.
Ségre, Morrison, and Feld, *Experimental Nuclear Physics,* New York, Wiley, 1953. A reference work in several volumes.

4. Electrochemistry

There are no large treatises on electrochemistry; the smaller ones that do exist are limited for the most part to applied or technical electrochemistry. Up-to-date discussions of the principles and theory of electrochemistry as separate publications are rare, but the larger works in physical chemistry cover this theoretical material. Some useful reference works are:

Blum, W., and Hogaboom, G. B., *Principles of Electroplating and Electroforming*, 3rd ed., New York, McGraw-Hill, 1949, 470 pp.
Creighton, H. J., and Koehler, W. A., *Principles and Applications of Electrochemistry*, 2 vols., New York, Wiley, 1943–1944.
Fichter, F., *Organische Electrochemie*, 2nd ed., Dresden, Steinkopff, 1951, 359 pp.
Gray, A. G., *Modern Electroplating*, New York, Wiley, 1953, 563 pp.
Handbuch der technischen Electrochemie, edited by V. Engelhardt and later by G. Eger, Leipzig, Akad., Verlagses, 1931– . Five vols. were announced and four have been issued.
Kortüm, G., and Bockris, J. O'M., *Textbook of Electrochemistry*, 2 vols., Amsterdam, Elsevier, 1951.
Mantell, C. L., *Industrial Electrochemistry*, 3rd ed., New York, McGraw-Hill, 1950, 781 pp.
Müller, R., *Allgemeine und technische Elektrochemie nichtmetallisher Stoffe*, Vienna, Springer, 1937, 440 pp.
Conway, B. E., *Electrochemical Data*, New York, Elsevier, 1952, 374 pp. A compilation of many kinds of data that are useful in electrochemical work.

5. Photography

There are no very extensive works on photography from the chemical and scientific point of view. The following books are useful:

Diserens, C., *Handbuch der Photographie*, 2 vols., Bern, Hallwag, 1951.
Diserens, C., *Traité de photographie*, Vol. 2, chimie photographique, Paris, Gauthier-Villars, 1953. This is a translation of the above work, of which Vol. 1 is devoted to optical equipment and Vol. 2 to the chemistry of photography.
Boni, A., *Guide to the Literature of Photography and Allied Subjects*, New York, Morgan and Lester, 1944.
Evans, R. M., and Hanson, W. T., *Principles of Color Photography*, New York, Wiley, 1953, 709 pp.
Neblette, C. B., *Photography: Its Materials and Processes*, 5th ed., New York, Van Nostrand, 1952, 500 pp.
Walls' Dictionary of Photography and Reference Book, 17th ed., London, Foundation Press, 1951, 705 pp.

6. Inorganic Chemistry

Gmelin's Handbuch der anorganischen Chemie has long held the leading position as an exhaustive reference work. The eighth edition, now in progress, when complete will be the most comprehensive treatise in its field. This edition began to appear in 1924 under the editorship of R. J. Meyer, who was succeeded by Erich Pietsch, and by 1956 most of it had been issued by the publisher, Verlag Chemie G.m.b.H., Weinheim/Bergstrasse, Germany. Dr. Pietsch [4] announced in 1952 that supplementary parts are being prepared for the volumes that do not cover the literature to January 1, 1950, and that this edition is to be completed by 1963 or 1964. The eighth edition, when entirely finished, will cover all of inorganic chemistry from about 1750 to 1950. The treatment of inorganic chemistry is more critical than that of the preceding editions. An effort is made to judge all available material critically from the standpoint of present knowledge and to include in the discussions of the elements and their compounds only those older portions of knowledge that are useful today. The references to the literature are very complete. Gmelin covers many fields related to inorganic chemistry: physical chemistry, mining, mineralogy, metallurgy, geochemistry, electrochemistry, chemical technology, and some phases of physics. The coverage of the eighth edition is broader in related fields than that of preceding editions. The information is arranged in 70 systems and the systems cover the rare gases first (system one), then the nonmetals, and finally the heavy metals. In most cases a system is devoted to one element. Each element in a system is treated thoroughly, together with all of its compounds with elements of lower system number than the one under consideration. For example, system 2 is devoted to hydrogen, 3 to oxygen, 4 to nitrogen, 9 to sulfur, and 59 to iron; and thus compounds of oxygen with hydrogen will be found under 3, of nitrogen with hydrogen and with oxygen under 4, and of iron with oxygen and with sulfur under 59. The work is being issued according to the Gmelin System Numbers and not by volumes; some "numbers" have several parts.

Gmelin's Handbuch der anorganischen Chemie is a lineal descendant to Leopold *Gmelin's Handbuch der theoretischen Chemie* (1817–1819); hence it has a history of over a century. In the sixth edition (1872) the editorship was taken over by Karl Kraut, whence the name *Gmelin-Kraut*, which was applied to the sixth and seventh editions. The seventh edition was not finished until 1927. In 1921 the German Chemical Society took over the *Handbuch* and restored the original author's name for the eighth edition. The Society later formed the Gmelin Institute, where the manuscript of the Handbuch is prepared by a scientific staff. Erich Pietsch is now director of the Institute and Editor-in-chief of the Handbuch.

An English translation of *Gmelin's Handbuch*, with many additions, was edited by Henry Watts and appeared in 1848–1872 in 19 volumes (London, The Cavendish Society); this is still an important reference work for the early literature of inorganic chemistry.

J. W. Mellor's Comprehensive Treatise on Inorganic and Theoretical Chemistry (16 vols., London, Longmans, Green, 1922–1937), is comprehensive, but is not as exhaustive as Gmelin's treatise. However, its bibliographies are very complete. Each volume has its own index and Volume 16 contains the general index. The work aims to give a complete description of all elements and compounds known in inorganic chemistry and to discuss them, where possible, in the light of physical chemistry. Supplementary volumes (editorial board: H. V. A. Briscoe, A. A. Eldridge, and G. M. Dyson) are being prepared to bring all 16 volumes of Mellor's *Treatise* up to date; publication began in 1956.

Traité de chimie minérale, P. Pascal (ed.) (12 vols., Paris, Masson, 1931–1934), is a critical treatise on inorganic chemistry. It covers all of the elements and their compounds, including industrial aspects, and the bibliographies are good. Some of the citations are vague. A new edition in 19 volumes began to appear in 1956 (*Nouveau traité de chimie minérale*).

Comprehensive Inorganic Chemistry, M. C. Sneed, J. L. Maynard, and R. C. Brasted (eds.) (New York, Van Nostrand), began to appear in 1953. This work is to be in 11 volumes, completed within five or six years. The editors introduce it "as a reference work on the chemical elements and their inorganic compounds . . . comprehensive in the extensiveness of the fields covered rather than in the fullness of their treatment." Technological aspects are stressed, and the theoretical aspects are up to date in the first volumes to appear. If the first volumes are a fair sample, this work will be more like an advanced textbook than a treatise.

OLDER TREATISES

Abegg's Handbuch der anorganischen Chemie (4 vols., in 14 parts, Leipzig, Hirzel, 1905–1939) was started by R. Abegg, and continued by F. Auerbach and I. Koppel. The work has not been completed; part of Volume 4 on the platinum subgroup of Group VIII in the periodic system is lacking. This treatise is a less exhaustive but more critical work than the 7th edition of Gmelin.

O. **Dammer's Handbuch der anorganischen Chemie** (4 vols. and supplement, Stuttgart, Enke, 1892–1905) was issued as a counterpart to Beilstein's work on organic chemistry and attained an important place. It is practically superseded by later works. It is an old— but good—treatise.

Doelter and Leitmeier's Handbuch der Mineralchemie (4 vols. in 8 parts, Darmstadt, Steinkopff, 1912–1931) differs from the other treatises on inorganic chemistry by placing greater stress on the mineralogical and geological aspects of the subject.

U. R. **Evans' Metals and Metallic Compounds** (4 vols., London, Arnold, 1923) is an advanced textbook that resembles a treatise and covers the metals, not all of inorganic chemistry, as the title indicates.

The Textbook of Inorganic Chemistry, edited by N. J. Friend (11 vols. in 20 parts, London, Griffin, 1914–1938), is both comprehensive and selective. It gives sufficient references to the literature to be a satisfactory reference work. Some of the volumes have been revised; the first volume originally issued in 1914 is now in the 3rd edition.

H. **Moissan's Traité de chimie minérale** (5 vols., Paris, Masson, 1904–1906), which he wrote with the help of several collaborators of repute, was the best French treatise on inorganic chemistry until Pascal's work appeared.

OTHER REFERENCE WORKS

The Encyclopedia of Chemical Reactions, edited by C. A. Jacobson and Clifford Hampel (New York, Reinhold), has been in progress since 1946. The material is arranged alphabetically. Certain features of an index are combined with the informational content of an abstract. References to the journal literature are given for each reaction. It is the only work in existence that attempts to list all the known inorganic chemical reactions. Vol. 5 (1953) goes through ruthenium.

Gould, E. S., *Inorganic Reactions and Structures,* New York, Holt, 1956, 470 pp.

Walter **Hückel's Structural Chemistry of Inorganic Compounds** (2 vols., New York, Elsevier, 1951–1952) is a discussion of structural and constitutional theory as a basis for systematizing inorganic chemistry.

A. F. **Wells' Structural Inorganic Chemistry** (2 ed., London, Oxford Univ. Press, 1951, 599 pp.) is an excellent book.

LABORATORY MANUALS

R. E. **Dodd** and P. L. **Robinson's Experimental Inorganic Chemistry** (Houston, Texas, Elsevier, 1953, 424 pp.) is a survey of general experimental methods that have proved useful in inorganic chemistry. It covers basic techniques and includes the handling of gases, vacuum technique, colloidal systems, and other fields that need attention in experimental work. It does not give preparations, except as illustrations of general techniques. It is apparently the only recent book in this field; for the most part, this type of information is scattered through the works on inorganic preparations and the journal literature. A bibliography of over 1,500 references is included.

Handbuch der praeparativen anorganischen Chemie, edited by Georg Brauer (Stuttgart, Enke, 1951–   ), is an invaluable work. It was announced in 8 vols., 6 of which appeared by 1955. It contains instructions for the preparation of all known inorganic substances. Extensive data and references to the literature are given for all preparations that are not available commercially.

Inorganic Syntheses (New York, McGraw-Hill, 1939–   ) is another indispensable work. The fourth volume appeared in 1953. The editorship rotates. It includes checked and tested methods of preparing important inorganic compounds. A volume appears about every two years at present.

A. **Stähler's Handbuch der Arbeitsmethoden in der anorganischen Chemie** (4 vols. in 7 parts, Leipzig, de Gruyter, 1913–1926) is another valuable work. Much of this work is devoted to general methods (mechanical operations, physical and chemical operations, and physio-chemical determinations); the number of preparations is not as large as one might expect in such a large work.

Ludwig **Vanino's Handbuch der präparativen Chemie** (Stuttgart, Enke, 1925, Vol. 1, Anorganischen Teil, 582 pp.) is still a useful work. It has been out of print for years, but reprints are available from J. W. Edwards, Ann Arbor, Michigan. This was the most comprehensive compilation available until *Inorganic Syntheses* and Brauer's work appeared.

7. Analytical Chemistry

There are few comprehensive references works on analytical chemistry; most of the books are limited to a specific phase of it. Also, the number of books devoted to one physical chemical method in chemical analysis is large.

GENERAL

Berl, W. G., *Physical Methods in Chemical Analysis*, 2 vols., New York, Academic Press, 1950–1951. This treatise gives an excellent survey of the methods now in use, as chromatographic analysis, potentiometric analysis, polarographic analysis, conductometric analysis, spectographic analysis, colorimetric analysis, etc., and it also points out possible uses of others.

Boettger, W. (ed.), *Physikalische Methoden der analytischen Chemie*, 2nd ed., 3 vols., Leipzig, Akad. Verlagsges, 1950– . Similar to Berl (see above).

Belcher, R., and Wilson, C. L., *New Methods in Analytical Chemistry*, New York, Reinhold, 1955, 300 pp. Not based on instrumental technique.

Chamot, E. M., and Mason, C. W., *Handbook of Chemical Microscopy*, 2nd ed., 2 vols., New York, Wiley, 1938–1940. A standard work, but rather out of date. There are few books in this field.

Chemische Analyse, Die. This is a publisher's series of monographs (Stuttgart, Enke) by various authors under the editorship of B. M. Margosches in the beginning (1907) and now edited by W. Boettger. New titles are being added and others revised. The books cover all phases of analytical chemistry and are usually outstanding works.

Feigl, Fritz, *Spot Tests*, 2 vols., Houston, Elsevier, 1949. This covers both organic and inorganic chemistry.

Fresenius, R., and Jander, G. (eds.), *Handbuch der analytischen Chemie*, Berlin, Springer, 1940– . A very comprehensive treatise that was announced in IV parts (Teile) and about 25 volumes. Only a few volumes were issued before 1946. Part II (Qualitative) and Part III (Quantitative) are nearing completion. The Handbuch is the successor to the famous works of C. R. Fresenius on qualitative and quantitative analysis which went through many editions; it is a valuable reference work.

Harley, J. H., and Wiberly, S. E., *Instrumental Analysis*, New York, Wiley, 1954, 440 pp. It covers the major analytical instruments.

Kolthoff, I. M., and Stenger, V. A., *Volumetric Analysis*, 2nd ed., 3 vols., New York, Interscience, 1946– .

McDonald, H. J., and Associates, *Ionography: Electrophoresis in Stabilized Media*, Chicago, Yearbook Pub., 1955, 267 pp. Covers both organic and inorganic substances.

Schaeffer, H. F., *Microscopy for Chemists*, New York, Van Nostrand, 1953, 264 pp.

Rüdisüle, A., *Nachweis, Bestimmung und Trennung der chemischen Elemente*, Bern, Paul Haupt, 1913–1937. This excellent but old work has not been entirely finished. Seven volumes and a supplement for vols. 1–4 had been issued by 1937. The volumes covering C, N, P, O, H, the halogens, and the inert gases were not issued.

Stouts, C. R. N., Gilfillan, J. H., and Wilson, H. N., *Analytical Chemistry*, 2 vols., Oxford, Clarendon Press, 1955. Both physical and chemical methods of analysis are considered with emphasis being placed on apparatus and instruments.

INORGANIC QUALITATIVE

Müller, Gerhard O., *Praktikum der qualitativen anorganischen-chemischen Analyse*, Stuttgart, S. Hirzel, 1948, 1648 pp.

Smith, O. C., *Identification and Qualitative Analysis of Minerals*, 2nd ed., New York, Van Nostrand, 1953, 385 pp.

Vogel, A. I., *Macro and Semimicro Qualitative Inorganic Analysis*, 4th ed., London, Longmans, Green, 1954, 662 pp. An advanced textbook.

Welcher, F. J., and Hahn, R. B., *Semimicro Qualitative Analysis*, New York, Van Nostrand, 1955, 497 pp. A comprehensive text.

INORGANIC QUANTITATIVE

Duval, Clement, *Inorganic Thermogravimetric Analysis*, Amsterdam, Elsevier, 1953, 531 pp. It includes pyrolysis curves and data for almost 1,000 precipitates.

Kolthoff, I. M., and Sandell, E. B., *Textbook of Quantitative Inorganic Analysis*, 3rd ed., New York, Macmillan, 1952, 768 pp.

Vogel, A. I., *A Textbook of Quantitative Inorganic Analysis*, 2nd ed., London, Longmans, Green, 1951, 941 pp. It is a comprehensive advanced text.

ORGANIC ANALYSIS

Houben-Weyl's Methoden der organischen Chemie, Müller, E. (ed.), 4th ed., Stuttgart, Thieme. Vol. 2 of this work (*Analytische Methoden*), issued in 1953, is the best and most comprehensive book available that covers all phases of organic analysis.

Organic Analysis, New York, Interscience. This annual publication, begun in 1953, provides information on new methods and procedures. Outstanding chemists are members of its editorial and advisory boards.

Siggia, S., *Quantitative Organic Analysis via Functional Groups*, 2nd ed., 1954, 227 pp.

Shriner, R. L., Fuson, R. C., and Curtin, D. Y., *The Systematic Identification of Organic Compounds*, 4th ed., New York, Wiley, 1956, 418 pp. An outstanding book on qualitative analysis.

MICRO-ANALYSIS

Briscoe, H. V. A., and Holt, P. F., *Inorganic Micro-Analysis*, London, Arnold, 1950, 171 pp.

Milton, R. F., and Waters, W. A., *Methods of Quantitative Micro-Analysis*, New York, Longmans, Green, 1949, 599 pp.

Pregl, F., and Grant, J., *Quantitative Organic Micro-Analysis*, 5th ed., London, Churchill, 1951, 342 pp.

Forensic Chemistry

Gonzales, I. A., *Legal Medicine*, 2nd ed., New York, Appleton-Century-Crofts, 1954, 1349 pp.

Kirk, P. L., *Crime Investigation*, New York, Interscience, 1953, 806 pp.

Lucas, A., *Forensic Chemistry and Scientific Criminal Investigation*, 4th ed., London, Arnold, 1945.

Simpson, Kieth, *Forensic Medicine*, Baltimore, Williams & Wilkins, 1952, 344 pp.

Official Methods

American Society for Testing Materials, Standards, Philadelphia, American Soc. Testing Materials. This is issued in 7 parts triennially. The 1955 edition is the latest, and covers almost everything of industrial importance.

American Public Health Association, Standard Methods for the Examination of Water and Sewage, 10th ed., New York, Amer. Pub. Health Assoc., 1955.

Bibliography of Standard Tentative and Recommended or Recognized Methods of Analysis. Compiled under the authority of the Analytical Methods Committee of the Society of Public Analysts and Other Analytical Chemists, Cambridge, England, W. Heffer, 1951, 225 pp. This covers both American and British methods and includes techniques, apparatus, books, periodicals, and bulletins.

Official Methods of Analysis of the Association of Official Agricultural Chemists, 8th ed., Washington, D. C., Assoc. Official Agr. Chem., 1955, 1008 pp. Includes food analysis.

Pharmacopoeia of the United States of America, 15th ed., Easton, Pa., Mack Pub. Co., 1955, 1232 pp. Only the latest edition is official.

Reagents and Indicators

Reagent Chemicals, Compiled by the ACS Committee on Analytical Reagents. Washington, D. C., The American Chemical Society, 1955, 428 pp.

Rosin, J., *Reagent Chemicals and Standards*, 3rd ed., New York, Van Nostrand, 1955, 640 pp.

Tomicek, O., *Chemical Indicators*, London, Butterworth, 1950, 234 pp.

Welcher, F. J., *Organic Analytical Reagents*, 4 vols., New York, Van Nostrand, 1947–1948.

Commercial Analysis

Allen's Commercial Organic Analysis, 5th ed. in 10 vols., Philadelphia, Blakiston, 1923–1933. Edited by Williams et al. A very comprehensive standard treatise that is rather outdated, but there is no more recent work of such coverage for all kinds of organic compounds and substances.

Lunge, G., and Berl, E., *Chemisch-technische Untersuchungsmethoden*, 8th ed., 5 vols. in 6 parts, and 3 vols. of supplements, Berlin, Springer, 1931–1940. A standard treatise on methods of analyzing and testing; it too is outdated, but has not been replaced by a more recent work.

Lunge, G., Keane, C. A., and Thorne, P. C. L., *Technical Methods of Chem-*

ical Analysis, 4 vols., London, Gurney & Jackson, 1931–1948. It is based on Lunge and Berl's work. See above.

Lundell, G. E. F., Bright, H. A., and Hoffman, J. I., *Applied Inorganic Analysis with Special Reference to the Analysis of Metals, Minerals and Rocks,* 2nd ed., New York, Wiley, 1953, 1034 pp.

Meurice, A., and Meurice, C., *Cours d'analyse des produits des industries chimiques,* 3rd ed., 2 vols., Paris, Dunod, 1949–1952. It covers both organic and inorganic substances.

Proske, O., and Blumenthal, H. (eds.), *Analyse der Metalle,* 2nd ed., Berlin, Springer, 1949– . Three volumes announced.

Scott, W. W., and Furman, N. H. (eds.), *Standard Methods of Chemical Analysis,* 5th ed., 2 vols., New York, Van Nostrand, 1939. This covers both organic and inorganic substances.

Young, R. S., *Industrial Inorganic Analysis,* New York, Wiley, 1943, 368 pp.

Some other works on chemical analysis appear in other sections of this list. The American Society for Testing Materials publishes many books and pamphlets on analytical chemistry in its industrial aspects and these may be located by consulting the society's publication list.

8. Mineralogical and Geological Chemistry

Chamber's Mineralogical Dictionary, New York, Chemical Pub. Co., 1948, 47 pp. Defines terms.

Dana, E. S., *Minerals and How to Study Them,* 3rd ed., New York, Wiley, 1949. An excellent elementary textbook.

Dana, J. D., *System of Mineralogy,* 7th ed., 3 vols., rewritten and enlarged by Charles Palache and others, New York, Wiley, 1944– . Vol. 3 in preparation. A standard treatise.

Doelter, C., and Leitmeier, H. (eds.), *Handbuch der Mineralchemie,* 4 vols., 8 parts, Darmstadt, Steinkopff, 1912–1931. A very elaborate treatise on the chemistry of minerals.

Goldschmidt, V. M., *Geochemistry,* Muir, Alex (ed.), New York, Oxford Univ. Press, 1953, 730 pp. A wide survey of geochemistry and its applications.

Hay, M. H., *Chemical Index of Minerals,* London, British Museum, 1950, 609 pp. An index of mineral species and varieties arranged chemically with an alphabetical list of accepted mineral names and synonyms.

Rankama, K., and Sahama, T. G., *Geochemistry,* Chicago, Univ. of Chicago Press, 1950, 927 pp.

Schoeller, W. R., and Powell, A. R., *Analysis of Minerals and Ores of Rarer Elements,* New York, Hafner, 1956, 408 pp.

Smith, O. C., *Identification and Qualitative Chemical Analysis of Minerals,* 2nd ed., New York, Van Nostrand, 1953, 385 pp.

Winchell, A. N., *Elements of Optical Mineralogy,* 3 vols., New York, Wiley, 1950–1951. It covers principles, methods, descriptions of minerals and gives determinative tables.

34 BOOKS

Bateman, A. M., *Economic Mineral Deposits*, 2nd ed., New York, Wiley, 1950, 916 pp.

Dolbear, S. H., et al., *Industrial Minerals and Rocks*, New York, American Institute Mining and Metallurgical Engineers, 1949, 1156 pp.

Johnstone, S. J., *Minerals for the Chemical and Allied Industries*, New York, Wiley, 1954, 671 pp.

Ladoo, R. B., and Myer, W. M., *Nonmetallic Minerals*, New York, McGraw-Hill, 1951, 605 pp.

Niggli, Paul, *Rocks and Mineral Deposits*, San Francisco, Freeman, 1954, 563 pp.

Van Royen, W., et al., *The Mineral Resources of the World*, New York, Prentice-Hall, 1952– . A series of volumes will be issued. Vol. 2 is an Atlas of the World's Resources.

9. Metallurgy and Metallography

There are no large treatises on the chemical aspects of metallurgy, but a considerable quantity of metallurgy is included in Gmelin's *Handbuch der Anorganischen Chemie* (see page 26). Most of the books on metallurgy are devoted to a specific metal or process, or to one field of metallurgy. There are so many specialized works; it is possible to give here only books of the most general nature that are frequently useful. There are two guides to the literature of metallurgy that are useful; both are published by Richard Rimbach Associates, 921 Ridge Avenue, Pittsburgh, Pennsylvania. (*Guide to Foreign Sources of Metallurgical Literature*, by J. T. Milek, 1951, 95 pp., and *How to Find Metallurgical Information*, by Richard Rimbach, 1936, 32 pp.)

GENERAL METALLURGY

Goetzel, C. G., *Treatise on Powder Metallurgy*, 3 vols., New York, Interscience, 1949–1952.

Hayward, C. R., *Outline of Metallurgical Practice*, 3rd ed., New York, Van Nostrand, 1952, 740 pp. A comprehensive small work that covers the production of both iron and nonferrous metals from their ores.

Henderson, J. G., and Bates, J. M., *Metallurgical Dictionary*, New York, Reinhold, 1953, 416 pp. It defines terms.

Hoyt, S. L., *Metal Data*, 2nd ed., New York, Reinhold, 1953, 526 pp. It covers a variety of metallic properties for both ferrous and nonferrous metals and for alloys.

Lyon, N. R., *Liquid Metals*, 2nd ed., Washington, D. C., Government Printing Office, 1952, 269 pp.

Metals and Alloys, 5th ed., London, Louis Cassier Co., 1949, 214 pp. Gives the composition and specifications for over 4,500 nonferrous alloys.

Pryor, E. J., *An Introduction to Mineral Dressing*, London, Mining Publications, 1955, 649 pp.

Samans, C. H., *Engineering Metals and Their Alloys*, New York, Macmillan, 1949, 915 pp. It is a good reference book for general information on ferrous and nonferrous metallurgy.
Taylor, L. (ed.), *Metals Handbook*, Cleveland, Ohio, American Society for Metals, 1948 edition, 1444 pp. Revised frequently. It is a very useful and comprehensive collection of data and general information on metals.
Smithells, J. C. (ed.), *Metals Reference Book*, 2nd ed., 2 vols., New York, Interscience, 1955. A comprehensive collection of data on metallurgy and metal physics.
Woldman, N. E., *Engineering Alloys*, 3rd ed., Cleveland, Amer. Soc. for Metals, 1954, 1034 pp.

FERROUS METALLURGY

Brashford, G. R., *The Manufacture of Iron and Steel*, 2 vols., London, Chapman & Hall, 1949–1951.
Piwowarsky, E., *Hochwertigs Gusseisen, seine Eigenschaften und die physikalische Metallurgie seiner Herstellung*, 2nd ed., Berlin, Springer, 1951, 1070 pp. A valuable work on cast-iron.
Teichert, E. J., *Ferrous Metallurgy*, 2nd ed., in 3 vols., New York, McGraw-Hill, 1944. This is apparently the most recent work for all of ferrous metallurgy.
The Making, Shaping and Treating of Steel, 6th ed., Pittsburgh, Pa., The United States Steel Co., 1952. A standard reference work for the practical side of making steel.

NONFERROUS METALLURGY

Liddell, D. M. (ed.), *Handbook of Nonferrous Metallurgy*, 2nd ed., 2 vols., New York, McGraw-Hill, 1945. It is not a handbook in the usual sense of the word, but a work on the principles and processes of metallurgy. It is, apparently, the most recent work for all of nonferrous metallurgy.
Mathewson, C. H., et al., *Modern Uses of Nonferrous Metals*, 2nd ed., New York, American Institute Mining and Metallurgical Engs., 1953, 530 pp.
Institute of Mining and Metallurgy, *Refining of Nonferrous Metals*, London, The Institute, 1950, 515 pp.

CORROSION

Uhlig, H. H., *The Corrosion Handbook*, New York, Wiley, 1948, 1118 pp. Sponsored by the Electrochemical Society.
Evans, U. R., *Metallic Corrosion; Passivity and Protection*, 2nd ed., London, Arnold, 1946, 900 pp.
Speller, F. N., *Corrosion: Causes and Prevention*, New York, McGraw-Hill, 1951, 686 pp.
Ritter, F., *Korrosionstabellen metallischer Werkstoffe*, 3rd ed., Vienna, Springer, 1952, 283 pp. It contains much foreign data that are not found in other works.
Rabald, E., *Corrosion Guide*, New York, Elsevier, 1951, 629 pp. It covers over 40 materials, metals and nonmetals, and over 250 corrosive agents.

Cleaning, Coating, Finishing

Burns, R. M., and Bradley, W. W., *Protective Coatings for Metals*, New York, Reinhold, 1955, 640 pp. ACS Monograph.

Siliman, H., *Chemical and Electroplated Finishes*, 2nd ed., London, Chapman & Hall, 1952.

Machu, W., *Metallische Überzüge*, 3rd ed., Leipzig, Geest-Portig, 1948, 672 pp. It includes electroplating.

Vogel, O., *Handbuch der Metallbeizerei*, 2nd ed., 2 vols., Berlin, Verlag Chemie, 1951. Edited by H. Vogel and A. Keller. It covers cleaning and pickling of both iron and nonferrous metals.

Metallography

Barrett, C. S., *Structure of Metals*, 2nd ed., New York, McGraw-Hill, 1952, 661 pp. It includes crystallographic methods, principles, and data; it is an inclusive and up-to-date work.

Darken, L. S., and Gurry, R. W., *Physical Chemistry of Metals*, New York, McGraw-Hill, 1953, 835 pp.

Masing, G. (ed.), *Handbuch der Metallphysik*, 3 vols., 5 parts, Berlin, Akad. Verlagsges, 1935–1941. A comprehensive treatise.

Rolfe, R. T., *Dictionary of Metallography*, 2nd ed., London, Chapman & Hall, 1949, 300 pp.

10. Organic Chemistry

Large Treatises

Beilstein's Handbuch der organischen Chemie long reigned supreme as the general reference work for its field. Perhaps it has a competitor in Elsevier's *Encyclopaedia of Organic Chemistry*. Both endeavor to cover all organic compounds known up to a certain date; the dates differ and this will be discussed later. At the present time Beilstein and Elsevier supplement each other because there is a big difference in their publication schedules and a reference library must own both works; this may continue to be true. Beilstein includes the patent literature and Elsevier changed its original policy and included patents in volumes published in 1951 and thereafter.

The third large treatise on organic chemistry is Grignard's *Traité de chimie organique*. This treats the subject in a different way than do Beilstein and Elsevier; they give detailed information for every compound, one by one, but Grignard summarizes the knowledge of many phases of organic chemistry and of the various classes of compounds.

BEILSTEIN

Beilstein's Handbuch der organischen Chemie, 4th edition, edited by Bernard Prager and Paul Jacobson and later by F. Richter, started publication in 1918 (Berlin, Springer). Main series (Hauptwerk), Vols. 1–31 (1918–1940); 1st supplement (Erganzungswerk), Vols. 1–27 (1928–1938); 2nd supplement, Vols. 1–27 (1941–1955); 3rd supplement 1956–   . The main series, Vols. 1–27, includes all organic compounds of known structure to 1910; the first supplement includes those that are new and new information on those in the main work for the period 1910 to 1920. Volume 28 for the main work and the first supplement is the collective subject index for both of them. Volume 29 for the main work and the first supplement is the formula index for both of them. Volumes 30 and 31 of the main series are not covered by the indexes in Volumes 28 and 29. The second supplement covers the literature of the period 1920 to 1930; the third supplement will cover 1930 to 1950. There are two issues of Volume 6 of the second supplement, one of 1943, and the other of 1949, which is the revised and corrected volume. Beilstein is invaluable to the organic chemist.

The system of classification used in Beilstein is elaborate and to make the most effective use of this reference work it should be understood. Volume 1 (1918) of the main work explains this system of classification; there are several separate publications devoted to it. The most comprehensive is Prager, Stern, and Ilberg's *System der organischen Verbindungen: ein Leifaden für Benutzung von Beilstein's Handbuch der organischen Chemie* (Berlin, Springer, 1929, 246 pp.); it explains the system, lists the 4,877 classes, and gives a class index. For most purposes E. H. Huntress' excellent book is sufficient (*A Brief Introduction to the Use of Beilstein's Handbuch der organischen Chemie*, 4th ed., New York, Wiley, 1938, 44 pp.). The subject and formula indexes for the main series and the first supplement are guides to the entire work, but they do not eliminate the need for a working knowledge of the system of classification. Each volume of Beilstein and its supplements has a subject index.

The 4th edition of Beilstein is divided into four divisions and 4877 classes (Systemnummer) of which the first three divisions have been issued completely in 27 volumes. The supplements carry the same volume numbers as the main series and refer to it.

The first three divisions, system numbers 1–4720, cover the compounds of known structure. The fourth division, system numbers

4271–4877, was intended to cover organic compounds of unknown or uncertain structure; this division is incomplete. Volume numbers 30 and above fall in division IV. How much of division IV will be issued is uncertain because the knowledge of naturally occurring substances, as, for example, carbohydrates, proteins and steroids, is growing so rapidly.

One may well pause to pay tribute to the founder of the "Handbuch"—Friederich Konrad Beilstein, who as a compiler possessed monumental patience and industry. He was a Russian by birth and a professor in the Technological Institute, St. Petersburg (Leningrad), but he studied in Germany and the handbook has always been in German. He issued the first edition in 1881–1883, the second in 1886–1890, and the third in 1892–1899, but thereafter gave over the task of continuing his labors to the Deutsche Chemische Gesellschaft.

An interesting account of Beilstein's life and the history of his "Handbuch" is found in the papers of Huntress [5] and Richter.[6]

The German Chemical Society actually assumed responsibility for Beilstein's *Handbuch* in 1896, and issued the supplement to the third edition in 1906, just before Beilstein's death. The first three editions of Beilstein are of interest now historically and for occasionally identifying the abbreviations of journal names. The German Chemical Society later formed the Beilstein Institute, which still prepares the manuscript of the *Handbuch*. Friederich Richter, present editor of Beilstein's *Handbuch*, is the director of the Institute.

ELSEVIER

Elsevier's Encyclopaedia of Organic Chemistry, edited by Dr. F. Radt, started publication in 1946 with volume 14 (Amsterdam and New York, Elsevier Press). This treatise is written in English. It is highly regarded by organic chemists as a comprehensive source of reliable information. Elsevier gives the formula, constitution, occurrence, physical properties, reactions, and methods of preparation, along with references to the literature, for each compound as Beilstein does, but more emphasis is put on the biochemical properties than is done in Beilstein. Elsevier's *Encyclopaedia* has other new features: tables, diagrams, and flow sheets that are helpful. This encyclopaedia was announced to appear in 20 volumes. However, by the end of 1956 only Volumes 12, 13, and 14, together with supplements for Volume 14, had appeared. It is understood that publication will probably cease after one more volume of the encyclopaedia is issued.

GRIGNARD

Grignard's Traité de chimie organique started publication in 1935 (Paris, Masson) and is very nearly complete. It was announced to be in 24 volumes; Volume 22 was issued in 1953 and Volume 19 in 1954. Victor Grignard was the editor in the beginning, but since his death G. Dupont and R. Locquin have edited it. Some of the volumes have been revised and some just reprinted since 1945. It is a very comprehensive work and is useful when a summary of knowledge on some class of compounds or some phase of organic chemistry is needed. It gives numerous references to the literature but does not attempt to cover all of the organic compounds known at the time it was published. Grignard's own scheme of nomenclature, explained in Volume 1, is used in this treatise.

A reference library should own this French work because it serves a different need than Beilstein and Elsevier do.

OTHER REFERENCE WORKS

A number of smaller reference works on organic chemistry exist, but only the most recent or generally useful ones are given here:

Fieser, L. F., and Fieser, M., *Organic Chemistry*, 3rd ed., New York, Reinhold, 1956, 1150 pp. A comprehensive text and reference work.

Gilman, Henry (ed.), *Organic Chemistry*, 4 vols., New York, Wiley, 1943–1954. This treatise is really a collection of reviews that cover nearly all phases of organic chemistry.

Groggins, P. H., *Unit Processes in Organic Syntheses*, 4th ed., New York, McGraw-Hill, 1952, 899 pp. It is a text, but it is useful for general information on industrial methods.

Heilbron's *Dictionary of Organic Compounds*, 2nd ed., 4 vols., New York, Oxford Univ. Press, 1953. Sir Ian Heilbron and H. M. Dunbury are editors-in-chief. This indispensable work is an encyclopedia that gives the constitution, physical and chemical properties of the principal carbon compounds and their derivatives, together with the relevant literature references.

Organic Reactions (Roger Adams, editor-in-chief), New York, Wiley. This valuable work started publication in 1942; a volume appears about annually. It gives critical discussions that include the selection of experimental techniques and references to the literature.

Patterson, A. M., and Capell, L. T., *The Ring Index*, New York, Reinhold, 1940, 661 pp. This is a systematized collection of parent ring systems found in the organic literature up to 1939.

Rodd, E. H. (ed.), *Chemistry of Carbon Compounds*, Houston, Texas, Elsevier, 1952–   . This work was announced to be in 5 volumes in 7 parts and to be completed in 1956. The major portion has appeared.

It is an excellent reference work that covers all of organic chemistry; it includes a wealth of references to the literature.

Whitmore, F. C., *Organic Chemistry*, 2nd ed., New York, Van Nostrand, 1951, 960 pp. An unusually comprehensive text that gives references to the literature. It is one of the most useful works in one volume.

SPECIAL TOPICS

The number of works on organic chemistry devoted to one class of compounds, to a specific topic, or to selected topics is too large to list even the most important ones here. See the section on analytical chemistry (page 31) for organic analysis. The following books on theoretical organic chemistry are given because this important phase of the subject is either omitted or given limited consideration in the reference works already listed.

Badger, G. M., *The Structures and Reactions of the Aromatic Compounds*, New York, Cambridge Univ. Press, 1954, 456 pp.

Hermans, P. H., *An Introduction to Theoretical Organic Chemistry*, Houston, Elsevier, 1954, 520 pp. The lists of books at the ends of the chapters include nearly all of the books on theoretical organic chemistry published before 1954.

Hine, Jack, *Physical Organic Chemistry*, New York, McGraw-Hill, 1955, 492 pp.

Hückel, Walter, *Theoretical Principles of Organic Chemistry*, 2 vols., Houston, Elsevier, 1955–1956. A translation and revision of the 7th German edition (Leipzig, Geest & Portig, 1954). A comprehensive and lucid discussion of an important subject.

Ingold, C. K., *Structure and Mechanism in Organic Chemistry*, Ithaca, Cornell Univ. Press, 1953, 835 pp. An outstanding book.

Pullman, B., and Pullman, A., *Les théories électroniques de la chimie organique*, Paris, Masson, 1952, 665 pp.

Wheland, G. W., *Resonance in Organic Chemistry*, New York, Wiley, 1955, 846 pp.

LABORATORY

Houben-Weyl's *Die Methoden der organischen Chemie* is one of the most important reference works; it covers synthesis, organic analysis, and methods for performing almost every kind of reaction. References to the literature are numerous. The 3rd edition (4 vols.) appeared in 1925–1941 (Stuttgart, Thieme). The 4th edition, edited by E. Müller and published by Thieme, started to appear in 1952; it was announced to be in about 14 volumes.

Meyer, H. J. L., *Lehrbuch der organisch-chemischen Methodik*, 5th and 6th eds., 3 vols. in 6 parts, Berlin, Springer, 1933–1940. Covers both synthetic and analytical work.

Organic Syntheses, editors vary, New York, Wiley, 1921– . An annual compilation of satisfactory and tested methods for preparing organic compounds. There is a collective volume every ten years. It is an indispensable work.

Technique of Organic Chemistry, A. Weissberger (ed.), New York, Interscience. Nine volumes have been issued since 1948, and others are in preparation. This is another important reference work; it describes the various techniques and the equipment used, and also gives the theoretical background.

Theilheimer, W., *Synthetic Methods of Organic Chemistry,* New York, Interscience, 1948– . An annual publication that gives a critical review of current literature on new methods and significant variations on known or older methods. Volume 1 covers the period 1942–1944.

Velluz, Leon, and others (eds.), *Substances naturelles de synthèse,* Paris, Masson, 1951– . Directions for preparing the substances are taken from modern literature and supplemented by notes based on the experience of industrial chemists. About three small volumes appear annually.

Wagner, R., and Zook, H., *Synthetic Organic Chemistry,* New York, Wiley, 1953, 887 pp. For a one-volume work this is unusually comprehensive. It gives over 550 summaries of methods used in synthetic organic chemistry and thousands of references to the literature.

11. Biological Chemistry

There are relatively few works that cover all of biochemistry; and these are either treatises which are largely out of date or textbooks. The tendency in this field is towards specialized works on the various aspects of biochemistry. Only books of general interest are given here, and those that cover laboratory methods are listed separately.

Abderhalden, Emil (ed.), *Biochemisches Handlexikon,* 15 vols., Berlin, Springer, 1911–1933. The last 8 volumes are supplements. This treatise attempts to cover all compounds that occur in nature and to give their chemical, physical and physiological properties. It is out of date in some respects, but it contains much useful information and is still an important reference work. The references to the literature are very complete.

Baldwin, E., *An Introduction to Comparative Biochemistry,* 3rd ed., London, Cambridge Univ. Press, 1949, 164 pp.

Baldwin, E. J., *Dynamic Aspects of Biochemistry,* 2nd ed., London, Cambridge Univ. Press, 1952, 544 pp.

Bonner, James, *Plant Biochemistry,* New York, Academic Press, 1950, 550 pp.

Bourne, G. H., and Kidder, G. W. (eds.), *Biochemistry and Physiology of Nutrition,* 2 vols., New York, Academic Press, 1953. It is not limited to human nutrition.

Buchanan, R. E., and Fulmer, E. J., *Physiology and Biochemistry of Bacteria,* 3 vols., Baltimore, Williams & Wilkins, 1928–1930.

Foster, J. W., *Chemical Activities of Fungi,* New York, Academic Press, 1949, 640 pp.

Fruton, J. S., and Simmonds, S., *General Biochemistry,* New York, Wiley,

1953, 940 pp. This is a graduate level textbook, and it has numerous references to the literature.

Flaschentrager, B., and Lehnartz, E. (eds.), *Physiologische Chemie*, Berlin, Springer, 1951– . It is a continuation of O. Hammarsten's *Lehrbuch der physiologischen Chemie*, which was a standard text and reference work for many years. The present work will be in several volumes.

Gortner's *Outline of Biochemistry*, 3rd ed., New York, Wiley, 1949, 1074 pp. Ross A. Gortner wrote this work, but this edition was edited by R. A. Gortner, Jr. and W. A. Gortner. It is a comprehensive text and gives references to the literature.

Heilbrunn, L. V., *The Dynamics of Living Protoplasm*, New York, Academic Press, 1956, 327 pp.

Hunter, E. H., and Lwoff, A., *Biochemistry and Physiology of Protozoa*, 2 vols., New York, Academic Press, 1955.

Oppenheimer, C., *Handbuch der Biochemie des Menschen und der Tiere*, Jena, Fischer, 1923–1936. The main work is in 9 vols. (1923–1930); supplements appeared for Vols. 1–2 (1933–1936). It is a very complete reference work.

Rabinowitch, E. I., *Photosynthesis and Related Processes*, 2 vols. in 3 parts, New York, Interscience, 1945–1956.

Sexton, W. A., *Chemical Constitution and Biological Activity*, 2nd ed., London, Spon, 1953, 412 pp.

Sherman, H. C., *Chemistry of Foods and Nutrition*, 8th ed., New York, Macmillan, 1952, 721 pp.

Thimann, K. V., *The Life of Bacteria*, New York, Macmillan, 1955, 775 pp. This book supplements and brings up to date many of the topics that Buchanan and Fulmer discussed in their books.

Walker, B. S., Boyd, W. C., and Asimov, I., *Biochemistry and Human Metabolism*, 2nd ed., Baltimore, Williams & Wilkins, 1954, 916 pp.

West, E. S., and Todd, W. R., *Textbook of Biochemistry*, 2nd ed., New York, Macmillan, 1954, 1345 pp. Comprehensive.

White, A., Handler, P., Smith, E. L., and Stetten, DeW., *Principles of Biochemistry*, New York, 1954, 1117 pp. A comprehensive work with numerous references to the literature.

LABORATORY

Abderhalden, Emil (ed.), *Handbuch der Biologischen Arbeitsmethoden*, 2nd ed., Berlin, Urban and Schwarzenberg, 1920–1939. A very comprehensive collection of treatises on all manner of laboratory procedure in biochemistry. There are 106 volumes and one index in this edition.

Biochemistry Preparations, editors vary, New York, Wiley, 1949– . It is now an annual publication that gives directions for satisfactory methods. This series should be in every chemical library.

Dunn, M. S., and Drell, W., *Experiments in Biochemistry*, New York, McGraw-Hill, 1951, 216 pp. An advanced laboratory manual.

Hawk, P. B., Oser, B. L., and Summerson, W. H., *Practical Physiological Chemistry*, 13th ed., Philadelphia, Blakiston, 1954, 1439 pp. A very comprehensive collection of directions for analytical and preparative work in biochemistry. A standard work.

Hoppe-Seyler and Thierfelder, *Handbuch der physiologisch und patholo-gisch chemischen Analyse*, K. Lang, and E. Lahnartz (eds.), 10th ed., 5 vols., Berlin, Springer, 1953–   .

Klein, G., *Handbuch der Pflanzeanalyse*, 4 vols. in 6 parts, Berlin, Springer, 1931–1933. A comprehensive work on the chemical analysis of plants for both organic and inorganic constituents.

Methods of Biochemical Analysis, David Glick (ed.), New York, Inter-science, 1954–   . This annual publication should be very useful.

Standard Methods of Clinical Chemistry, M. Reiner (ed.), New York, Academic Press, 1953–   .

12. Foods

Blanck, F. C. (ed.), *Handbook of Food and Agriculture*, New York, Rein-hold, 1955, 1000 pp.

Bömer, Juckenack, and Tillmans, *Handbuch der Lebensmittel-chemie*, 9 vols., Berlin, Springer, 1933–1942. A comprehensive work on the composition and analysis of foods.

Crosbie-Walsh, T., et al., *Food Industries Manual*, 16th ed., London, Hill, 1949, 1172 pp. It covers food technology and analysis, and summarizes progress in the industry.

Jacobs, M. B., *The Chemical Analysis of Foods and Food Products*, 2nd ed., New York, Van Nostrand, 1951, 926 pp.

Jacobs, M. B. (ed.), *The Chemistry and Technology of Foods and Food Products*, 2nd ed., 3 vols., New York, Interscience, 1951. A comprehen-sive standard work.

Nicholls, J. R., *Aids to the Analysis of Foods and Drugs*, London, Bailliere-Tindall-Cox, 1952, 516 pp.

Parker, M. E., et al., *Elements of Food Engineering*, 3 vols., New York, Reinhold, 1952–1954.

Sherman, H. C., *Food Products*, 4th ed., New York, Macmillan, 1948, 428 pp. A standard text and reference work.

Winton, A. L., and Winton, K. B., *Structure and Composition of Foods*, 4 vols., New York, Wiley, 1932–1939. A very comprehensive, standard reference work.

13. Chemical Industry

Aeby, J., *Dangerous Goods and Others*, 4th ed., Antwerp, Aversois, 1955, 670 pp.

Baud, Paul, *Traité de chimie industrielle*, 4th ed. in 3 vols., Paris, Masson, 1951. It is unusually comprehensive and is useful as a small encyclopedia.

Brown, G. G., et al., *Unit Operations*, New York, Wiley, 1950, 612 pp.

Carlson, A. S. (ed.), *Economic Geography of Industrial Materials*, New York, Reinhold, 1956, 500 pp. This book gives the facts and data needed to determine the location of a plant for a process industry and discusses the factors involved.

Coulson, J. M., and Richardson, J. F., *Chemical Engineering*, 2 vols., New York, McGraw-Hill, 1955–1956. A textbook.

Dammer, O., *Chemische Technologie der Neuzeit*, 2nd ed., 5 vols., Stuttgart,

Enke, 1925–1932. This and the first edition deal with a wide variety of products and are still useful in patent searches.

Encyclopedia of Chemical Technology, edited by R. E. Kirk, and D. F. Othmer, 15 vols. and index, New York, Interscience, 1947–1956. The arrangement is alphabetical, the bibliographies are extensive, and patents are included in the references. It is an indispensable work. It gives a comprehensive summary of industrial knowledge on materials, processes and equpiment. The very full system of cross references facilitates its use.

Eucken, A., and Jakob, M. (eds.), *Der Chemie-Ingenieur: Ein Handbuch der physikalischen Arbeitsmethoden in chemischen und verwandten Industrie-Betrieben,* 3 vols. in 14 parts, Leipzig, Akad. Verlagsges, 1932–1940. This treatise is out of date in some respects, but it is the most comprehensive work available and is still a valuable reference work.

Faith, W. L., Keyes, D. B., and Clark, R. L., *Industrial Chemicals,* New York, Wiley, 1950, 652 pp. It gives the manufacture, uses, and data for 106 of the most important chemicals.

Freund, Hugo (ed.), *Handbuch der Mikroskopie in der Technik,* Frankfurt/ Main, Umschau Verlag, 1951– . A treatise that covers a wide variety of materials, most of them of chemical interest. Announced to be in 8 vols.

Gregory, T. C. (ed.), *Uses and Applications of Chemicals and Related Materials,* 2 vols., New York, Reinhold, 1939–1944. It covers nearly 8,000 substances, includes synonyms and gives a list of patents.

Handbuch der Werkstoffprufung, E. Siebel (ed.), 2nd ed., 6 vols., Berlin, Springer, 1950– . A standard German work that is similar to, but does not have exactly the same coverage as, the American Society for Testing Materials publication (page 32 of this book).

Hougen, O. A., Watson, K. M., and Ragatz, R. A., *Chemical Process Principles,* 2nd ed., 3 vols., New York, Wiley, 1954 (in progress).

Jordon, D. G., *Chemical Pilot Plant Practice,* New York, Interscience Chemical Engineering and Technology Library, 1955, 152 pp.

Merewether, E. R. A. (ed.), *Industrial Medicine and Hygiene,* 3 vols., London, Butterworth, 1954.

Modern Chemical Processes, edited by the Editors of *Industrial and Engineering Chemistry,* New York, Reinhold, 1950– . These volumes, published every two years, are a collected group of articles that appeared originally in the periodical *Industrial and Engineering Chemistry;* these are augmented somewhat by the editors in conjunction with the technical staffs of cooperating chemical organizations. These volumes are among the most valuable reference sources available on modern American chemical technology.

Perry, John H. (ed.), *Chemical Engineers Handbook,* 3rd ed., New York, McGraw-Hill, 1950, 1884 pp.

Perry, J. H. (ed.), *Chemical Business Handbook,* New York, McGraw-Hill, 1954, 1335 pp.

Riegel, E. R., *Industrial Chemistry,* 5th ed., New York, Reinhold, 1949, 1020 pp.

Rodger's *Manual of Industrial Chemistry,* C. C. Furnas (ed.), 2 vols., New York, Van Nostrand, 1942.

Sax, N. I., *Handbook of Dangerous Materials*, New York, Reinhold, 1951, 848 pp.

Shreve, R. N., *The Chemical Process Industries*, 2nd ed., New York, McGraw-Hill, 1956, 1000 pp.

Snell, F. D., and Snell, C. T., *Chemicals of Commerce*, New York, Van Nostrand, 1952, 587 pp.

Ullmann's *Enzyklopaedie der technischen Chemie*, edited by Wilhelm Foerst, 3rd ed., 14 vols., Berlin, Urban & Schwarzenberg, 1950– . A standard reference work. This edition has a new feature: two supplementary volumes are included that cover the construction of chemical apparatus, chemical engineering processes, factory laboratories, and industrial analyses. The alphabetical arrangement of the topics is retained. The bibliographies are good and include patents. The older editions are still useful in patent searches because material has been omitted to keep the size of the work down. The 1st edition (12 vols.) appeared in 1914–1923, and the 2nd (11 vols.) in 1928–1932. Ullmann's work was the best of its kind until the *Encyclopedia of Chemical Technology* appeared.

Winnacker, K., and Weingartner, E. (eds.), *Chemische Technologie*, 5 vols., Munich, Carl Hanser Verlag, 1950–1954. This encyclopedia covers organic and inorganic chemicals and metallurgy.

13a. Chemical Market Research

Campbell, M. J., and Crass, M. F., *Chemical Facts and Figures*, 3rd ed., Washington, D. C., The Manufacturing Chemists Assoc., 1950, 429 pp.

Chaddock, R. S. (ed.), *Chemical Market Research in Practice*, New York, Reinhold, 1956, 208 pp. Contributors of chapters in this book are members of the Chemical Market Research Association. A chapter on effective utilization of the literature, bibliographies, and lists of information sources are included.

Guide to Foreign Government Information Services, Washington, D. C., Chamber of Commerce of U. S., 1949, 31 pp.

Chemical Economics Handbook, Stanford, California, Stanford Research Institute, 1950– . An annual publication.

Coman, E. T., *Sources of Business Information*, New York, Prentice-Hall, 1949, 406 pp. This is an indispensable book.

Corley, H. M., *Successful Commercial Chemical Development*, New York, Wiley, 1955, 374 pp. Sponsored by the Commercial Chemical Development Association.

Lawrence, R. M. (ed.), *Sources of Information for Industrial Market Research*, New York, Chemical Industries, 1948, 95 pp. This work is limited to the chemical process industries; the papers were originally published in *Chemical Industries*, 1945–1947.

Literature Resources for Chemical Process Industries, no. 10 in *Advances in Chemistry Series*, Washington, D. C., American Chemical Society, 1954, 582 pp.

Randall, L. E., and Sharpnach, D. M., *Market Research Sources* (U. S. Bureau of Foreign and Domestic Commerce, *Domestic Commerce Series*, no. 20, 9th ed., 1950), Washington, D. C., Government Printing Office.

46 BOOKS

This is a comprehensive and exhaustive guide to domestic sources of information. It is indispensable. This edition emphasizes the postwar materials; it is not cumulative, so those who are interested in older material must consult earlier editions.

Thompson, R. B., *A Selected and Annotated Bibliography of Marketing Research*, Austin, Texas, Univ. of Texas (College of Business Administration, Bibliography no. 8, 1951, 32 pp.). This is comprehensive and contains much of interest to chemical industries.

World Chemical Directory, New York, Atlas Publishing Co., 1949, 702 pp. An international index of manufacturers, importers, and exporters of chemicals, drugs, plastics, and oils.

World Production of Raw Materials, Information Paper no. 18, New York, The Royal Institute of International Affairs, 542 Fifth Avenue, 1953, 104 pp.

14. Water, Sewage and Sanitation

Babbit, H. E., *Sewage and Sewage Treatment*, 7th ed., New York, Wiley, 1953, 674 pp.

Hobbs, A. T., and Hobbs, J. E., *Manual of British Water Supply Practice*, London, Institution of Water Engineers, 1950, 927 pp.

Hopkins, E. S., and Shultz, W. H., *The Practice of Sanitation*, 2nd ed., Baltimore, Williams & Wilkins, 1954, 466 pp.

Nordell, Eskell, *Water Treatment for Industrial and Other Uses*, New York, Reinhold, 1951, 526 pp.

Phelps, E. B., *Public Health Engineering*, 2 vols., New York, Wiley, 1948–1950.

Rudolfs, Willem (ed.), *Industrial Wastes: Their Disposal and Treatment*, New York, Reinhold, 1953, 450 pp. ACS Monograph.

Water Quality and Treatment, 2nd ed., New York, The American Water Works Association, 1950.

15. Soils and Fertilizers

Bear, F. E., *Chemistry of the Soil*, New York, Reinhold, 1955, 384 pp. ACS Monograph.

Blanck, F. C. (ed.), *Handbook of Food and Agriculture*, New York, Reinhold, 1955, 1000 pp.

Frear, D. E. H. (ed.), *Agricultural Chemistry*, 2 vols., New York, Van Nostrand, 1950–1951.

Hall, A. D., *Fertilizer and Manure*, rev. ed., London, Murray, 1949, 333 pp.

Jacob, K. D., *Fertilizer Technology and Resources in the United States*, New York, Academic Press, 1953, 454 pp.

Kitchen, H. B., *Diagnostic Techniques for Soils and Crops*, Washington, D. C., American Potash Institute, 1948, 308 pp. An excellent book.

Lyon, L. T., Buchman, H. D., and Brady, N. C., *Nature and Properties of Soils*, 5th ed., New York, Macmillan, 1952, 608 pp. An excellent textbook.

Menozzi, A., *Trattato di chimica vegetale e agraria*, 4 vols., Milan, Hoepli, 1946–1952. Volume 4 is on chemical analysis.

Scheffer, Fritz, *Lehrbuch der Agrikulturchemie*, 3rd ed., 5 vols., Stuttgart,

Enke, 1952–   . Most of it is devoted to soils, plant nutrition, and microbiology of soils.

Shawarbi, M. Y., *Soil Chemistry*, New York, Wiley, 1952, 417 pp. A comprehensive work with good bibliographies.

15a. Pesticides and Crop-Control Agents

Frear, D. E. H., *Pesticide Handbook*, State College, Penn., College Science Publishers, 1954, 196 pp. Gives 5,763 product listings on fungicides, herbicides, rodenticides, soil conditioners, and equipment.

Frear, D. E. H., *A Catalogue of Insecticides and Fungicides*, 2 vols., Waltham, Mass., Chronica Botanica, 1947–1948. It lists 1,450 substances.

Frear, D. E. H., *Chemistry of Pesticides*, New York, Van Nostrand, 1955, 469 pp. A valuable reference book.

DeOng, E. R., *Chemistry and Uses of Pesticides*, 2nd ed., New York, Reinhold, 1956, 500 pp.

Hunt, G. M., and Garrett, G. A., *Wood Preservation*, New York, McGraw-Hill, 1953, 417 pp.

Marine Fouling and Its Prevention, Annapolis, Md., U. S. Naval Institute, 1952, 388 pp.

Martin, H., and Mills, J. R. W., *Guide to the Chemicals Used in Crop Protection*, London, Canada, Univ. of Western Ontario, 1952, 236 pp.

Tukey, H. B., *Plant Regulators in Agriculture*, New York, Wiley, 1955, 269 pp.

16. Fermentation Industries

Herstein, K. M., and Jacobs, M. B., *Chemistry and Technology of Wines and Liquors*, New York, Van Nostrand, 1948, 436 pp.

Hopkins, R. H., and Krause, B., *Biochemistry Applied to Malting and Brewing*, London, Allen & Unwin, 1948, 342 pp.

Lüers, H., *Die Hefe*, Nürnberg, H. Carl, 1949, 356 pp. This work on yeast includes an annotated bibliography of over 1,200 references to its chemistry, physiology, and technology.

Prescott, A. C., and Dunn, C. G., *Industrial Microbiology*, New York, McGraw-Hill, 1949, 923 pp.

Underkofler, L. A., and Hickey, R. J. (eds.), *Industrial Fermentations*, 2 vols., New York, Chemical Publishing Co., 1954. A comprehensive work, not limited to alcoholic fermentation; it covers the production of a number of chemicals and pharmaceuticals.

17. Pharmaceuticals, Cosmetics, and Perfumes

PHARMACEUTICALS

Burger, Alfred, *Medicinal Chemistry*, 2 vols., New York, Interscience, 1951–1953. It is the best and most comprehensive work available at the present time.

Dolique, R., *Précis de chimie minérale pharmaceutique*, Paris, Maloine, 1952, 1380 pp. This work supplements Burger (see above) who gives little space to inorganic compounds.

Findlay, G. M. (ed.), *Recent Advances in Chemotherapy*, 3rd ed., 4 vols., London, Churchill, 1950– . A very comprehensive reference work.

Garratt, D. C., *The Quantitative Analysis of Drugs*, 2nd ed., New York, Philosophical Library, 1955, 670 pp.

Howard, M. E. (ed.), *Modern Drug Encyclopedia and Therapeutic Index*, 5th ed., New York, Drug Publications, 1952, 1431 pp. Revised frequently.

Houben, Joseph, *Fortschritte der Heilstoffchemie*, Berlin, de Gruyter, 1926–1939. The first part in 6 volumes and 7 parts covers the German patents on medicinals from 1877 through 1928, and the second part in 4 volumes and 4 parts covers journal literature.

International Pharmacopoeia, Geneva, The World Health Organization, 1951– . It is available from the Columbia Univ. Press, New York. To be in several volumes.

Jenkins, G. L., Christian, J. E., and Hager, G. P., *Quantitative Pharmaceutical Chemistry*, 4th ed., New York, McGraw-Hill, 1953, 534 pp.

Kaufmann, H. P., *Arzneimittel-Synthese*, Berlin, Springer, 1953, 834 pp.

The Merck Index of Chemicals and Drugs, 6th ed., Rahway, New Jersey, Merck & Co., 1952, 1167 pp. A very useful encyclopedia.

The National Formulary, 10th ed., Washington, D. C., American Pharmaceutical Assoc., 1955, 867 pp.

Osol, A., and Farrar, G. E. (eds.), *The Dispensatory of the United States of America*, 25th ed., Philadelphia, Lippincott, 1950, 2,000 pp. It is a wealth of information.

Reddish, G. F. (ed.), *Antiseptics, Disinfectants, Fungicides, and Chemical and Physical Sterilization*, Philadelphia, Lea & Febiger, 1954, 841 pp. This work covers antimicrobic agents generally, but excludes antibiotics and chemotherapeutic agents.

Suter, C. M. (ed.), *Medicinal Chemistry*, New York, Wiley, 1951– . A series of reviews prepared under the auspices of the Division of Medicinal Chemistry of the American Chemical Society.

The United States Pharmacopoeia, 15th ed., Easton, Pennsylvania, Mack Printing Co., 1955, 1,232 pp.

PERFUMES AND COSMETICS

Bedoukian, P. Z., *Perfumery Synthetics and Isolates*, New York, Van Nostrand, 1951, 496 pp.

Guenther, Ernest, *The Essential Oils*, 6 vols., New York, Van Nostrand, 1948–1952. It is the best and most comprehensive work available in this field of chemistry.

Greenberg, L. A., Lester, D., and Haggard, H. W., *Handbook of Cosmetic Materials*, New York, Interscience, 1954, 455 pp. It gives formulas, properties, uses, toxic action, and dermatologic action for about 1,000 materials.

Moncrieff, R. W., *The Chemistry of Perfumery Materials*, London, United Trade Press, 1949, 344 pp. A very comprehensive work.

West, T. F., et al., *Synthetic Perfumes; Their Chemistry and Preparation*. London, Arnold, 1949, 388 pp.

Poucher, W. A., *Perfumes, Cosmetics and Soaps*, 6th ed., 3 vols., New York,

Van Nostrand, 1942. A standard work. A French translation is being issued by Dunod (Paris).

Janistyn, Hugo, *Reichstoffe, Seifen, Kosmetika,* 2 vols., Heidelberg, Hüthig, 1950. This work is similar to Poucher's (see above).

18. Acids, Alkalies, Salts, and Other Heavy Chemicals

There is no comprehensive work in this field; only monographs, each of which is on a specific compound or on several closely related ones, exist. See the works on industrial chemistry (page 43) for information on heavy chemicals.

19. Glass, Clay Products, Refractories, and Enameled Metals

Davis, Pearce, *The Development of the American Glass Industry,* Cambridge, Mass., Harvard Univ. Press, 1949, 300 pp.

Dralle, Robert, *Die Glasfabrikation,* 2nd ed., 2 vols., Munchen, Oldenbourg, 1926–1931. A standard reference work.

Koenig, J. H., and Earhart, W. H., *Literature Abstracts of Ceramic Glazes,* 2nd ed., Philadelphia, College Offset Press, 1951, 395 pp.

Morey, G. W., *The Properties of Glass,* 2nd ed., New York, Reinhold, 1954, 650 pp. ACS Monograph.

Norton, F. H., *Refractories,* New York, McGraw-Hill, 1950, 782 pp.

National Research Council, *Data on Chemicals for Ceramic Uses,* Washington, D. C., The National Research Council, Bulletin no. 107, 1943. A very comprehensive compilation that includes a bibliography of 1,128 references to periodical literature.

orton, F. H., *Elements of Ceramics,* Cambridge, Mass., Addison-Wesley, 1952, 246 pp. A very good textbook.

merican Ceramic Society, *Refractories Bibliography,* 1928–1947 (inclusive), Columbus, Ohio, American Ceramic Society, 1950, 2,109 pp. It was prepared in cooperation with the American Iron and Steel Institute.

Rosenthal, E., *Pottery and Ceramics; from Common Brick to Fine China,* London, Penguin Books, 1949, 304 pp. A good semipopular book.

Searle, A. B., *Refractory Materials,* London, Griffin, 1950, 895 pp. A standard British work that has been revised several times.

Searle, A. B., *The Clayworkers Handbook,* London, Griffin, 1949, 392 pp.

Salmang, H., *Die physikalischen und chemischen Grundlagen der Keramik,* 2nd ed., Berlin, Springer, 1951, 321 pp. It is one of the few books devoted to the scientific aspects of ceramics, and one of the best ones.

Thiene, Hermann, *Glas,* 2 vols., Jena, G. Fischer, 1931–1939.

20. Cement, Concrete, and Other Building Materials

Bogue, R. H., *The Chemistry of Portland Cement,* 2nd ed., New York, Reinhold, 1955, 793 pp.

Comprehensive Bibliography of Cement and Concrete, 1925–1947, Lafayette, Indiana, The Director of the Engineering Experiment Station of Purdue Univ., 491 pp. It covers the literature of the world.

37970

Lea, F. M., and Desch, C. H., *The Chemistry of Cement and Concrete*, 4th ed., London, Arnold, 1953.
Kühl, H., *Zement-Chemie*, 3 vols., Berlin, Verlag Technik, 1951–1953.

21. Fuels and Carbonization Products

Coal Tar Data Book, Gomersal, near Leeds, England, The Coal Tar Research Association. The Association began to issue this in 1953 by publishing about 100 pages at a time. It covers pure compounds, tars, tar oils, pitches, chemical engineering data, and conversion tables.
Huntington, R. L., *Natural Gas and Natural Gasoline*, New York, McGraw-Hill, 1950, 605 pp.
Lowry, H. H. (ed.), *The Chemistry of Coal Utilization*, 2 vols., New York, Wiley, 1945. It was prepared by a staff of experts under the auspices of the National Research Council. It is a very comprehensive work on coal and all the products that can be obtained from it by carbonization, hydrogenation, and other methods.
Johnson, A. J., and Auth, G. H. (eds.), *Fuels and Combustion Handbook*, New York, McGraw-Hill, 1950, 915 pp. A comprehensive reference work covering properties, uses, and combustion of all solid, liquid, and gaseous fuels.
Storch, H. H., et al., *The Fisher-Tropsch and Related Syntheses*, New York, Wiley, 1951, 603 pp.

22. Petroleum, Lubricants, and Asphalt

There are few up-to-date books in this field:

Abraham, H., *Asphalt and Allied Substances*, 5th ed., 2 vols., New York, Nostrand, 1944.
Bell, H. S., *American Petroleum Refining*, 3rd ed., New York, Van Nostra: 1945, 631 pp.
Boone, L. P., *Petroleum Dictionary*, Norman, Oklahoma, Univ. of Oklaho Press, 1952, 338 pp.
Brooks, B. T. (ed.), *The Chemistry of Petroleum Hydrocarbons*, 3 vols., New York, Reinhold, 1954–1955. An excellent work that includes the technology of petroleum.
Brooks, B. I., and Dunstan, E. A. (eds.), *The Science of Petroleum*, London, Oxford Univ. Press, 1938 (in progress). Vols. 1–4 (1938); Vol. 5 in several parts began to appear in 1950; Vol. 6 in several parts began to appear in 1953. It is the most comprehensive treatise on petroleum; it covers occurrence throughout the world, the principles and practice of production, refining, and manufacture of synthetic products, among other topics. The synthetic products of petroleum are discussed in Vol. 5.
Egloff, G., and Hulla, G., *The Alkylation of Alkanes*, New York, Reinhold, 1948, 1,144 pp.
Ellis, Carleton, *Chemistry of Petroleum Derivatives*, 2 vols., New York, Reinhold, 1934–37. A very comprehensive work that has extensive bibliographies that cover the literature to 1935.
Goldstein, E. F., *The Petroleum Chemicals Industry*, London, Spon, 1949, 449 pp.

Gruse, A. W., *Chemical Technology of Petroleum*, 2nd ed., New York, McGraw-Hill, 1942, 733 pp.
Institute of Petroleum, *Modern Petroleum Technology*, 2nd ed., London, Institute of Petroleum, 1955, 702 pp.
Kalichevsky, V. A., and Kobe, *Petroleum Refining with Chemicals*, London, Cleaver-Hume, 1956, 700 pp.
Kalichevsky, V. A., and Stanger, B. A., *Chemical Refining of Petroleum*, New York, Reinhold, 1942, 250 pp. ACS Monograph.
Marthe, A., *Bibliographie des livres, thèse, et conférences relatifs à l'industrie du pétrole (1847-1947)*, Paris, Gauthier-Villars. A bibliography of over 6,000 references.
Pétrole, propriétés et utilisations, Paris, Presses Documentaires, 1953– . It is a work in several volumes devoted to petroleum, its products, and products synthesized from it. A number of authors have contributed to each volume.
Sachanen, A. M., *The Chemical Constituents of Petroleum*, New York, Reinhold, 1945, 451 pp.
Sachanen, A. M., *Conversion of Petroleum*, New York, Reinhold, 2nd ed., 1948, 602 pp.
Rossi, F. D., Mair, B. J., and Streiff, A. J., *Hydrocarbons from Petroleum*, New York, Reinhold, 1953, 600 pp. ACS Monograph.
Weil, B. H., and Lane, J. C., *Synthetic Petroleum from the Synthine Process*, New York, Chemical Publishing Co., 1948, 303 pp. It is largely a bibliography of U. S. Government reports and patents on making petroleum from coal.

23. Cellulose and Paper

Casey, J. P., *Pulp and Paper: Chemistry and Chemical Technology*, 2 vols., New York, Interscience, 1952. A reference work.
Heuser, E., *The Chemistry of Cellulose*, New York, Wiley, 1944, 660 pp. It is devoted to the scientific aspects, not to applications.
Ott, E., and Spurlin, H. (eds.), *Cellulose and Cellulose Derivatives*, 2nd ed., in 3 parts, New York, Interscience, 1954-1955. A comprehensive reference work that emphasizes industrial uses.
Stephenson, J. N. (ed.), *Pulp and Paper Manufacture*, 4 vols., New York, McGraw-Hill, 1950-1953. A very comprehensive textbook that covers all aspects of the industry, including machinery.
West, C. J., *Dictionary of Paper*, 2nd ed., New York, American Paper and Pulp Association, 1953, 393 pp.
West, C. J., *Bibliographies on Paper Making*. There are a number of these; some of them were published by Tappi (Technical Assoc. of the Pulp and Paper Industry, New York) and others by the Institute for Paper Chemistry, Appleton, Wisconsin. They cover the period 1900-1951.
Wise, L. E., and Jahn, E. C., *Wood Chemistry*, 2 vols., New York, Reinhold, 1952. A very comprehensive reference work. ACS Monograph.

24. Explosives and Explosions

The number of books that deal with the chemical aspects of the subject is small. The United States Bureau of Mines and other government agencies publish a great deal of material on explosives and explosions.

Davis, T. L., *Chemistry of Powder and Explosives*, New York, Wiley, 1943, 490 pp.

25. Dyes and Textile Chemistry

Analytical Methods for a Textile Laboratory, Lowell, Mass., The Lowell Textile Institute, 1949, 287 pp. This book was compiled by a Committee of the American Association of Textile Chemists and Colorists.

The Color Index, 2nd ed., Lowell, Mass., The American Association of Textile Chemists and Colorists, 1957. The American Association has compiled this edition of the index. The first edition, compiled by the Society of Dyers and Colourists (Great Britain) and edited by F. M. Rowe, was issued 1924–1928, and a supplement appeared later. This index is invaluable for information on dyes; it gives commercial and scientific names, formulas, indicates methods of preparation, and includes references to the literature. The "Color Index" numbers positively identify dyes having many names.

Diserens, Louis, *Neueste Fortschritte und Verfahren in der chemischen Technologie der Textilfasern*, 2 parts in 6 vols., Basel, Birkhauser, 1948 (in progress). The first part "Die neuesten Fortschritte in der Anwendung der Farbstoffe" in 3 vols. (2nd and 3rd ed., 1949–1951) is the internationally recognized work on the chemical technology of dyeing and printing; there is an English translation (see below) and a French translation began to appear in 1952 (Paris, Editions Teintex). The second part "Neue Verfahren in der Technik der chemischen Veredelung der Textilfasern" is nearly finished; Vols. 1–2 (1948–1953); Vol. 3 (in preparation).

Diserens, Louis, *The Chemical Technology of Dyeing and Printing*, 2 vols., New York, Reinhold, 1948–1951. This is a translation and revision of the 2nd edition (1946–1949) of "Die neuesten Fortschritte in der Anwendung der Farbstoffe."

Fierz-David, H. E., and Blangey, L., *Grundlegende Operationen der Farbenchemie*, 8th ed., Berlin, Springer, 1952, 416 pp.

Fierz-David, H. E., and Blangey, L., *Fundamental Processes of Dye Chemistry*, New York, Interscience, 1949. An English translation of the 5th edition (1943) of the preceding work; it is primarily a laboratory manual.

Friedländer, P., *Fortschritte der Teerfarben-fabrikation*, Berlin, Springer, 1888–1942. It covers the German patent literature from 1877. Volume 26 appeared in 1942.

Hill, Roland (ed.), *Fibers from Synthetic Polymers*, Amsterdam, Elsevier, 1953, 554 pp. A comprehensive work.

Lawrie, L. G., *A Bibliography of Dyeing and Textile Printing*, London, Chapman & Hall, 1949, 143 pp. A list of books from the 16th century to 1946.

Lubs, H. A. (ed.), *The Chemistry of Synthetic Dyes and Pigments*, New York, Reinhold, 1955, 735 pp. ACS Monograph.

Luniak, B., *The Identification of Textile Fibers*, London, Pitman, 1953, 177 pp. A translation and revision of the 2nd edition of the Swiss text on qualitative and quantitative analysis of fiber blends.

Matthews–Mauersberger, *Textile Fibers: Their Physical, Microscopic, and Chemical Properties*, 6th ed., New York, Wiley, 1954, 1283 pp. A comprehensive reference work.

Moncrieff, R. W., *Artificial Fibers*, 2nd ed., New York, Wiley, 1954, 455 pp. It covers some fibers that are not considered by Hill and supplements the information on others given by Matthews–Mauersberger.

Preston, J. M., *Fibre Science*, Manchester, England, The Textile Institute, 1954, 421 pp. A survey of constitution, structure, and reaction of fibers.

Pummerer, R. (ed.), *Chemische Textilfasern, Filme und Folien: Grundlagen und Technologie*, Stuttgart, Enke, 1951– . Nine parts (Lieferung) had been issued by 1955.

Schultz, G., and Lehmann, L., *Farbstofftabellen*, 7th ed., 2 vols. and 2 supplements, Leipzig, Akad. Verlagsges., 1931–1939. This is outdated by the *Color Index*, but reference is often made to the Schultz numbers to identify dyes.

Speel, H. C., *Textile Chemicals and Auxiliaries*, New York, Reinhold, 1952, 500 pp.

Weber, F., and Martina, A., *Die neuzeutlichen Textilveredelungs-Verfahren der Kunstfasern*, 6 parts, Vienna, Springer, 1950–1952. It covers the literature from 1939 to 1950 and includes references to about 7,500 patents.

Venkataraman, K., *The Chemistry of Synthetic Dyes*, 2 vols., New York, Academic Press, 1951–1952. An excellent and comprehensive reference work.

26. Paints, Varnishes, Lacquers, and Inks

Casey, R. I., *Writing Inks*, New York, Reinhold, 1945. ACS Monograph.

Gardner, H. A., and Sward, G. G., *Physical and Chemical Examination of Paints, Varnishes, Lacquers, and Colors*. Bethesda, Md., Gardner Laboratories, 1950, 722 pp.

Payne, H. F., *Organic Coating Technology*, 2 vols., New York, Wiley, 1954– . Vol. 2 in preparation.

Magnier's *Encyclopédie pratique du fabricant de vernis, laques, émaux, peintures*, 3rd ed., L. Clevet and R. Nebut (eds.), Paris, Girardot et Cie, 1952– . Vol. 4 (1955).

Mattiello, J. J., *Protective and Decorative Coatings*, 5 vols., New York, Wiley, 1941–1946. A comprehensive work on the chemistry and technology of paints, varnishes, and lacquers.

Remington, J. S., and Francis W., *Pigments: Their Manufacture, Properties and Use*, 3rd ed., London, Hill, 1954, 222 pp.

Stewart, J. R., *The National Paint Dictionary*, 3rd ed., Washington, D. C., Stewart Research Laboratories, 1949.

Voet, A., *Ink and Paper in the Printing Process*, New York, Interscience, 1952, 213 pp. The chemistry of ink, and the interaction between paper and ink in the major printing processes are covered.

54   BOOKS

Wolfe, H. J., *Printing and Litho Inks*, 4th ed., New York, MacNair Dorland, 1949, 478 pp.

27. Fats, Fatty Oils, Waxes, and Detergents

Bailey, A. E., *Industrial Oil and Fat Products*, 2nd ed., New York, Interscience, 1951, 992 pp.

Cooke, E. I. (ed.), *The Modern Soap and Detergency Industry*, 3rd ed., 2 vols., London, Technical Press, 1950.

Davidsohn, J. B., Better, E. J., and Davidsohn, A., *Soap Manufacture*, 2 vols., New York, Interscience, 1953.

Doss, M. P., *Properties of the Principal Fats, Fatty Oils, Waxes, Fatty Acids, and Their Salts*, New York, The Texas Co., 1952, 244 pp.

Eckey, E. W., *Vegetable Fats and Oils*, New York, Reinhold, 1954, 864 pp. ACS Monograph.

Elliot, A. B., *The Alkaline Earth and Heavy Metal Soaps*, New York, Reinhold, 1946, 340 pp.

Hilditch, T. P., *The Chemical Constitution of Natural Fats*, 3rd ed., London, Chapman & Hall, 1956, 554 pp.

Hilditch, T. P., *The Industrial Chemistry of Fats and Waxes*, 3rd ed., London, Baillière-Tindall and Cox, 1949, 604 pp.

McCutcheon, J. W., *Synthetic Detergents*, New York, MacNair Dorland, 1950, 435 pp. Useful for its wide coverage.

Niven, W. W., *Industrial Detergency*, New York, Reinhold, 1955, 340 pp.

Schwartz, A. M., and Perry, J. W., *Surface Active Agents*, New York, Interscience, 1949, 575 pp. An excellent discussion of their chemistry and technology.

Sisley, J. P., *Index des huiles sulfonées et détergents modernes*, 2 vols., Paris, Editions Tientex, 1949–1954. It covers properties, commercial names, the names of manufacturers, and uses in the textile, metallurgical, and other industries for thousands of substances.

Sisley, J. P., and Wood, P. J., *Encyclopedia of Surface Active Agents*, New York, Chemical Pub. Co., 1952, 540 pp. A translation of Vol. 1 of the preceding French work.

Warth, A. H., *The Chemistry and Technology of Waxes*, 2nd ed., New York, Reinhold, 1956, 1,000 pp.

28. Sugar, Starch, Gums

Brautlecht, A. C., *Starch—Its Sources, Production and Uses*, New York, Reinhold, 1953, 408 pp. The emphasis is on white potato starch.

Howes, F. N., *Vegetable Gums and Resins*, Waltham, Mass., Chronica Botanica, 1949, 188 pp.

Honig, Peter (ed.), *Principles of Sugar Technology*, Amsterdam, Elsevier, 1953, 767 pp. A work on cane sugar.

Kerr, R. W. (ed.), *Chemistry and Industry of Starch*, New York, Academic Press, 1950, 719 pp. This work places more emphasis on the chemistry of starch than does Brautlecht; it also covers starches from various sources.

McGinnis, R. A., *Beet Sugar Technology*, New York, Reinhold, 1951, 580 pp.
Mantell, C. L., *The Water Soluble Gums*, New York, Reinhold, 1947, 279 pp.

29. Leather and Glue

Bergmann, M., and Grassmann, N. W. (eds.), *Handbuch der Gerberei-chemie und Lederfabrikation*, 3 vols., 5 parts, Vienna, Springer, 1931–1944.
Gustavson, K. H., *The Chemistry and Reactivity of Collagen*, New York, Academic Press, 1956, 342 pp.
Gustavson, K. H., *The Chemistry of the Tanning Processes*, New York, Academic Press, 1956, 403 pp.
McLaughlin, G. D., and Theis, E. R., *The Chemistry of Leather Manufacture*, New York, Reinhold, 1945, 800 pp. ACS Monograph.
Progress in Leather Science 1920–1945, 3 vols., London, British Leather Manufacturers Research Association, 1946–1948.
Smith, P. I., *Glue and Gelatin*, London, Chapman & Hall, 1943.

30. Rubber and Other Elastomers

There is no comprehensive modern treatise on the chemistry and technology of natural rubber. There is one comprehensive treatise on all of the various synthetic rubbers. Much of the recent literature, in book form, on rubber and elastomers is covered in works that also deal with plastics; see the next section for these.

ASTM, *Rubber and Rubber-like Materials*, 2nd ed., Philadelphia, American Society for Testing Materials, 1951, 652 pp. This gives considerable information in addition to tests and specifications.
Bibliography of Rubber Literature, Akron, Ohio, Division of Rubber Chemistry of the American Chemical Society, 1935– . This is distributed by the Rubber Age Publishing Co., New York. A volume appears about every second year.
Davis, C. C., and Blake, J. T., *The Chemistry and Technology of Rubber*, 3rd ed., New York, Reinhold, 1937, 941 pp. Reprinted 1946. ACS Monograph. It contains an excellent chapter on the literature of rubber up to 1935. This book is still a valuable reference work on natural rubber.
LeBras, J., and Delalande, A., *Les dérivés chimiques du caoutchouc naturel*, Paris, Dunod, 1950, 486 pp.
Whitby, G. S. (ed.), *Synthetic Rubber*, New York, Wiley, 1954, 1044 pp. A very comprehensive treatise that contains much previously unpublished work. See *Chemical Abstracts* **49**, 2768–2769 (1955).

31. Synthetic Resins and Plastics

Blount, E. R., and Mark, H. (eds.), *Monomers* (A collection of data and procedure on the basic materials for the synthesis of fibers, plastics and rubbers), New York, Interscience, 1949– . A series of monographs that vary considerably in quality.

Boundy, R. H., and Boyer, R. F. (eds.), *Styrene—Its Polymers, Copolymers, and Derivatives,* New York, Reinhold, 1952, 1304 pp. ACS Monograph.

Bjorksten, Johan, et al., *Polyesters and Their Applications,* New York, Reinhold, 1956, 626 pp. It includes extensive bibliographies.

D'Alelio, G. F., *Fundamental Principles of Polymerization—Rubbers, Fibers, Plastics,* New York, Wiley, 1952, 517 pp. It is not a highly technical book, but it is very useful. The author is an authority in this field; he discusses and evaluates much of the polymer research of the last 25 years.

Flory, P. J., *Principles of Polymer Chemistry,* Ithaca, Cornell Univ. Press, 1953, 688 pp. An outstanding book.

High Polymers, New York, Interscience, 1940–   . A publisher's series of monographs on the chemistry, physics, and technology of polymers. The members of the editorial board (H. F. Mark, C. S. Marvel, H. W. Melville, and G. S. Whitby) are authorities on the subject.

Houwink, R. (ed.), *Elastomers and Plastomers,* 3 vols., New York, Elsevier, 1948–1950. A comprehensive work on their physics, chemistry, and technology; natural and synthetic rubbers are included.

Kunin, R., and Myers, R. J., *Ion Exchange Resins,* Wiley, New York, 1950, 212 pp. This book contains an excellent bibliography.

Laughton, H. M. (ed.), *Synthetic Resins and Allied Plastics,* 3rd ed., London, Oxford Univ. Press, 1952, 747 pp.

Meyer, K. H., *Natural and Synthetic High Polymers,* New York, Interscience, 1950, 891 pp. Rubber is among those considered.

Schildkneckt, C. E., *Vinyl and Related Polymers,* New York, Wiley, 1952, 723 pp. It is a comprehensive book and contains excellent bibliographies.

Saechling, H., and Zebrawski, W., *Kunstoff-Taschenbuch,* 10th ed., Munich, C. Hanser, 1954, 353 pp. This is an excellent source of information on German plastics.

Simonds, H. R., Weith, A. W., and Bigelow, M. H., *Handbook of Plastics,* 2nd ed., New York, Van Nostrand, 1949, 1463 pp. It covers physical and chemical properties, methods of fabricating, and patents on commercial plastics.

Wakeman, L. R., *The Chemistry of Commercial Plastics,* New York, Reinhold, 1947, 836 pp.

SOURCES OF INFORMATION ABOUT BOOKS

There are two points to consider in discussing sources of information about chemical books. One is keeping up with new chemical books and evaluating them; the other is determining the existence of a book, or books, on a specific topic. There is no one source of information in either case. Some of the sources serve both purposes. Therefore, to avoid repetition, the general situation is outlined and then an annotated list of sources of information follows. Some other sources of information are given in Thornton and Tully's book.[7]

One type of publication that some persons regard as a book because it is often issued in book form is the *Annual Review*. For a discussion of reviews, and a list, see page 206.

To keep up with all of the new books on chemistry it is necessary continually to watch sources 1–6, mentioned below, and to select titles that seem promising. *Chemical Abstracts* announces a very large percentage of the new chemical books issued each year; *Chemisches Zentralblatt* does not announce so many. If these two abstract journals are watched, many of the new books are found and probably nearly all of the important ones. But there is often a long delay in announcing a new book in the abstract journals. Evaluating new books before purchasing them is difficult if the book is not at hand for examination, because the reviews of a book, if it is reviewed, often appear long after the book. The publishers' catalogs vary as to how much information is given on the content of a book. To determine the existence of a chemical book, the subject indexes of *Chemical Abstracts*, the library catalogs, the Cumulative Book Index, and the book lists are most generally useful.

1. Scientific and Chemical Journals

Many of these journals announce new chemical books, many review them, and some do both. *Chemical Abstracts* is the only abstract journal, apparently, that has always (1907–   ) included the titles of the new chemical books of the world; it indexes the book by both author and subject, and since 1919 frequently refers the reader to a review. *Chemisches Zentralblatt* started this practice in 1927 and treats books in the same way as does *Chemical Abstracts*. *Bulletin signalétique* (1940–   ) reviews some scientific books and gives indicative annotations for the others. The announcements of books in chemical journals from foreign countries are particularly useful for American libraries. There are two journals of general science that announce and review many chemical books: *Science* (US), and *Nature* (Great Britain).

2. Publishers' Catalogs

By writing for them one can obtain the latest catalogs of publishers of scientific books and can be put on mailing lists to receive notices. A list of the principal publishers with their addresses is given in Appendix 7. Publishers' catalogs do not always give the publication date of a book. Many publishers separate books on pure chemistry from those on industrial chemistry and chemical technology and put them into separate catalogs. It is best to ask for catalogs to cover

chemistry, chemical engineering, chemical technology, and technology
to get complete coverage for all fields of chemistry. Some libraries
keep files of publishers' catalogs.

3. Catalogs of Book Dealers

Dealers in scientific books often issue catalogs of new scientific
books, compiled from the publishers' catalogs, and the trade and
national bibliographies. These vary greatly in the amount of information given about the new books. Book dealers often separate chemical books into several classes and list them in different catalogs in
the same way publishers do, so this should be kept in mind when asking for catalogs. Some dealers also issue catalogs of second-hand
books.

Some dealers publish catalogs to cover new chemical books written
in German, French, Italian, and other languages. Among these are
Stechert-Hafner (New York), Walter J. Johnson (New York), Maxwell and Co. (London), and Henry Sotheran and Co. (London). The
names and addresses of dealers in chemical books are given in Appendix 7.

One of Sotheran's catalogs is worth special comment: H. C. Sotheran and H. Zeitlinger (eds.), *Bibliotheca Chemico-Mathematica*.
This was issued in 2 volumes in 1921, and supplements were issued in
1932, 1937, and 1952. It has been carefully prepared and contains
much information about chemical books of all ages. Copies of this
catalog and of the first 2 supplements are becoming rare, but are
available at most reference libraries.

4. Library Accession Lists

A few libraries print accession lists and distribute them on a subscription basis; others make mimeographed or similar duplicate copies
for free distribution to a limited number of other libraries or individuals. These can be obtained by writing to the librarian. See
Appendix 3 for libraries of interest to chemists. The Library of the
Chemical Society (London), one of the world's most important chemical libraries, publishes a monthly list *Additions to the Library* in the
Proceedings of the Chemical Society, which appears in the *Journal of
the Chemical Society* (London). Some useful lists available on subscription are:

Carnegie Library, Pittsburgh, *Science and Technology: A Record of Literature Recently Added to the Carnegie Library*. A quarterly annotated
list. This library has an extensive chemical collection.

Library of Congress, Washington, D. C., *Monthly List of Russian Accessions.* 1949–   . Includes both books and periodicals received by the Library of Congress and a large number of cooperating libraries in the United States. Classified.
New York Public Library, New York, N. Y., *New Technical Books*, bimonthly. A select, annotated list. This library has a large chemical collection.
Science Museum Library, London, England, *Monthly List of Accessions to the Science Library.* There are about 4,700 titles a year on this list. A very large scientific library which has an extensive chemical collection.

5. General Book Guides

These are the trade and national bibliographies of which there are several for nearly every country of the world. See *Guide to Reference Books* by C. M. Winchell (Chicago, American Library Association, 7th ed., 1951 and supplements) for others than those given here. See also Conover, Helen, *Current National Bibliographies*, Washington, D. C., Government Printing Office, 1955, 132 pp. A Library of Congress publication.

UNITED STATES

Publishers Weekly, New York. It lists books published each week in the United States. Occasionally there are brief annotations. There are several collective lists of which *New Scientific, Technical, and Engineering Books of all Publishers* is the most valuable; these have been issued annually or semiannually since 1950.
The *Cumulative Book Index*, New York, Wilson Co., 1898–   . Monthly. Annual and 5-year cumulations. A world list of books published in the English language.

GREAT BRITAIN

The British National Bibliography, London, The British Museum, 1950– Weekly. Cumulates annually.

GERMANY

Bibliographie der deutschen Bibliothek, Frankfurt am Main, Deutsche Bibliothek, 1947–   . Monthly. It covers the Western zone of Germany.

FRANCE

"Biblio," Catalogue des ouvrages parus en langue française dans le monde entier, Paris, Hachette, 1933–   . Monthly. A world list of books published in the French language.

6. Periodicals Devoted to Books

Das Deutsche Buch (Neuerscheinung der deutsche Verlage), Frankfurt am Main, Buchhändler Vereingung, 1950–   , six issues per year. This is an annotated listing of books selected from the German national bibliography that will be of interest outside of Germany.

French Bibliographical Digest (*Science*), New York, The Cultural Division of the French Embassy, 1949– . It gives reviews and annotations in English for significant scientific and technical books published in the French language. Series I, nos. 1–8, covers books for 1940–1948. Series II, nos. 9– , covers 1949– .

Neuerscheinungen wissenschaftlichen Literatur aus den Landern den Volksdemokratie, Berlin (Soviet Sector), Zentralstelle für Wissenschaftliche Literatur, 1951– . Bimonthly. A select list, annotated in part, of current scientific literature of Albania, Bulgaria, Czechoslovakia, Hungary, Poland, Rumania, and China.

Technical Book Review, London, E. W. Publications, 1954– . Bimonthly. International coverage.

Technical Book Review Index, New York, Special Libraries Association, 1935– . Monthly. This has brief extracts from reviews of American and foreign books that appear in a number of periodicals. It was published (1917–1929) by the Carnegie Library, Pittsburgh, Pa.

7. Catalogs of Libraries

One naturally turns to the card catalog of a library to find a book on a given subject. Some localities in the United States now have a union card catalog. There is also the **National Union Catalog of Books in North American Libraries,** which is maintained at the Library of Congress, Washington, D. C.; it was started in 1927 and is very comprehensive. This card catalog is being kept up to date, but it has not been duplicated or printed to make it available in other libraries.

Libraries seldom issue catalogs of their holdings in book form. A few are available: Library of the Chemical Society, London (1903); Library of the German Chemical Society, issued with the 1920 index to *Berichte der deutschen chemischen Gesellschaft;* Library of the British Patent Office (1911); Library of the German Patent Office (1913); and the Carnegie Library of Pittsburgh, Pennsylvania (1907–1922). See the *Guide to Reference Books,* mentioned on page 59, for the published catalogs of the Library of the British Museum, Bibliothèque Nationale (Paris), and Staatsbibliothek (Berlin).

The Library of Congress, Washington, D. C., does not issue a printed catalog in book form, but the Association of Research Libraries published such a catalog (Edward Brothers, Ann Arbor, Michigan) called **A Catalog of Books Represented by Library of Congress Printed Cards Issued to July 31, 1942,** and a supplement for cards issued to December 31, 1947. A complete file of these cards was available in a few large libraries before 1942. These cards represent most of the books in the Library of Congress, together with those in many government libraries, and other libraries throughout the United States. These libraries cooperate with the Library of Congress in its cataloging.

The Library of Congress is issuing two monthly publications: **Library of Congress Author Catalog** and **Library of Congress Subject Catalog** (1948–   ); these periodicals and their cumulations continue the catalog published by the Association of Research Libraries and have the same coverage. These catalogs are useful in determining the existence of books, particularly foreign ones, and in other ways because the Library of Congress catalog cards give considerable information about the books.

8. Book Lists

ASLIB Book List of Recently Published Scientific and Technical Books. This was started by ASLIB (Assoc. of Special Libraries and Information Bureaux) of London in 1935 as a quarterly publication. It is now a monthly publication devoted to books in the English language, mostly British publications, and titles are selected by a group of scientists.

ASLIB, A Select List of Standard British Scientific and Technical Books, 1952. This edition has about 1,000 titles. Revised frequently.

Gaudenzi, Nerio, *Guida bibliografica internazionale per il chimico: Libri e reviste,* Florence, Sansoni Edizioni Scientifiche, 1952, 500 pp. A classified list of about 4,000 books and about 900 periodicals. No indication is given of the relative values of the books. Titles are annotated only if they do not indicate the content of the book. Most of the books were published during 1935–1950. Gaudenzi attempts to cover all of chemistry and chemical technology, except metallurgy for which he is preparing a separate work.

Hawkins, R. R. (ed.), *Scientific, Medical and Technical Books Published in the United States of America,* 1930–1944, Washington, D. C., The National Research Council, 1946, 1114 pp. (Distributed by R. R. Bowker, New York, N. Y.) Supplement of books published 1945–1948, Washington, 1950. Supplement of books published 1949–1952, Washington, 1953. More supplements will be issued. This is an invaluable selected list. It includes the most important federal government publications. A table of contents and evaluative annotations are given for each title. Most secondary school texts are omitted.

Journal of Chemical Education. The Division of Chemical Education of the American Chemical Society has an annual book exhibit at the fall meeting of the Society. The titles are published in its Journal, usually the September issue. This is quite an extensive list; it rarely includes books in languages other than English; and it is useful in keeping up with new chemical books.

Lewis' Medical, Scientific, and Technical Lending Library Catalog, London, H. K. Lewis & Co., 1950, 1152 pp. This contains about 27,000 titles of books published up to 1950. Supplement for 1950–1952 (1953). Bimonthly lists, 1953– .

9. Sources for Old Books

Bolton, H. C., *A Select Bibliography of Chemistry,* 4 vols., Washington, D. C., The Smithsonian Institution, 1893–1904. This covers the period 1492–1902, and includes about 18,000 items. It is not limited to books, but includes dissertations and periodicals. This is the most complete list of chemical books for the period covered.

International Catalogue of Scientific Literature (page 283 for a description). It includes nearly all of the chemical books for the period 1901–1914.

Subject Indexes to Chemical Abstracts, 1907– .

10. Translations of Books

Index Translatorium (1932–). Now published by UNESCO.

CHOOSING AND ORDERING BOOKS

It is well to remember in choosing books to purchase that most scientific books are either short-lived, or else are revised to bring them up to date. Hence it is a good rule not to buy a book until one actually has need for it and expects to use it. The depreciation on books is, in general, greater than on periodical files. After the first drop to secondhand value, the volumes of a standard journal set increase in value year by year as more customers enter the market, whereas the value of books diminishes steadily unless they have some peculiar merit or become rarities.

Books may be ordered directly from the publishers; this is often the best plan for those engaged in teaching, as they usually obtain a substantial discount. Many American publishers are agents for the books of foreign publishers; for these see *Literary Market Place,* a complete directory of American book publishing, published annually by R. R. Bowker, New York. Unless foreign books are purchased this way, it is usually more satisfactory to order them through book dealers. Some foreign publishers have branches in the United States. The names and addresses of dealers in scientific books are given in Appendix 7.

The date on the title page of a book is not a safe guide to its age. United States books are usually copyrighted, and the latest copyright date is the date of the last revision. British books do not usually bear copyright dates, but German books are often copyrighted for the United States. In the absence of a copyright date, the date of the latest preface is a useful indication of the time of publication.

LITERATURE CITED

(1) Taylor, H. S., "Annual Tables of Constants and Numerical Data," *Ind. Eng. Chem. News Ed.* **16**, 134–135 (1938).
(2) Sparks, W. J., "NRC Division of Chemistry and Chemical Technology," *Chem. Eng. News* **32**, 1801–1802 (1954).
(3) Maizell, R. E., "Techniques of Data Searches in Chemical Libraries," *J. Chem. Educ.* **32**, 309–311 (1955).
(4) Anon, "Gmelin Handbuch Progress Reviewed," *Chem. Eng. News* **30**, 1144 (1954).
(5) Huntress, E. H., *J. Chem. Educ.* **15**, 303–309 (1938).
(6) Richter, Friedrich, *J. Chem. Educ.* **15**, 310–316 (1938).
(7) Thornton, J. L., and Tully, R. I. J., *Scientific Books, Libraries and Collectors*, London, Library Association, 1954, 288 pp.

CHAPTER 3

PERIODICALS

IIIIIIIIIIIIIIIIIIIIIIIIIIIIIIIIIIIIIIIIIIIIIIIIIIIIIIIIIIIIIIIIIIIIII

GENERAL CONSIDERATIONS

The importance of scientific periodicals cannot be overestimated. The journal literature is the storehouse of a large mass of reports of experimental work and interpretations thereof, and of discussions of observations and conclusions from wider experience, together with a smaller proportion of reviews, general reports, and statements of news and opinions. It is the original source material of the collection. This literature differs most markedly from the book literature in its relatively unorganized state and in its prompter and more regular advancement on the frontiers of our knowledge. A book is soon out of date, but a live journal can and does keep up with the onward march of scientific discovery. On this account every literature search of a comprehensive nature must include examination of the journal literature in addition to books dealing with the subject in question. The journal literature on a subject supplements any existing book literature in three ways: (1) it brings it up to date, (2) it covers material that was omitted from the books, and (3) it gives more detailed information than the books may carry. Books are usually secondary sources based largely on the journal literature, the primary source. Periodicals are essential in retrospective literature searches; they are equally valuable for keeping up with current research.

The **bulk of the journal literature** is almost staggering in its proportions and it is increasing rapidly. In 1927 there were 1,263 journals of interest to chemists; now there are over 7,000 that are examined regularly by the editors and abstractors of *Chemical Ab-*

stracts. The number of journals of greatest direct chemical interest can be judged by glancing at the descriptions further on in this chapter. There is such a mass of this literature that it is a heavy task to keep abreast of even that part of interest in one's special field and to use it effectively when needed. It behooves the chemist to learn to use all the means that have been provided to make this sea of information navigable: abstract journals, indexing periodicals, reviews, indexes, bibliographies, and mechanical aids, to mention the principal ones. Otherwise he will be lost at sea.

The volume of current research presents other problems that concern users of chemical journals. Although the number of journals of chemical interest has increased rapidly, the amount of research in many fields has grown more rapidly; there is not sufficient space in existing periodicals to publish all manuscripts offered and many journals have a large backlog of manuscripts. It is not always financially possible to increase the size of an existing periodical or to start a new one. Some journals have partially solved the problem of more prompt publication of new work by keeping all papers as brief as possible and sometimes valuable experimental detail is sacrificed; others use the auxiliary publication plan to save space. The journals published by the American Chemical Society use auxiliary publication for some papers; the most essential part appears in the journal with a note stating that the complete manuscript has been deposited with the American Documentation Institute from which photographic copies are available. Davis[1] has pointed out the need for more journals to use auxiliary publication and its advantages. Lamb[2] in his paper "Publication—Lifeblood of Science" has proposed radically different printing methods and format to enable chemical journals to publish "promptly, clearly, and economically all the novel, valid, and significant research" that they receive.

The **importance of reading scientific journals** as they appear should be emphasized, particularly to students and those entering the chemical profession. Since the volume of current research is so large and it is necessary to depend on abstracting journals to keep in touch with most of it, there is a tendency to rely on them too much. One gains a knowledge of the line of thought, of the way in which one piece of research suggests another, of the method of attacking a problem, and of experimental methods and details from the regular reading of a periodical, which the best of abstract journals cannot convey. A chemist should read widely, not restricting himself to his special field; many suggestions for his work will come from other fields of chemistry and sometimes from other sciences. Another reason for reading periodicals is worth comment; abstract journals rarely abstract everything that is published in a given periodical. The major abstract journals, as *Chemical Abstracts* or *Chemisches Zentralblatt*, endeavor to cover all of the new chemical information in the periodicals and serials of the world. Useful information, not covered by abstract journals, is most abundant in periodicals devoted in whole or in part to the various phases of industrial and applied chemistry; the most frequent types of information being advertisements, news items, lists of trade bulletins, market and price data, various types of business and economic information, lists of patents, book reviews, announcements of new books, and preliminary announcements of research. Also, in a field where a large amount of research is being done, the time lag between the publication of a paper and its abstract is a serious consideration. So the habit of reading current periodicals is worth while and should be cultivated.

The **older journal literature** is worth consideration. There are times when one will feel justified in ignoring all but the more modern literature on a subject, but to do so always would be a mistake. Ideas and facts are still to be found in the older publications even though the methods, interpretations, and theories may have been outgrown or carried over into more recent periodical literature and books. Just as it can be said that the journal literature is never out of date because of the continuous appearance of units of it, so it can also be said that the older parts of it are never entirely out of date because it is original source material.

New scientific periodicals start publication almost every month; there are several ways of learning of those of chemical interest. *Chemical Abstracts* announces new periodicals along with the new books, and indexes them. *New Serial Titles*, a monthly publication of the Library of Congress, covers periodicals that began publication after 1950. The periodical *College and Research Libraries* semiannually publishes an annotated list of the most important new periodicals.

For information about periodicals that have been published for some time numerous **lists of periodicals** are available. Those of general interest that also include chemical publications are given in Appendix 4 of this book; those of particular interest to chemists are given in Appendix 6.

The **purchase** of chemical periodicals by individuals or libraries involves some points that are outside the realm of this book. In selecting journals for which to enter subscriptions, it is hoped that the descriptions of current journals of greatest chemical interest, see pp. 75–123, will be of help. Publishers' addresses will be found in the List of Periodicals Abstracted by *Chemical Abstracts* (see Appendix 6) and in *Ulrich's Periodicals Directory*, which includes the most important chemical periodicals, both foreign and domestic.

The purchase of **Russian scientific periodicals** presents particular problems because editions are limited and the Soviet government controls their distribution. Many individuals and libraries in the United States have found periodicals published in the USSR difficult to obtain from the Soviet publishing houses. However, a limited number of subscriptions to a specified list of journals are available through dealers in the United States; one of the most satisfactory dealers is the Four Continent Book Corp. (see page 372).

Fortunately the Library of Congress and several other organizations in the United States are doing much to make scientific journals originating in the Soviet Union more available to scientists in the United States. The Library of Congress receives a very large number of scientific periodicals from the Soviet Union, part of them through the State Department (see the paper by Peiss [3]). The Library publishes the titles of all papers in the Soviet periodicals which it receives in its *Monthly List of Russian Accessions* and provides photocopies of the papers for a nominal fee.

The Microcard Foundation (Box 2145, Madison 5, Wisconsin) and the Microtext Publishing Corporation (112 Liberty Street, New York 6, N. Y.) are publishing copies of back volumes of Russian chemical periodicals on microcards, and are selling microcard copies of a number of current Russian chemical and scientific journals on a subscription basis.

The Consultants Bureau, 152 West 42nd Street, New York 18, N. Y., publishes the complete English translation of several current Russian chemical journals and distributes these on a subscription basis; this practice started in 1950.

It is usually cheaper to obtain foreign periodicals directly from the publishers; also, periodicals are usually received more promptly that way. It is more convenient, however, and not much more expensive, to order through dealers (see Appendix 7). Often the best and cheapest way to obtain a journal published by a scientific or technical society is to join the society in question if eligible.

HISTORY AND CLASSIFICATION

History

The present practice of communication among scientists by means of journals, their main method of cooperation, is a development from the period when personal contact and correspondence were the only means. Correspondence in the form of "letters to the editor" is still a means utilized to a minor degree.

The first journals were published by scientific societies whose members came to realize the need of a more effective way of announcing results and of exchanging ideas upon scientific topics than letters and meetings provided. *The Transactions of the Royal Society* (England), begun in 1665 and still appearing regularly, is the pioneer scientific journal. Its influence has been very great. The *Comptes rendus hebdomadaires des séances de l'académie des sciences* (Paris), publication of which began in 1835, is another early journal whose influence has been notable. The Academy of Sciences of Paris was established in 1666 and published, irregularly, certain proceedings before the starting of *Comptes rendus*. The first scientific journal in the United States was *Silliman's Journal*, now known as the *American Journal of Science*. It was started in 1818. Not long after, in 1826, *The Franklin Journal*, now called the *Journal of the Franklin Institute*, was established. These scientific journals, which are the earliest in their respective countries and are still being published, were and still are devoted to the sciences in general although some of them have emphasized one field of science in recent years.

With the development of scientific knowledge and its increasing divisions into branches, the tendency that grew up was for the scientific society and the scientific journal to become more specialized. This specialization, which is steadily increasing, extends into the present.

The **first chemical journal** apparently was the *Chemisches Journal* (1778–1784); it was later called *Crell's Chemische Annalen* (1784–1803). The oldest chemical journal that is still being published is the *Annales de chimie* (France), begun in 1789. Another early chemical journal of much importance that is still appearing in Germany is *Justus Liebig's Annalen der Chemie*, which was founded in 1832 under the name *Annalen der Pharmacie* and passed during the period from 1840 to 1874 under the name *Annalen der Chemie und Pharmacie*. William A. Noyes [4] in a presidential address before the American Chemical Society has expressed the opinion that it was the most valuable journal for the development of chemistry through the middle of the nineteenth century.

The **first American chemical periodical** was the *American Chemist*, which was published from 1870 to 1877 by that venerable pioneer among American chemists, Charles F. Chandler, and his brother. It was an outgrowth of an unsuccessful venture on the part of the *London Chemical News*, which involved the issuance of a monthly reprint in New York City with an appended American supplement prepared by Chandler. *The American Chemist*, which was a monthly, contained not only original papers by American chemists but also abstracts from American and foreign journals. This journal was discontinued because of the decision of the American Chemical Society to publish a journal. While the *American Chemist* seems properly to be considered the first American chemical periodical, mention should be made of the single volume of the *Memoirs of the Columbian Chemical Society* issued in 1813. *The American Chemical Journal*, founded in 1879 by Ira Remsen, another eminent American chemist, had a strong influence on the development of chemistry in the United States and contributed towards the recognition in Europe of the work of American chemists. It was for many years better known than *The Journal of the American Chemical Society* among foreign chemists. It was incorporated with the latter journal in 1914. Another American journal of interest from the historical point of view is Edward Hart's *Journal of Analytical Chemistry*, begun in 1887. Its name was changed to *Journal of Analytical and Applied Chemistry* in 1891. It was also incorporated with *The Journal of the American Chemical Society* in 1893. *The Journal of the American Chemical Society* was established in 1876 and has become one of the world's most valuable journals devoted to theoretical or pure chemistry.

In the earlier days of chemistry in America a number of chemists in the United States made a practice of publishing their papers in German journals, a tendency that just about ceased after 1914. Some chemists in other countries also published in German periodicals, particularly Russian and Scandinavian chemists, but in these cases it was often duplicate publication and this practically stopped by 1939.

A class of early journals that has developed into the most important group of all is that made up of the **journals published by the chemical societies.** These journals have been devoted on the whole to the entire field of chemistry except the industrial side in so far as that can be separated from pure chemistry. On that account and because of their wide distribution and use, they have had a notable educational influence and broadening effect in addition to their value as storehouses of information. The first of these journals was the *Quarterly Journal of the Chemical Society of London,* begun in 1847; it now appears monthly as the *Journal of the Chemical Society* (London). Chemical societies in other countries where chemistry has been developing have followed this example. The order is: *Bulletin de la société chimique de France* (1858), *Berichte der deutschen chemischen Gesellschaft* (1867–1945), *Journal of the Russian Physical-Chemical Society* (1869–1930), *Gazzetta chimica italia* (1871), *Journal of the American Chemical Society* (1876), *Journal of the Chemical Society of Japan* (1880), *Bulletin de la société chimique de Belgique* (1887), *Svensk Kemisk Tidskrift* (1899), *Chemisch Weekblad* (Holland, 1903), *Helvetica Chimica Acta* (Switzerland, 1918), *Journal of the Indian Chemical Society* (1924), and *Acta Chemica Scandinavica* (1947). In addition to these there are publications of chemical societies in several other countries where chemical activity is not so great.

Just as the starting of periodicals devoted to science in general was followed after a time by the appearance of journals devoted to the whole of chemistry, so after a while there began to appear **journals limited** in their scope **to specific branches of chemistry.** The broadest branch of chemistry is industrial chemistry, and so it seems natural that the first of these specialized chemical publications should have been devoted to the technical side of chemistry. It is *Wagner's Jahresberichte über chemische Technologie,* which was founded in 1855; it is not a journal in the true sense. The next one to appear, a still more specialized one, was *Fresenius's Zeitschrift für analytischen Chemie,* founded in 1862. These were followed by other specialized chemical journals. Now there is at least one journal for each of the major fields of chemistry (one in each major country in some fields) and in many cases for subdivisions of a major field. The journals described later in this chapter are classified according to branches of chemistry and illustrate this point.

Many of the more important general industrial journals and some of the journals devoted to more specialized branches are published by organizations of chemists specially interested in the respective fields involved. Examples of these are *Journal of the Society of Chemical Industry* (1882–1950) and *Journal of Applied Chemistry* (London 1951–   ), published by the Society of Chemical Industry (London); *Transactions of the American Institute of Chemical Engineers*

(1909–   ); *Chimie et industrie,* published by La société de la chimie industrielle (France) since 1918; *The Analyst,* the official organ of the (British) Society of Public Analysts (1877); and the *Transactions of the Electrochemical Society* (1902–   ).

A type of **journal** showing still further specialization is the one **devoted to a specific industry,** the conducting of which involves chemistry and chemical engineering. There are journals, in some cases many of them, for all of the large industries involving chemistry, as the petroleum journals, the dye journals, the rubber journals, the plastics journals, and the glass journals. Some of these are published by organizations of scientific and technical men interested in the industries involved; examples are the *Journal of the American Leather Chemists' Association* and the *Journal of the Society of Glass Technology* (Great Britian). These industrial publications sponsored by societies are usually filled with original papers, the papers being many times close to, if not indeed pure, science products, and an abstract section is often included.

Another kind of specialization is shown by periodicals devoted exclusively to reviews. The rapid growth of chemistry stimulated the introduction of reviews to help scientists keep in touch with current developments. Review journals supplement the abstract journals and are an outgrowth of annual reviews and yearbooks. This type of journal is quite numerous after 1920. Examples are *Chemical Reviews* (United States), *Reviews of Pure and Applied Chemistry* (Australia), *Fortschritte der chemischen Forschung* (Germany), *Quarterly Reviews* (The Chemical Society, London), and *Uspekhi Kimii* (USSR).

The latest development in chemical periodicals is the news publication, which started out as a news section in another journal in most cases, but is now a separate journal. The demand for the latest chemical news caused the establishment of a number of weekly chemical news journals; examples are *Chemical and Engineering News* (United States), and *Chemistry and Industry* (England).

Classification

The journals of interest to chemists can be classified in several ways and a number of classifications are in use to serve different purposes.

Periodicals are sometimes classified as primary or secondary sources of information. The primary sources of information are those that contain new or previously unpublished information. The secondary sources are more highly organized and include the abstract journals, the review journals, and the indexing serials; they contain information obtained from the primary sources and serve as a guide or a key to the literature in the primary group. No distinct line can be drawn between these two classes of periodicals. Some journals publish both new material and reviews, others include both new material and abstracts, while some cover all three (original papers, reviews, and abstracts). The current journals of greatest chemical interest that are described later in this chapter fall into the primary source group in most cases because for practical purposes that is their main function. The abstract journals that are considered separately in this chapter include those devoted exclusively to abstracts and those from the first group that publish a large enough number of abstracts regularly to be useful as abstract journals.

Journals can be **classified as scientific,** sometimes called theoretical (devoted to pure science, as the *Journal of the American Chemical Society*), **or industrial,** sometimes called technical (devoted to applied science, as *Industrial and Engineering Chemistry*).

Journals may be **classified as philanthropic or published for profit,**[5] which is nearly the same as a classification into society organs and journals published as private enterprises. Some privately published journals are really of the philanthropic class, as the *Archives of Biochemistry and Biophysics.* Government publications and the bulletins and circulars issued by universities, like society publications, are classed as philanthropic. The journals of the so-called philanthropic group are usually devoted almost exclusively to original papers (with sometimes abstracts and with society proceedings if society journals); and, as far as the purely scientific and technical side of chemistry is concerned, they make up by far the most valuable part of the journal literature. As a rule these journals have the first right to the publication of papers presented at the meetings of the organizations responsible for them. Most of the great outstanding contributions have appeared in journals of this type. The fact that a journal is published by a scientific society is a pretty sure indication that it is a source of reliable information. Such a journal may be expected to stand for whatever the sponsoring society stands for and to report the best work of its members in so far as this work is disclosed at all.

As one would expect, most of the **journals published for profit** are of an industrial nature. This class includes the numerous trade journals. A situation to be reckoned with in evaluating the journals published for profit is the fact that, with the exception of a few journals with high subscription rates, as the *Zeitschrift für physikalische Chemie*, the profit comes mainly from advertisements. The natural tendency is to publish material of a character calculated best to carry the advertising and an amount just sufficient for that purpose. Quality has sometimes been lowered. The wise editor recognizes, however, that a high standard of business ethics and practice, with the establishment of a reputation for supplying useful, up-to-date and accurate information, is the best policy in the long run from every point of view. Long establishment is at least a partial test of reliability.

Other characteristics of trade journals published for profit are that they are usually devoted largely to industrial and trade news and statistics, commonly of economic or business interest; the amount of new technical or scientific information is usually rather small. Such journals frequently contain copied articles or parts thereof and general reports of interest to the more or less casual reader but of little value to the research investigator. These reports are designed to help the readers keep up with a general trend; sometimes they have bibliographies that are useful. Editorial sections are usually included and sections devoted to a limited number of patents are common. The material published by these trade journals has its value but, since most of it lacks the same degree of permanency as that published in journals devoted to the initial reporting of scientific and technical research, the back files of trade journals are of lesser importance.

A more recent development is the publication for profit of strictly **technical journals** for the chemical and allied industries. *Chemical Engineering* (United States) is an example. The journals of this class are usually well edited. They obtain by contribution, special reporting, and reprinting (sometimes translations from foreign journals) first-class material, and their importance is not to be underestimated. As contrasted with the trade journals these periodicals serve more as tools for the profession than for industry. As the business and economic problems of the chemical industries have become more prominent, these journals have added much of the material included in the trade journals.

It is not intended to give the impression that privately published journals are the only sources of the kind of business and economic news and information valued by industry. **The most valuable journals serving chemical industry** are published by chemical societies in the various countries and they contain such news and information in addition to the large amount of new and original material.

Another difference between the philanthropic journal and the journal published for profit, which has some significance as regards the **quality of the material published,** is the fact that in the former case high-grade material for publication usually pours in without editorial effort whereas for the latter class material has in many cases to be sought. Good material is obtained by many of the journals published for profit. Some trade journals are largely parasites on the philanthropic journals as far as their scientific and technical information service is concerned. Editors of society and philanthropic publications usually have boards of advisors to help to evaluate papers that are contributed and to select the best and most valuable ones.

Another **classification** of some interest is **based on the countries** in which the journals are published. The more important journals of chemical interest now appearing are arranged by countries as a secondary classification in the grouping by subjects or fields as shown in the list further on in this chapter. This arrangement gives one a rough idea of the extent of chemical activity in the various countries. The latest figures available on this basis of classification are those of Crane [6] who compiled them for the 5,236 journals given in the *List of Periodicals Abstracted by Chemical Abstracts* (1951 ed.) ; these show that 64.6 per cent of the journals were then published in seven countries: United States, England, Italy, Germany, France, Japan, and Russia.

A **classification** of journals of chemical interest **by languages** would correspond in a general way with that by country of origin. Again the latest figures available are those of Crane [6] that showed that in 1951 44.8 per cent of the journals abstracted came from English-speaking countries and that journals in the German, Russian, French, Japanese, Spanish, and Italian languages accounted for a large proportion of the others. Swiss journals are often published in several languages, partly in French, partly in German, and occasionally in Italian or English. Some Japanese journals are published in several languages too, the most frequent being Japanese and English. Scandinavian journals frequently carry papers in English, or are published entirely in English. Some journals published in Holland are printed in French with occasional papers in English or German.

Classification of current periodicals of chemical interest according to subject or field is another useful one; this is used for the journals described below. The broadest classification of this sort is the separation of the strictly chemical journals from those of related sciences but still of distinct interest to chemists. Of the related science journals it is worthy of note that those of physics and the various branches of biology are particularly prolific sources of papers of direct interest to the chemist.

CURRENT JOURNALS OF GREATEST CHEMICAL INTEREST, CLASSIFIED ACCORDING TO SUBJECTS OR FIELDS AND SECONDARILY ACCORDING TO COUNTRIES

The classification is that used for abstracts in *Chemical Abstracts*, with three exceptions: journals devoted to physical chemistry have been separated from the general chemical journals, a general science class has been introduced, and class 15 (Agricultural Chemistry) is not divided. A few journals that have ceased publication recently have been included if they are important journals. The comments accompanying many of the journals are made in an effort to give an impression of the nature, scope, and usefulness to the chemist of the journals as gained by the authors in their use of them. The journals entered without comment are either strictly chemical journals (pure or applied) or journals that frequently publish papers of chemical interest. No attempt has been made to describe the journals in detail. Some journals are difficult to classify so a few are entered in more than one class and there are a few cross references. Abstract journals are considered in a separate section farther on in this chapter, but there is some duplication because no sharp line of demarcation can be drawn between journals that are devoted to abstracts exclusively and those that publish both abstracts and papers. Journals published in the United States are entered first and the others follow in alphabetical order according to the country of origin in these lists. In nearly all cases the date on which the journal started publication is given. An effort has been made to note all of the existing collective indexes and to give part of the changes in the names of the periodicals.

General Science

The results of a considerable amount of chemical research are published in journals of general science.

76 PERIODICALS

UNITED STATES

American Journal of Science. 1818– . This pioneer American journal covered all phases of science until 1900 when geology and related sciences became predominant. Collective indexes, 1818–1935, in 18 vols.

Journal of the Franklin Institute. 1826– . Collective indexes, Vols. 1–180 (1826–1926).

Journal of the Washington Academy of Sciences. 1911– .

Memoirs of the American Academy of Arts and Sciences. 1780– .

Proceedings of the American Academy of Arts and Sciences. 1846– .

News Report, National Academy of Sciences (Research Council of U.S.A). 1951– .

Proceedings of the National Academy of Sciences of the United States. 1915– .

Proceedings of the American Philosophical Society. 1838– .

Science. 1883– . The official organ of the American Association for the Advancement of Science. It includes articles on topics of general interest, scientific news, book reviews, lists of new books, and brief announcements of experimental work. It is particularly useful for keeping in touch with the activities of scientific men.

ARGENTINA

Anales de la sociedad científica argentina. 1876– .

Ciencia e investigación (Buenos Aires). 1945– .

AUSTRIA

Österreichische Akademie der Wissenschaften. 1848– . The name of this journal was *Sitzungsberichte der Akademie der Wissenschaften in Wien* until 1947. There are four parts, of which Abteilung IIB is devoted to chemistry.

AUSTRALIA

Australian Journal of Science. 1938– . It has a supplement, *Australian Science Abstracts*, which is valuable.

Australian Journal of Scientific Research. 1948–1952. Series A covers physical sciences and Series B, biological sciences. Split up into *Australian Journal of Physics* and *Australian Journal of Chemistry* in 1953.

Proceedings of the Royal Society of Victoria.

BELGIUM

Annales de la société scientifique de Bruxelles. 1875– .

Bulletin de la classe des sciences, Académie royale de Belgique. 1835– .

Osiris. 1936– . This is really an international journal of the history of science.

BULGARIA

Comptes rendus de l'académie bulgare des sciences. 1948– .

CANADA

Canadian Journal of Research. 1926–1950. This was first published in six parts, of which A, B, and F (physical sciences, chemical sciences, technology) are of most interest. It was replaced by six entirely separate journals. Collective index, Vols. 1–12, 1926–1935.

National Research Council Bulletin. 1951– .

Transactions of the Royal Society of Canada. 1882– . Sections III and IV cover chemical, mathematical, and physical sciences. Collective index. 1882–1906.

FINLAND

Annales Academiae Scientiarum Fennicae. 1909– . There are five parts in Series A, of which Part II is devoted to chemistry. Printed in English or German.

FRANCE

Comptes rendus hebdomadaires de séances de l'académie des sciences (Paris). 1835– . All papers are brief; some appear elsewhere in greater detail. The number of chemical papers is large, and this is one of the most important French journals for chemists.

GERMANY

Forschungen und Fortschritte. 1935– . This review journal for German scientific work once had an English edition entitled *Research and Progress;* it was published from 1935 to 1945.

Naturwissenschaften, Die. 1913– . This journal is similar to *Nature* (England). Many brief early announcements of German research appear here. Collective indexes, Vols. 1–15; 16–20, 1913–1932.

Zeitschrift für Naturforschung. 1946– . Much of this journal is devoted to summaries and reviews of research done in both Germany and other countries in physics, chemistry, and biology.

GREAT BRITAIN

Advancement of Science (London). 1939– . Published by the British Association for the Advancement of Science.

Annals of Science. 1936– . A quarterly review of the history of science since the Renaissance.

Discovery. 1920– .

Endeavour. 1942– . A review journal.

Isis. 1913– . An international review of the history of science.

Nature. 1869– . *Nature,* which surveys the whole field of scientific activity, is an excellent journal to use for keeping in touch with scientific advances. Many announcements and brief reports of important new investigations appear promptly. *Nature* announces and reviews many scientific books. Chemistry receives its full share of attention.

Philosophical Magazine, The. 1798– . This is a valuable journal that is now devoted to theoretical, experimental, and applied physics, but it was an excellent general science journal until about 1920 when papers on atomic

78   PERIODICALS

structure, the structure of matter, and physics became predominant. Many important chemical papers were published. The name has changed several times: *Philosophical Magazine*, 1798–1814; *Philosophical Magazine and Journal* from its combination with the *Philosophical Journal* (1797–1814) in 1814 to 1827; *Philosophical Magazine or Annals of Chemistry, Mathematics, Astronomy, Natural History and General Science* from 1827 to 1832; *The London, Edinburgh and Dublin Philosophical Magazine and Journal of Science*, 1832–1944 (*Dublin* was added in 1840). *The Philosophical Magazine* (1945–   ), now in the seventh series, has collective indexes for two series, Vols. 1–68 (1798–1826) and Vols. 1–11 (1827–1831).

Proceedings of the Cambridge Philosophical Society. 1843–   .
Transactions of the Cambridge Philosophical Society. 1822–1928.
Proceedings of the Royal Institution of Great Britain. 1851–   . Collective index, Vols. 1–24, 1851–1925.
Proceedings of the Royal Society of Edinburgh. 1832–   .
Transactions of the Royal Society of Edinburgh. 1783–   . Collective indexes, 1783–1908.
Proceedings of the Royal Society (London). 1800–   .
Transactions of the Royal Society (London). 1665–   . The Royal Society in both its *Proceedings* and *Transactions* publishes two sets of papers under separate covers: *Series A. Mathematical and Physical Sciences* and *Series B. Biological Series*. The papers are usually of high quality and many are of chemical interest. Collective indexes (*Proceedings*, Series B) 1800–1930. Collective index (*Transactions*, Series A) 1665–1830.
Research (London). 1947–   . A review of science and its applications.

HOLLAND

Koninklijke Nederlandse Akademie van Wetenschappen, Proceedings. Formerly called *Proceedings of the Royal Academy of Sciences of Amsterdam.* 1853–   . Many valuable chemical papers are published. Printed in English, French, and German.

INDIA

Current Science. 1932–   .
Journal of the Indian Institute of Science. 1914–   .
Journal of Scientific and Industrial Research. 1941–   . Carries some abstracts.
Proceedings of the Indian Academy of Sciences. 1934–   .

IRELAND

Proceedings of the Royal Irish Academy. 1836–   .
Scientific Proceedings of the Royal Dublin Society, The. 1877–   . Collective indexes, Vols. 1–11.

ITALY

Atti della academia nazionale dei Lincei, Rendiconti. 1847–   .
Scientia (Milan) 1907–   . This is an international review of science, with papers in English, French, German, Italian, and Spanish.

Journal of the Faculty of Science, Hokkaido University. 1930–   .
Journal of the Faculty of Science, University of Tokyo. 1887–   .
Journal of the Scientific Research Institute (Tokyo). Formerly *Scientific Papers of the Institute of Physical and Chemical Research.* 1922–   .
Memoirs of the College of Science, University of Kyoto. 1914–   .
All of these Japanese journals give considerable space to chemistry.

MEXICO

Ciencia. 1940–   . A review of pure and applied sciences.

PERU

Revista de ciencias. 1897–   .

PHILIPPINE ISLANDS

Philippine Journal of Science, The. 1906–   . Collective indexes, Vols. 1–28 (1906–1925).

POLAND

Bulletin international de l'académie polonaise des sciences et des lettres. Formerly *Bulletin international de l'académie des sciences de Cracovie.* 1889–   .

SOUTH AFRICA

South African Journal of Science. 1903–   .

SPAIN

Euclides (Madrid). 1941–   . This is one of the most important Spanish journals. It reviews the sciences, including chemistry. Publishes some abstracts.

SWITZERLAND

Archives des sciences (Geneva). 1846–   . Until 1948, it was called *Archives des sciences physiques et naturelles.* Collective indexes, Vols. 1–36; [N.S.] Vols. 1–64 (1889–1910).
Experientia. 1945–   . It is similar to *Nature* (England).

TURKEY

Communications de la faculté des sciences de l'université d'Ankara. 1948–   . Articles in English, French, or German.

USSR (SOVIET UNION)

Doklady Akademii Nauk Soyuza Sovetskikh Sotsialisticheskikh Respublik. 1828–   . These are the reports of the Academy of Sciences of the USSR and continue *Comptes rendus de l'académie des sciences de Russie.* The papers are short and may be reported in more detail in other journals at a later date. This very important journal covers all sciences, including much chemistry. It is printed in Russian. There was another edition, *Comptes rendus (Doklady) de l'académie des sciences de l'USSR* (printed in English, French, or German), which was discontinued in 1947. The present title was adopted in 1933.

Izvestiya Akademii Nauk Soyuza Sovetskikh Sotsialisticheskikh Respublik (Bulletin of the Academy of Sciences of USSR). 1836– . Formerly *Bulletin de l'académie des sciences de Russie*. It is printed in Russian. This important journal for keeping up with Russian research is now published in nine separate parts of which *Izvest. Akad. Nauk SSSR, Otdelenie Khimicheskikh Nauk* (Chemistry) and *Izvest. Akad. Nauk SSSR, Otdelenie Tekhnicheskikh Nauk* (Technology) are of most interest to chemists. The present title was adopted in 1937.

VENEZUELA

Acta científica venezolana. 1950–   .

1. Apparatus, Plant Equipment, Unit Operations

Very few journals are devoted specifically to these fields. Many papers, or portions of papers, on apparatus and equipment appear scattered through a great variety of journals devoted primarily to other subjects. Most of the papers on unit operations are published in journals devoted to chemical engineering or to industrial chemistry.

UNITED STATES

Instruments and Automation. 1928–   . Formerly *Instruments*.
Journal of the Optical Society of America. 1917–   .
Review of Scientific Instruments. 1930–   .

FRANCE

Revue d'optique, théorique et instrumentale. 1922–   .

GERMANY

Brennstoff-Warme-Kraft. 1949–   .
Chemie-Ingénieur-Technik. 1928–   . A continuation of *Die Chemische Fabrik*, 1928–1941.
Chemische Technik, Die (Berlin). 1949–   . *Chemische Apparatur* (1914–1942) was merged in *Chemische Technik* in 1943.

GREAT BRITAIN

British Journal of Applied Physics. 1950–   .
Instrument Engineer. 1952–   .
Journal of Scientific Instruments. 1924–   .
Laboratory Practice. 1952–   .
Vacuum. 1951–   . A review of development in vacuum research and engineering. It includes a classified abstract section.

Microtecnic. 1947–   . An international review for measuring and gauging techniques, optics, and precision mechanics.

2. General Chemistry

UNITED STATES

Armed Forces Chemical Journal. 1946–   .
Chemical and Engineering News. 1923–   . Formerly the *News Edition* of *Industrial and Engineering Chemistry,* it has been published as a separate journal since January 1942. This weekly publication of the American Chemical Society is invaluable for keeping up with the chemical news both of the United States and of foreign countries. Prices of chemicals, lists of trade publications, announcements of new books, and book reviews are included. Beginning with 1953, the annual index is not included in the journal but is sold separately. See *Chem. Eng. News* **32,** 1975 (1954). The activities of the American Chemical Society are reported.
Chemical Reviews. 1924–   . Excellent reviews that usually have extensive bibliographies. Collective indexes, Vols. 1–10; Vols. 11–20.
Journal of the American Chemical Society. 1879–   . This is one of the world's most important journals devoted to pure chemistry. Collective index, Vols. 1–20 (1879–1898).
Journal of Chemical Education. 1924–   . In addition to papers on chemical education, there are papers on the history of chemistry and many reviews of chemical books. Collective index, Vols. 1–25 (1924–1949).

ARGENTINA

Anales de la asociación química argentina. 1913–   .

AUSTRALIA

Australian Journal of Chemistry. 1952–   .
Reviews of Pure and Applied Chemistry. 1951–   .

AUSTRIA

Mikrochemie vereinigt mit Mikrochimica Acta. 1923–   . This journal is the only one devoted to microchemistry. *Mikrochemie* was started in 1923 and *Mikrochimica Acta* merged with it in 1938. Resumed publication as *Mikrochimica Acta* in 1953.
Monatshefte für Chemie und verwandte Teile anderer Wissenschaften. 1880–   . Collective index, Vols. 1–50 (1880–1931).

BELGIUM

Bulletin des sociétés chimiques Belges. 1887–   . This is a continuation of the *Bulletin de la société chimique de Belgique.* Collective index, 1907–1916.

BRAZIL

Anais da associação química do Brasil. 1942–   .
Revista da sociedade brasileira de química. 1939–   .

CANADA

Canadian Journal of Chemistry. This is a continuation of section B of the *Canadian Journal of Research* (1929–1950); it became a separate journal in 1951. This valuable journal is published by the National Research Council of Canada.
Chemistry in Canada. 1949–   . This is largely devoted to news and general information about chemistry in Canada.

CHINA

Journal of the Chinese Chemical Society (Peking). 1933–   . Printed in English with occasional papers in Chinese, French, or German.
Journal of the Chinese Chemical Society (Tiwan). 1954–   .

COLOMBIA

Revista colombiana de química. 1945–   .

CZECHOSLOVAKIA

Chemické Zvesti. 1949–   .
Chemické Listy. 1905–1950. Replaced by *Chemicky Prumysl* in 1951.
Chemicky Obzor. 1925–   .
Collection of Czechoslovak Chemical Communications. 1929–   . Publication suspended 1940–1946. Printed in English, French, German, or Russian.

DENMARK

Acta Chemica Scandinavica. 1947–   . This is published in Denmark but it is a joint publication of the Danish, Finnish, Norwegian, and Swedish chemical societies. Printed in English, French, German, or Scandinavian. It is an important journal.
Comptes rendus des travaux du laboratoire Carlsberg. 1878–   . These are now two series: chemistry and physiology.

FINLAND

Finska Kemistsamfundets Meddelanden. 1892–   . Collective index, Vols. 23–36 (1914–1927).
Suomen Kemistilehti (Acta Chemica Fennica). 1928–   . See also *Acta Chemica Scandinavica* under Denmark.

FRANCE

Annales de chimie. 1789–   . This is the oldest chemical journal still appearing. It appeared from 1816 to 1914 under the name *Annales de chimie et de physique*, when it was divided into two separate journals, *An-*

nales de chimie and *Annales de physique.* Collective indexes at about 10-year intervals.

Bulletin de la société chimique de France. 1858– . An important chemical journal which is, and has been, devoted to pure chemistry. It published a large number of abstracts from the beginning until 1945. Collective indexes for these periods: 1858–1874; 1875–1888; 1889–1898; 1899–1906; 1907–1916; 1917–1926.

GERMANY

Chemische Berichte. 1868– . This is a continuation of the valuable *Berichte der deutschen chemischen Gesellschaft* (see below), which ceased publication with Vol. 77, no. 11/12, 1945. *Chemische Berichte* continues the volume numbers of *Ber. deut. chem. Ges.* and started publication with Vol. 80 (1947).

Berichte der deutschen chemischen Gesellschaft. 1868–1945. Continued as *Chemische Berichte* (see above). This journal and its successor should be in every chemical library. Abstracts were published from 1868 to 1896. Collective indexes were issued every ten years through 1937, but since 1896 these are author indexes only.

Chemiker-Zeitung mit Chemie Börse. 1877– . This journal, called *Chemiker Zeitung* until 1951, is a general chemical journal with emphasis on applied chemistry. It published a large number of abstracts from 1882 to 1940; there are fewer now. Since 1951 chemical markets and general business information have been added.

Fortschritte der Chemie, Physik und physikalischen Chemie. 1909–1932. These are critical reviews; most of them are of monograph length.

Fortschitte der chemischen Forschung. 1949– . A review journal.

Zeitschrift für anorganische und allgemeine Chemie. 1892– . This is a good journal and always has been devoted entirely or largely to inorganic chemistry, as the title changes below indicate: 1943–1950, *Zeitschrift für anorganische Chemie;* 1915–1945, same title as the present; 1892–1915, same title as for 1943–1950. Abstracts in Vols. 1–37. Collective indexes for Vols. 1–200 (1892–1931) at 50-volume intervals.

GREAT BRITAIN

Journal of the Chemical Society (London). 1841– . This is an outstanding journal. It had a large abstract section from 1871 to 1926. The original name was *Memoirs and Proceedings of the Chemical Society,* which continued until 1847 when it was changed to the *Quarterly Journal of the Chemical Society.* In 1862, the journal became a monthly publication and the present name was adopted. A collective index covers the period 1841–1872. The first decennial index covered the period 1873–1882 and one has been issued at regular intervals ever since. *The Proceedings,* except for 1885–1914, when published separately, appear in the *Journal.*

Quarterly Reviews. 1947– . These valuable chemical reviews are published by The Chemical Society (London).

Transactions of the Faraday Society. 1905– . This very valuable journal covers electrochemistry, physical chemistry, colloids, electrometal-

84	PERIODICALS

lurgy, and many other subjects of interest to chemists. Collective indexes, Vols. I–XX; XXI–XL (1905–1944).

HOLLAND

Recueil des travaux chimiques des Pays-Bas. 1882–　. A valuable journal. Collective index, Vols. 1–50 (1882–1931). Printed in French, German, and English.
Chemisch Weekblad. 1903–　. After 1920 this journal is devoted largely to industrial chemistry.

HUNGARY

Acta Chimica Academiae Scientiarum Hungaricae. 1951–　. Printed in English, French, German, or Russian.
Magyar Kémiai Folyóirat. 1895–　. Printed in Hungarian with summaries in German.
Magyar Kémikusok Lapja (The *Journal of the Hungarian Chemical Society*). 1946–　.

INDIA

Journal of the Indian Chemical Society. 1924–　. A good journal that has grown rapidly as more Indian scientists have been publishing here rather than in British journals. The *Industrial and News* edition of the *Journal of the Indian Chemical Society* is also useful.

ITALY

Gazzetta chimica italiana. 1871–　. This is the most important chemical journal published in Italy. Only papers in pure chemistry have been published since 1913. Collective indexes, Vols. 1–20; Vols. 21–40.

JAPAN

Bulletin of the Chemical Society of Japan. 1926–　. This useful journal publishes, in English, French, or German, papers communicated to the Society and lists of titles of papers published in other Japanese journals.
Journal of the Chemical Society of Japan. 1880–　. (*Nippon Kagaku Zassi*). Divided into two sections in 1948: pure chemistry and industrial chemistry. The Japanese language only is used. Collective indexes, 1880–1937.

MEXICO

Química. 1942–　.

NEW ZEALAND

Journal of the New Zealand Institute of Chemistry. 1937–　.

NORWAY

Acta Chemica Scandinavica. See listing under **Denmark**.

PERU

Boletin del químico peruano (Lima). 1943–　.
Boletin de la sociedad química del Peru. 1935–　.

Roczniki Chemii. 1921–   .

Journal of the South African Chemical Institute. 1919–   . Collective indexes. Vols 1–10; Vols. 11–20.

Anales de la real sociedad española de física y química (Madrid). 1903–   . Formerly *Anales de física y química* and before then *Anales de la sociedad española de física y química.* 1903–1940.

Arkiv för Kemi. 1903–   . Formerly *Arkiv för Kemi, Minerolagi och Geologi,* until 1949. Printed in English and German.
Svensk Kemisk Tidskrift. 1889–   . Printed in English, French, German, or Swedish.
See also *Acta Chemica Scandinavica* under Denmark.

Helvetica Chimica Acta. 1918–   . An important and valuable journal that publishes papers originating in several countries, in addition to Switzerland. Collective indexes, Vols. 1–15; Vols. 16–30.

Journal of the Russian Physical-Chemical Society. 1869–1930. This was not a journal of physical chemistry but one that covered both physics and chemistry. Only the Russian language is used, but there was usually a table of contents in French. Many valuable papers appeared in this journal. In 1930 the journal was divided to form two new journals, *Zhurnal Obshcheĭ Khimii (Journal of General Chemistry)* and *Zhurnal Fizicheskoĭ Khimii (Journal of Physical Chemistry).*
Uspekhi Khimii. 1932–   . This is a review publication to help Russian chemists keep up to date on the progress of chemistry—mostly outside of Russia.
Zhurnal Obshcheĭ Khimii (Journal of General Chemistry). 1930–   . This is a continuation of the chemical part of the *Journal of the Russian Physical-Chemical Society* (see above) and Series A of *Khimicheskiĭ Zhurnal.* Only the Russian language is used. This is an important journal both for keeping up with Russian research work and for the number of significant papers.

Arhiv za Kemiju. 1927–   .
Bulletin de la société chimique Belgrade. 1930–   .

86   PERIODICALS

2a. Physical Chemistry

The publication of research in physical chemistry is not confined to journals of physical or general chemistry; much of it appears in journals of physics, of which those most frequently of interest to chemists are included here.

UNITED STATES

Journal of Applied Physics. 1929– .
Journal of Chemical Physics. 1933– .
Journal of Colloid Science. 1946– . This is one of the few journals devoted to this field of physical chemistry.
Journal of Physical Chemistry, The. 1896– . This journal should be in every chemistry library. Abstracts in physical chemistry were published in Vols. 1–10. The name was *The Journal of Physical and Colloid Chemistry* from Vol. 51 (1947) through Vol. 56 (1951).
Physical Review, The. 1893– . With few exceptions, the research reported in this journal of physics is of interest to chemists. *Chemical Abstracts* abstracts nearly all of the papers and classifies most of the abstracts under electronic or nuclear phenomena. Collective index, 1893–1920.
Physics Today. 1948– . This journal does not include details of experimental work in physics as does *Physical Reviews* or such highly technical reviews as *Reviews of Modern Physics,* the other publications of the *American Institute of Physics,* but it is useful for keeping track of current work.
Reviews of Modern Physics. 1928– . Formerly *Physical Review Supplement.* A review journal. Collective index, 1929–1938.

CANADA

Canadian Journal of Physics. 1951– . This is a continuation of Section A of the *Canadian Journal of Research,* 1929–1950; it became a separate journal in 1951. It includes many papers of chemical interest, especially in the field of nuclear phenomena.

FRANCE

Annales de physique. 1915– .
Journal de chimie physique et de physicochimie biologique. 1903– . Formerly *Journal de chimie physique.* This journal of physical chemistry was originally published in Switzerland. It is really an international journal. Collective indexes, 1903–1933.
Journal de physique et Le radium. 1872– . The *Journal de physique, théorique et appliquée,* founded in 1872, was combined in 1920 with *Le Radium,* founded in 1904, and then assumed the title of *Journal de physique et Le radium.* Since 1922 it has printed a large number of abstracts annually. Many of the papers in this journal are of chemical interest.

GERMANY

Annalen der Physik. 1799– . Some papers of chemical interest, particularly on electronic phenomena, appear in this physical journal.
Kolloidchemische Beihefte. 1909–1943. This journal published long papers, often in the nature of monographs, on pure and applied colloid chemistry that are still useful. From 1931 to 1943 it was called *Kolloid-Beihefte.*
Kolloid-Zeitschrift. 1906– . It covers both pure and applied colloid chemistry. It has always had a very extensive abstract section. Collective index, Vols. 1–50 (1906–1930).
Zeitschrift für Kristallographie (Kristallgeometrie, Kristallphysik, Kristallchemie). 1877– . Suspended publication 1945–1954. Abstracts were included up to 1940. Collective index for Vols. 1–50; 51–75.
Zeitschrift für Physik. 1920– . This physical journal publishes many papers of chemical interest each year.
Zeitschrift für physikalische Chemie. 1887– . Suspended publication, Vol. 194, no. 3 (1944). Resumed publication, Vol. 194, no. 4–6 (1950). Collective indexes, 1887–1936. Abstracts were published up to 1906. This is the oldest and one of the most important journals of physical chemistry.
Zeitschrift für physikalische Chemie (Frankfurt). 1954– .
Zeitschrift für wissenschaftliche Photographie, Photophysik, und Photochemie. 1903– . The current numbers have an abstract section.

GREAT BRITAIN

Philosophical Magazine. See under General Science.
Proceedings of the Physical Society of London. 1874– . Many papers of chemical interest are published here; Section A contains mainly papers on atomic and subatomic subjects.
Transactions of the Faraday Society. See under General Chemistry.

HOLLAND

Physica. 1933– . Series IVA of *Archives néerlandaises des sciences exactes et naturelles.* Recent volumes of this physical journal have published many papers in physical chemistry, particularly in the fields of electronic and nuclear phenomena.

JAPAN

Journal of the Physical Society of Japan. 1946– .
Nippon Butsuri Gakkai Shi (Nippon Buturi Gakkai Si) (Proceedings of the Physical Society of Japan). 1946– . Printed in Japanese.
Progress of Theoretical Physics. 1946– .
Review of Physical Chemistry of Japan, The. 1925– .

SWITZERLAND

Helvetica Physica Acta. 1928– . Recent volumes of this physical journal contain a number of papers of chemical interest.

USSR (SOVIET UNION)

Acta Physicochimica USSR. 1934–1947. This had English or French summaries of the papers that were printed in Russian.

Kolloidnyi Zhurnal. 1935–   . A colloid chemistry journal.

Uspekhi Fizicheskikh Nauk (Progress of Physical Science). 1920–   . This is a review journal to help Russian scientists keep up with current research, mostly outside of Russia.

Zhurnal Eksperimental'noĭ i Teoreticheskoĭ Fiziki (Journal of Experimental and Theoretical Physics). 1930–   . Formerly Series A of *Fizicheskiĭ Zhurnal.* Part of the research here is of chemical interest, particularly in the field of nuclear phenomena.

Zhurnal Fizicheskoĭ Khimii (Journal of Physical Chemistry). 1930–   . This is a continuation of the physical part of the *Journal of the Russian Physical-Chemical Society,* see page 85. It is an important Russian journal.

Zhurnal Tekhnicheskoĭ Fiziki (Journal of Technical Physics). 1931–   . Some papers on physical chemistry are included.

3. Electronic Phenomena and Spectra

There is only one journal that specializes in this field; most of the papers are widely scattered in journals of general science, physics, chemistry, and physical chemistry.

GREAT BRITAIN

Spectrochimica Acta. 1939–   . An international journal.

OTHERS

Among the journals listed in Part 2a (Physical Chemistry), the following publish a number of papers on electronic phenomena:

Annalen der Physik (Germany).
Journal of Chemical Physics (U. S.).
Journal de physique et Le radium (France).
Physical Review, The (U. S.).
Transactions of the Faraday Society (Great Britain).
Zeitschrift für Physik (Germany).

3a. Nuclear Phenomena

There are very few journals that specialize in this field; part of the papers appear in journals of general science, chemistry, and physical chemistry, but many of the papers appear in physical journals.

UNITED STATES

Bulletin of the Atomic Scientists. 1945–   . This does not include reports of research work but is devoted to the general aspects of the field.

Nucleonics. 1947–   . This is mostly concerned with atomic power, atomic engineering, and industrial uses. It publishes some abstracts.

FRANCE

Atomes (Paris). 1946– . This is similar to the *Bulletin of the Atomic Scientists*.

GREAT BRITAIN

Journal of Nuclear Energy. 1954– .
Atomics and Atomic Technology. 1950– . This journal deals with the practical applications of nuclear energy.

OTHERS

Journals listed in Part 2a (Physical Chemistry) that publish many papers on nuclear phenomena are:

Canadian Journal of Physics.
Journal of Applied Physics (U. S.).
Journal of Chemical Physics (U. S.).
Journal of the Physical Society of Japan.
Helvetica Physica Acta (Switzerland).
Izvestiya Akademii Nauk SSSR, Seriya Fizicheskaya (Physics). Many papers of physical chemical interest are published.
Physica (Holland).
Physical Review (U. S.). This publishes more papers on nuclear science than any other journal at the present time.
Proceedings of the Physical Society (London).
Zhurnal Eksperimental'noĭ i Teoreticheskoĭ Fiziki (*Journal of Experimental and Theoretical Physics*) (USSR).
Zeitschrift für Physik (Germany).

THE NETHERLANDS

Nuclear Physics. 1956– .

4. Electrochemistry

There are few journals that specialize in this field. Much electrochemical work is reported in journals of physical chemistry, general chemistry, metallurgy, and industrial chemistry; some is included in electrical engineering journals.

UNITED STATES

Electrical Engineering (New York). 1905– .
Electronics. 1930– . The primary coverage of this journal is the design of all kinds of electrical equipment.
Journal of the Electrochemical Society. 1902– . (A combination of the *Journal* and the *Transactions of the Electrochemical Society.*) The *Transactions* were a separate publication until 1948. This is an important journal.

Plating. 1914–   . Formerly *Monthly Review of the American Electro-plater s Society.* The title changed in 1948. Some abstracts are included.

Transactions of the Electrochemical Society. 1902–1948. The title was *Transactions of the American Electrochemical Society* until 1931. Now appearing in the *Journal of the Electrochemical Society.*

FRANCE

Journal du four electrique et des industries electrochimiques. 1895–   . This is an international review.

GERMANY

Zeitschrift für Electrochemie und angewandte physikalische Chemie. 1894–   . Collective indexes, Vols. 1–10 (1894–1904); Vols. 11–30 (1905–1924).

GREAT BRITAIN

Electroplating and Metal Finishing. 1948–   . This has a large abstract section.

JAPAN

Journal of the Electrochemical Society of Japan. 1933–   .

5. Photography

There are many periodicals devoted to photography that occasionally publish a paper of chemical interest, but there are relatively few that give the scientific aspects of photography much space. Much of the chemistry of photography is published in a variety of chemical journals.

UNITED STATES

American Photography. 1907–   .

Journal of the Society of Motion Picture Engineers and Television Engineers. 1916–   . Collective index, 1916–1930. Formerly *Journal of Motion Picture Engineers.*

FRANCE

Bulletin de la société française de photographie et de cinématographie. 1855–   .

Science et industries photographiques. 1921–   . It has a large abstract section.

GERMANY

Die Fotografie. 1947–   . A continuation of several German photographic journals.

Photographische Korrespondenz. 1864–   . This is now published in Austria.

Zeitschrift für wissenschaftliche Photographie, Photophysik, und Photochemie. 1903–   . This is an important journal and the current numbers include some abstracts.

British Journal of Photography. 1854–   . A good journal that includes abstracts of British patents.

Journal of Photographic Science. 1953–   .

Photographic Journal. 1853–   . An excellent journal. Section B, devoted to the scientific aspects of photography, was split off in 1953 to form a new journal, *Journal of Photographic Science.*

SWITZERLAND

Camera (Lucerne). 1921–   .

6. Inorganic Chemistry

There are only two journals devoted to this field. Papers on inorganic chemistry appear in journals of general science, of general chemistry, industrial chemistry, and mineralogical and geological chemistry.

GERMANY

Zeitschrift für anorganische und allgemeine Chemie. 1892–   . At the present time it includes very little general chemistry. See page 83.

GREAT BRITAIN

Journal of Inorganic and Nuclear Chemistry. 1955–   . An international journal.

7. Analytical Chemistry

Many of the journals of applied chemistry include some papers on analytical chemistry.

UNITED STATES

Analytical Chemistry. 1929–   . Formerly *Industrial and Engineering Chemistry, Analytical edition).* The change in title concerned in 1947. This is an indispensable journal.

Chromatography Bulletin. 1950–   .

Journal of the Association of Official Agricultural Chemists. 1915–   . See section 12, p. 101, for a description.

FRANCE

Annales des falsifications et des fraudes. 1908–   . See Section 12 for a description.

Chimie analytique. 1896–   . Its name from 1942 to 1947 was *Annales chimie analytique* and from 1919 to 1942 was *Annales de chimie analytique et de chimie appliquée et Revue de chimie analytique réunis*. It is a good journal and has included abstracts from the beginning.

GERMANY

Mikrochemie vereinigt mit Mikrochimica Acta. 1923–1953. Much of this journal is devoted to microanalytical chemistry.
Mikrochimica Acta. 1953–   .
Zeitschrift für analytische Chemie. 1862–   . An excellent journal that had a good abstract section from 1862 to 1935. Ten-year collective indexes for Vols. 1–120 (1862–1940).

GREAT BRITAIN

Analyst, The. 1876–   . It covers all phases of analytical chemistry and included abstracts up to 1950. Collective indexes. Vols. 1–60 (1876–1935) at ten-year intervals.
Spectrochimica Acta. 1939–   . An international journal.

HOLLAND

Analytica Chimica Acta. 1947–   . This journal is the publication of the Section of Analytical Chemistry of the International Union of Pure and Applied Chemistry. It covers both pure and applied analytical chemistry. It is published in English, French, or German.

SPAIN

Información de química analítica (Madrid). 1947–   . A supplement of *Ion,* which is a journal of industrial chemistry.

USSR (SOVIET UNION)

Zhurnal Analiticheskoi Khimii (*Journal of Analytical Chemistry*). 1946–   .
Zavodskaya Laboratoriya (*Factory Laboratory*). 1935-   . It is devoted to industrial analytical methods.

8. Mineralogical and Geological Chemistry

UNITED STATES

American Journal of Science. 1819–   . This is almost entirely devoted to geology, mineralogy and related sciences at present.
American Mineralogist, The. 1916–   .
Bulletin of the Geological Society of America. 1889–   . Collective indexes, Vols. 1–50 (1889–1939), were issued at ten-year intervals beginning with 1900.
Economic Geology and the Bulletin of the Society of Economic Geologists. 1905–   . This journal includes a large number of abstracts. Collective indexes, Vols. 1–20 (1905–1925); Vols. 21–30 (1926–1935).
Geophysics. 1930–   . Collective index, 1931–1937.
Journal of Geology, The. 1893–   . Collective indexes, 1893–1927.

FRANCE

Bulletin de la société française de minéralogie et de cristallographie. 1878–   .
Bulletin de la société géologique de France. 1830–   .

Revue de l'industrie minérale. 1855–   . This journal is divided in three parts: I, *Memoires* (original papers), II, *Comptes rendus* (abstracts and reviews), and III, *Documents.* Former name, *Bulletin de la société de l'industrie minérale de St. Etienne.*

GERMANY

Chemie der Erde. 1914–   . This covers chemical mineralogy, petrography, geology, and related fields.

Geochimica et Cosmochimica Acta. 1950–   .

Fortschritte der Mineralogie. 1911–   . Formerly *Fortschritte der Mineralogie, Kristallographie und Petrographie.* A good review journal.

Neues Jahrbüch für Mineralogie, Geologie und Palaontologie. 1807–1950. This was divided into two journals, see below.

Neues Jahrbüch für Mineralogie. 1950–   .

Neues Jahrbüch für Geologie und Palaontologie. 1950–   .

GREAT BRITAIN

Geological Magazine, The. 1864–   . Collective indexes, 1864–1903.

Mineralogical Magazine and Journal of the Mineralogical Society. 1876–   . *Mineralogical Abstracts* is a part of this publication. See under Abstract Journals. Collective indexes, Vols. 1–20 (1876–1925) in two volumes.

Quarterly Journal of the Geological Society of London. 1845–   . Collective indexes, Vols. 1–50 (1845–1894).

NORWAY

Norsk Geologisk Tidsskrift. 1905–   .

SWEDEN

Arkiv för Mineralogi och Geologi, utgivet av Kungl. 1949–   . Printed in English.

Geologiska Föreningens i Stockholm Forhandlingar. 1872–   . Printed in English, French, German, or Swedish.

SWITZERLAND

Schweizerische mineralogische und petrographische Mitteilungen. 1921–   .

USSR (SOVIET UNION)

Doklady Akademü Nauk SSSR. 1827–   . See General Science Journals, p. 79.

9. Metallurgy and Metallography

Part of the literature in this field is widely scattered in a great variety of journals. Papers on metallurgy often appear in journals of general industrial chemistry and journals of electrochemistry.

Acta Metallurgica. 1953– .

Blast Furnace and Steel Plant, The. 1913– . A trade journal.

Corrosion. 1945– .

Engineering and Mining Journal. 1866– . A trade journal that includes some metallurgy.

Iron Age, The. 1859– . A valuable trade journal.

Iron and Steel Engineer. 1924– .

Journal of Metals. 1949– . A very important publication that covers a considerable part of the scientific work on metallurgy in the United States. It is a continuation of *Metals Technology;* it is a publication of the American Institute of Mining and Metallurgical Engineers.

Light Metal Age. 1943– . Devoted to nonferrous metallurgy and includes abstracts.

Metal Finishing. 1903– . Formerly *Metal Industry, New York.* Devoted exclusively to metallic surface treatments and includes abstracts.

Materials and Methods. 1929– . The magazine of materials engineering (a continuation of *Metals and Alloys*). A trade type of journal that formerly included abstracts.

Metal Progress. 1920– . Includes a few abstracts.

Metals Review. 1928– . A news digest that has a department known as "A.S.M. Review of Metal Literature," which gives very complete coverage, about 9,000 annotated entries each year. An American Society for Metals publication.

Mining Engineering. 1949– . Incorporating *Mining and Metallurgy, Mining Technology,* and *Coal Technology.* This is an important publication of the American Institute of Mining and Metallurgical Engineers.

Modern Metals. 1945– . Nonferrous metals.

Powder Metallurgy Bulletin. 1946– . Abstracts are included.

Products Finishing. 1937– . Cleaning, plating, and polishing are covered.

Transactions of the American Institute of Mining and Metallurgical Engineers. 1871– . At the present time all papers in the transactions are published earlier in the journals of the Institute (*Journal of Metals,* or *Mining Engineering*).

Transactions of the American Society of Metals. 1920– . Formerly *Transactions of the American Society for Steel Treating.* Many of the papers are issued as preprints and are included in a regular issue at a later date.

Proceedings of the Australasian Institute of Mining and Metallurgy. 1897– . Collective indexes, 1897–1931.

Revue universelle des mines, de la metallurgie, des travaux publiques, des sciences, et des arts appliqués à l'industrie. 1857– . Some abstracts are included.

JOURNALS CLASSIFIED 95

BRAZIL

Engenharia, mineração e metalurgia. 1936– . Formerly *Mineração e metalurgia.*

CANADA

Canadian Mining and Metallurgical Bulletin. 1908– . Formerly the *Bulletin of the Canadian Institute of Mining and Metallurgy.*
Canadian Mining Journal. 1882– .
Canadian Metals. 1938– . Formerly *Canadian Metals and Metallurgical Industries.*

FRANCE

Galvano. La surface métallique. 1932– .
Revue de l'aluminium. 1924– .
Revue de métallurgie. 1904– . This is the most important French metallurgical journal. It includes abstracts.

GERMANY

Archiv für Eisenhüttenwesen. 1927– .
Metall. 1947– . Formerly *Metallwirtschaft.*
Metall und Erz. Discontinued in 1944. See *Zeitschrift für Erzbergbau und Metallhüttenwesen.*
Stahl und Eisen. 1881– . A good journal. Current numbers include abstracts. Collective indexes, Vols. 1–50 (1881–1930) in 3 volumes.
Werkstoffe und Korrosion. 1950– . A continuation of *Archiv für Metallkunde* and *Korrosion und Metallschutz.*
Zeitschrift für Erzbergbau und Metallhüttenwesen. 1948– . A continuation of *Metall und Erz.* It includes abstracts.
Zeitschrift für Metallkunde. 1918– . The most important of the German metallurgical journals. There was an extensive abstract section but there are few abstracts at present.

GREAT BRITAIN

Alloy Metals Review. 1936– . Abstracts are included.
Aluminum and the Nonferrous Review. 1935– . Temporarily suspended in 1948.
Bulletin and Foundry Abstracts of the British Cast Iron Research Association. 1923– .
Bulletin of the Institution of Mining and Metallurgy. 1904– . An important journal. Current numbers include some abstracts.
Iron and Steel (London). 1927– . A good trade publication.
Journal of the Institute of Metals and Metallurgical Abstracts. 1909– . A very important journal that covers general and nonferrous metallurgy. The abstract section is very large and comprehensive. Collective indexes, 1909–1938.
Journal of the Iron and Steel Institute (London). 1869– . Iron and steel metallurgy is covered thoroughly in its abstract section. Many important papers are published. Collective indexes, 1869–1931.
Light Metals. 1938– . Nonferrous metallurgy.

Metal Industry, The (London). 1909– . A trade publication devoted to nonferrous metals.

Metallurgia. 1929– . (*The British Journal of Metals* incorporating *The Metallurgical Engineer*).

Mining Magazine. 1909– . This seldom publishes a paper on metallurgy, but its abstracts and patent information are useful.

INDIA

Quarterly Journal of the Geological, Mining, and Metallurgical Society of India. 1926– .

ITALY

Metallurgia italiana, La. 1909– .

JAPAN

Nippon Kinzoku Gakkai Shi. 1937– . Formerly *Nippon Kinzoku Gakukai-Shi* (Journal of the Japan Institute of Metals).

SOUTH AFRICA

Journal of the Chemical, Metallurgical, and Mining Society of South Africa. 1894– . A few abstracts are included.

USSR (SOVIET UNION)

Izvestiya Sektora Platiny i Drugikh Blagorodnykh Metallov. Akademiya Nauk SSSR. (*Platinum and precious metals.*)

Tsvetnye Metally. (*Nonferrous metallurgy.*)

See also under General Science: *Doklady Akademii Nauk SSSR, Izvestiya Akademii Nauk SSSR.*

See also under General Industrial Chemistry: *Zhurnal Prikladnoi Khimii.*

10. Organic Chemistry

There are few journals devoted exclusively to organic chemistry.

UNITED STATES

Journal of Organic Chemistry. 1936– .

GERMANY

Annalen der Chemie, Justus Liebigs. 1832– . The name was *Annalen der Chemie und Pharmacie* from 1840 to 1874. This is still an important journal but does not hold the preeminent place that it once did. Collective indexes for Vols. 1–550.

Journal für praktische Chemie. 1834– . Except for the early years, this journal is devoted almost exclusively to organic chemistry and it is an important journal. Collective indexes (old series) Vols. 1–30, 31–60, 61–90, 91–108 and (new series) Vols. 1–50, 51–100. Publication was suspended 1943–1954. The 4th series started with Vol. 1 (1954).

Makromolekulare Chemie. 1947– . This journal is devoted to the chemistry of organic compounds of high molecular weight.

JAPAN

Journal of the Society of Organic Synthetic Chemistry (Japan) (*Yûki Gôsei Kagaku Kyôkai Shi*). 1943– .

OTHERS

Journals of general chemistry or general science that publish large numbers of papers on organic chemistry are listed below. For descriptions of the journals see General Chemistry or General Science.

Acta Chemica Scandinavica (Denmark).
Bulletin de la société chimique de France.
Comptes rendus hebdomadaires des séances de l'académie des sciences. (France).
Chemische Berichte. (Germany).
Doklady Academii Nauk SSSR.
Gazzetta chimica italiana.
Helvetica Chimica Acta. (Switzerland).
Journal of the American Chemical Society.
Journal of the Chemical Society. (London).
Recueil des travaux chimiques des Pays-Bas. (Holland).
Zhurnal Obshchei Khimii (*Journal of General Chemistry USSR*), which is much more important than the *Doklady Akademii Nauk SSSR*.

11. Biological Chemistry

The number of journals devoted exclusively to biochemistry is relatively small. The number of journals devoted to biology, medicine, or some specific phase thereof is very large; most of them contain at least an occasional paper of chemical interest, some of them many such papers. Only biological or medical journals of special value to chemists are listed here.

UNITED STATES

American Journal of Medical Technology. 1934– . Analytical methods of biochemical interest. Some abstracts are included.
American Journal of Physiology. 1898– . Many papers of chemical interest. Collective indexes, 1898–1939.
Antibiotics and Chemotherapy. 1951– . Many papers of chemical interest.
Applied Microbiology. 1953– . Deals with the applications of bacteriology to industry, foods, and sanitation but does not cover plant and animal diseases.
Archives of Biochemistry and Biophysics. 1942– . "And Biophysics" was added to the name in 1951. This is next to the *Journal of Biological Chemistry* in importance in the United States.
Endocrinology. 1917– . Abstracts are included.

Journal of the American Dietetics Association. 1925– . Abstracts are included.

Journal of the American Medical Association. 1883– . A considerable number of papers and abstracts of chemical and pharmaceutical interest are published. Collective indexes, Vols. 1–49.

Journal of Applied Physiology. 1948– .

Journal of Bacteriology. 1916– . Many papers of chemical interest.

Journal of Biological Chemistry, The. 1905– . This is America's most important biochemical journal. Collective indexes, Vols. 1–25; Vols. 26–50.

Journal of Clinical Endocrinology and Metabolism. 1940– . Formerly the *Journal of Clinical Endocrinology.* Many papers of chemical interest.

Journal of Clinical Nutrition. 1952– . Abstracts are included.

Journal of General Physiology, The. 1918– . Many papers of chemical interest.

Journal of Histochemistry and Cytochemistry. 1953– . Both original papers and reviews are included.

Journal of Laboratory and Clinical Medicine. 1915– . Abstracts are included. Many papers of chemical interest.

Journal of Nutrition. 1928– . Collective indexes, Vols. 1–15 (1928–1938); Vols. 16–36 (1938–1948).

Journal of Pharmacology and Experimental Therapeutics. 1909– . Many papers of chemical interest. Collective indexes, Vols. 1–20 (1910–1923); Vols. 21–40 (1923–1930).

Journal of Urology. 1917– .

Metabolism, Clinical and Experimental. 1952– .

Nutrition Reviews. 1942– .

Pharmacological Reviews. 1949– .

Physiological Reviews. 1921– .

Plant Physiology. 1926– .

Proceedings of the Society for Experimental Biology and Medicine. 1903– . Many papers of chemical interest.

Stain Technology. 1926– . Collective indexes, 1926–1940.

ARGENTINA

Revista de la asociación bioquímica argentina. 1936– .

AUSTRIA

Protoplasma. 1926– . *Internationale Zeitschrift für physikalische Chemie der Protoplasten.* It was originally published in Germany. Publication was suspended during 1944–1948.

Zeitschrift für Vitamin, Hormon und Fermentforschung. 1947– .

BELGIUM

Archives internationales de pharmacodynamie. 1894– . Collective indexes, Vols. 1–50.

DENMARK

Acta Pharmacologica et Toxicologica. 1945– .

Acta Endocrinologica. 1946– .

These two publications are issued jointly by Scandinavian societies, although the journals are published in Denmark.

FRANCE

Annales de l'institut Pasteur. 1887– .
Annales de la nutrition et de l'alimentation. 1947– .
Bulletin de la société de chimie biologique. 1914– . An important biochemical journal. Collective index, Vols. 1–20.
Comptes rendus des séances de la société de biologie. 1849– . Collective indexes, 1849–1923.
Journal de chimie physique et de physicochimie biologique. 1903– . See under section on Physical Chemistry.
Journal de physiologie (Paris). 1899– . Formerly *Journal de physiologie et de pathologie générale*. Many abstracts are included.

GERMANY

Arzneimittel-Forschung. 1951– . Biochemistry in relation to pharmaceuticals is frequently reported.
Biochemische Zeitschrift. 1906– . An important biochemical journal. Collective indexes at each 30-vol. interval for Vols. 1–300 (1906–1939).
Endokrinologie. 1928– .
Fermentforschung. 1916–1945. Good papers on enzymes.
Hoppe-Seyler's Zeitschrift für physiologische Chemie. 1877– . This was the first of the more important biochemical journals to appear. Thirty-volume collective indexes for Vols. 1–250 (1877–1937) in 8 vols.
Naunyn-Schmiedeberg's *Archiv für experimentelle Pathologie und Pharmakologie.* 1873– . Many papers of biochemical interest. Collective indexes, Vols. 1–50.
Pfluger's *Archiv für die gesamte Physiologie des Menschen und der Tiere.* 1868– . Collective indexes, Vols. 1–240 (1868–1938) in 5 vols.

GREAT BRITAIN

Biochemical Journal, The (London). 1906– . An invaluable journal that covers all phases of plant and animal biochemistry. Collective indexes at 10-year intervals (1906–1936).
British Journal of Nutrition, The. 1947– .
British Journal of Pharmacology and Chemotherapy. 1946– .
British Medical Journal, The. 1857– .
Journal of Experimental Biology. 1930– .
Journal of General Microbiology. 1947– .
Journal of Physiology, The (London). 1878– . Collective indexes, Vols. 1–60.
Lancet, The. 1823– .
Nutrition Abstracts and Reviews. 1931– . Publishes a large number of abstracts.
Quarterly Journal of Experimental Physiology and Cognate Medical Sciences. 1908– .
Review of Applied Mycology. 1922– . Frequently of chemical interest since chemical compounds synthesized by fungi have become important.

Biochimica et Biophysica Acta. 1947– . This is an international journal. Printed in English, French, or German.

Enzymologia. Acta Biocatalytica. 1936– . Printed in English, French, or German.

INDIA

Annals of Biochemistry and Experimental Medicine. 1941– .

ITALY

Acta vitaminologica (Milan). 1947– .

Bollettino della societa italiana di biologia sperimentale. 1927– . Many papers of chemical interest.

JAPAN

Journal of Biochemistry (Japan). 1922– . Printed in English or German. It suspended publication from 1944 to 1950.

Igaku to Seibutsugaku (*Medicine and Biology*). Many papers of chemical interest.

SWEDEN

Experimental Cell Research. 1950– . This is an international journal.

SWITZERLAND

Helvetica Physiologica et Pharmacologica Acta. 1943– .

Internationale Zeitschrift für Vitaminforschung (*International Review of Vitamin Research*). 1932– . Includes a large number of abstracts.

Schweizerische medizinische Wochenschrift. 1920– . Many papers of biochemical and pharmaceutical interest.

USSR (SOVIET UNION)

Biokhimiya. 1936– . Biochemistry.

Mikrobiologiya. 1932– . Microbiology, general and industrial.

12. Foods

For foods in relation to nutrition, see Section 11, Biochemistry.

UNITED STATES

Cereal Chemistry. 1924– . Both cereals and bakery products are covered. Collective indexes, Vols. 1–20 (1924–1943).

Food Engineering. 1928– . Formerly *Food Industries.* It is a good trade publication.

Food Research. 1936– . Publishes a large number of papers on food chemistry. Collective index, Vols. 1–12 (1936–1947).

Food Technology (Champaign, Ill.). 1947– . Publishes many papers of chemical interest. Abstracts are included.

Journal of Agricultural and Food Chemistry. 1953– . This is a publication of the American Chemical Society.

Journal of the Association of Official Agricultural Chemists. 1915– .
Many papers on foods appear in this journal. Much of this journal is
devoted to analytical methods.
Journal of Dairy Science. 1917– . Many papers on research work on
the chemistry of milk and milk products appear here. Abstracts are
included.

BELGIUM

Revue des fermentations et des industries alimentaires. 1946– .

FRANCE

Annales des falsifications et des fraudes, Les. 1908– . Part of the papers
in this journal relate to foods. Much of this journal is devoted to analytical methods.

GERMANY

Die Milchwissenschaft. 1946– . Includes papers on the chemistry of
milk and milk products.
Zeitschrift für Lebensmittel-Untersuchung und -Forschung. 1882– . This
is a useful journal devoted exclusively to scientific studies of foods. It
has an abstract section. Its name has changed several times in its long
history: 1943– , present title; 1926–1943, *Zeitschrift für Untersuchen
der Lebensmittel;* 1898–1926, *Zeitschrift für Untersuchung der Nahrungs-
und Genussmittel, sowie der Gebrauchsgegenstände:* and 1882–1892, *Vierteljahresschrift über der Chemie der Nahrungs- und Genussmittel.*

GREAT BRITAIN

Journal of Dairy Research (London). 1929– .
Journal of the Science of Food and Agriculture. 1950– . Devoted to
scientific research in the fields indicated. It is not a trade journal.

JAPAN

Bulletin of the Japanese Society of Scientific Fisheries. 1932– . A number of papers of interest to food chemists appear here.
Memoirs of the Research Institute of Food Science, Kyoto University.
1951– .

SWITZERLAND

Mitteilungen aus dem Gebiete der Lebensmitteluntersuchung und Hygiene.
1910– . This journal deals mainly with the analytical chemistry of
foods.

13. General Industrial Chemistry

Each of the journals on general industrial chemistry given below
is concerned with several phases of industrial chemistry; abstracts
of papers appearing in these journals appear in many sections of
abstracting journals. Section 13 of *Chemical Abstracts,* devoted to
Chemical Industry and Miscellaneous Industrial Products, covers
only papers that do not fall into special fields of industrial chemistry.

For journals that are publications of the patent offices of the various countries, see the chapter on Patents, page 167.

UNITED STATES

A.M.A. Archives of Industrial Health. 1950–   . This is a continuation of the *Journal of Industrial Hygiene and Toxicology* (1919–1949). It includes abstracts and frequently covers problems of concern to chemical industries.

ASTM Bulletin (American Society for Testing Materials). 1921–   . This is one of three publications of the Society for Testing Materials that are issued at regular intervals; all cover the composition, standardization of specifications, and methods of testing of engineering materials. Most of the information is of interest to chemists. The Bulletin is issued eight times a year at present.

American Society for Testing Materials, Proceedings. 1898–   . This is an annual publication at present and has the same coverage as the ASTM Bulletin. Collective Indexes, 1898–1935.

American Society for Testing Materials, Standards. This is issued triennially, the last being dated 1955. For the main entry see page 32.

Chemical Engineering. 1902–   . The number of papers on research work is not large. It is a good source of chemical engineering news, market statistics, and general information. This journal carries a large amount of advertising that is useful. It includes some abstracts. There have been several changes in name: 1918–1946, *Chemical and Metallurgical Engineering;* 1910–1918, *Metallurgical and Chemical Engineering;* 1905–1910, *Electrochemical and Metallurgical Industry;* 1902–1905, *Electrochemical Industry.*

Chemical and Engineering News. 1923–   . See under General Chemistry.

Chemical Engineering Progress. 1947–   . This journal was started in 1947 by the American Institute of Chemical Engineers and is an enlargement and continuation of the *Transactions of the American Institute of Chemical Engineers,* 1909–1947. It includes original papers and discussions. The *Chemical Engineering Progress, Monograph Series,* and *Symposium Series* were started in 1951 and numbers are sold separately.

Chemical Processing. 1938–   . It is a trade publication that covers a number of industries.

Chemical Week. 1914–   . A trade publication with emphasis on the business and economic phases of chemical industries. There have been several changes in its name: 1951, *Chemical Industries Week;* 1933–1950, *Chemical Industries;* and 1914–1932, *Chemical Markets.*

Chemurgic Digest. 1942–   . This journal reports on the use of agricultural products to make chemicals.

Industrial and Engineering Chemistry. 1909–   . This journal of the American Chemical Society is indispensable. It publishes more good papers reporting new work of value to industrial chemists than any other journal in the world. Although it emphasizes research, it includes valuable symposia, reviews, and much of the trade information provided by the trade journals. One feature, "Facts and Figures for the Chemical Process

Industries," published biennially beginning with 1948, is the most complete and authoritative record published for the chemical industries in the United States. Before 1923 the name was *Journal of Industrial and Engineering Chemistry.*

Mechanical Engineering. 1906– . Papers of chemical interest frequently appear in this journal.

Standardization. 1930– . Formerly *Industrial Standardization.* This publication includes reports of current work of the American Standards Association on standard abbreviations of words for use in technical publications, standard letter symbols, standard specifications for equipment and some chemicals, and other standards of interest to chemists.

Transactions of the American Institute of Chemical Engineers. 1908–1947. Valuable papers were published here. The *Transactions* are continued in *Chemical Engineering Progress,* see above.

ARGENTINA

Industria y química (Buenos Aires). 1935– .
Revista de química (Buenos Aires). 1950– .

AUSTRALIA

Chemical Engineering and Mining Review. 1909– .

AUSTRIA

Mitteilungen des chemischen Forschungs-Institutes der Wirtschaft Österreichs. 1946– .
Praktische Chemie. 1950– .

BELGIUM

Industrie chimique belge, La. 1930– . Formerly *Bulletin de la fédération des industries chimiques de Belgique* and bound with the *Bulletin de la société chimique de Belgique,* 1921–1929. Some abstracts are included.

BRAZIL

Engenharia e química (Rio de Janeiro). 1949– .
Química e industria (São Paulo). 1933– .
Revista brasileira de química (Ciencia e industria) (São Paulo). 1936– . Includes some patents. Collective index, Vols. 1–10 (1936–1940).
Revista de química industrial (Rio de Janeiro). 1932– .

CANADA

Canadian Chemical Processing. 1917– . Note changes in name. The present one was adopted in 1951. 1938–1951, *Canadian Chemistry and Process Industries;* 1921–1938, *Canadian Chemistry and Metallurgy;* 1917–1921, *Canadian Chemical Journal.* This journal covers all fields of industrial chemistry including research work, raw materials, economics, markets, and trade literature.

Canadian Journal of Technology. 1950–   . Continuation of Section F (Technology) of the *Canadian Journal of Research.* Some papers of chemical interest are published.

CHINA

Chemical Industry and Engineering. 1950–   .

FRANCE

Chimie et industrie. 1918–   . This is an important journal and is the best industrial chemical journal of France. It has an abstract section that covers both papers and patents.

Revue des produits chimiques, La, et L'Actualité scientifique. 1898–   .

GERMANY

Angewandte Chemie. 1888–   . This is Germany's most important industrial chemical journal. It includes research papers as well as trade news. Abstracts of papers and patents were published until 1918. Collective indexes, Vols. 1–40 (1887–1927). There have been several changes in name: 1947–   , present name; 1944–1947, suspended publication; 1942–1944, *Die Chemie;* 1932–1941, *Angewandte Chemie;* and 1888–1931, *Zeitschrift für angewandte Chemie.*

Chemiker-Zeitung mit Chemie Börse. 1876–   . See page 135.

Chemische Technik, Die (Berlin). 1949–   . This journal puts emphasis on equipment.

Chemie-Ingenieur-Technik. 1928–   . A good journal.

Chemische Industrie (Düsseldorf). 1949–   . *Zeitschrift für die deutsche Chemie-wirtschaft.* It includes some patents. It is a useful trade journal.

Kunststoffe. 1911–   . This is of most interest now for plastics

Zeitschrift des Vereines deutscher Ingenieure. 1857–   . This is a good engineering journal which often publishes papers of chemical interest. Collective indexes, Vols. 1–79.

GREAT BRITAIN

Chemical Age. 1919–   . The number of research papers is not large, but this journal is useful for its coverage of developments in industrial and engineering chemistry.

Chemical Engineering Science. 1951–   .

Chemical Trade Journal and Chemical Engineer, The. 1887–   . Strictly a trade journal.

Chemistry and Industry. 1937–   . Formerly a part of the *Journal of the Society of Chemical Industry.* Issued as a separate journal since 1937. This is a valuable news publication and does not include reports of research work.

Chemical and Process Engineering. 1920–   . Formerly *International Chemical and Process Industries,* 1920–1952.

Chemical Products and the Chemical News. 1938–   .

Engineering. 1866–   . Some papers of chemical interest are included.

Industrial Chemist and Chemical Manufacturer. 1925–   . This is a useful journal. Abstracts and patents are included.
Journal of Applied Chemistry (London). 1951–   . This is the successor of the *Journal of the Society of Chemical Industry.* This journal publishes reports of new research and includes abstracts.
Journal of the Society of Chemical Industry. 1882–1950. This valuable journal will be useful for many years. Collective indexes at 10-year intervals through 1950.
Transactions of the Institution of Chemical Engineers (London). 1923–   . This was an annual publication until 1952.

HOLLAND

Chemisch Weekblad. 1903–   . This publishes original research as well as trade news of interest to industrial chemists.

INDIA

Transactions of the Indian Institute of Chemical Engineers. 1947–   .

ITALY

Annali di chimica (Rome). 1914–   . Formerly *Annali di chimica applicata.*
La chimica e l'industria. 1935–   . This is Italy's most important journal of industrial chemistry and includes a large number of abstracts.

JAPAN

Chemical Engineering. 1937–   .
Journal of the Society of Chemical Industry. 1898–1937. In 1938 this journal was made the industrial section of the *Journal of the Chemical Society of Japan.* See under General Chemical journals.
Kagaku to Kogyo (Chemistry and Chemical Industry). 1948–   . Printed in Japanese.
Reports of the Government Chemical Industrial Research Institute (Tokyo).

POLAND

Przemysł Chemiczny (Chemical Industry). 1932–   .

SOUTH AFRICA

South African Industrial Chemist. 1947–   .

SPAIN

Afinidad. 1921–   . A journal of industrial chemistry. It includes abstracts.
Ion, Revista española de química aplicada. 1941–   . It includes some abstracts.

SWEDEN

Acta Polytechnica. 1947–   . This covers several fields of engineering, including chemical engineering and metallurgy.

Chimia. 1947–   . This includes research in industrial chemistry, news, patents, and abstracts.

USSR (SOVIET UNION)

Zhurnal Prikladnoi Khimii (Journal of Applied Chemistry). 1928–   . An important journal.

14. Water, Sewage, and Sanitation

UNITED STATES

American Journal of Hygiene, The. 1921–   . Collective indexes, 1921–1938.
American Journal of Public Health and the Nation's Health. 1911–   .
A.M.A. Archives of Industrial Health. 1950–   . Abstracts are included.
Engineering News-Record. 1874–   .
Journal of the American Water Works Association. 1881–   . An excellent abstract section is included. Collective indexes, 1881–1939, 1940–1944. The name was *Proceedings of the American Water Works Association, 1881–1913.*
Journal of Industrial Hygiene and Toxicology. 1920–1949.
Public Works. 1920–   .
Sewage and Industrial Wastes. 1929–   . Formerly the *Sewage Works Journal.* Title changed in 1949. Abstracts are included. Collective index, Vols. 1–20 (1929–1948).
Wastes Engineering. 1930–   . Formerly *Sewage and Industrial Waste Engineering.*
Water and Sewage Works. 1929–   . Formerly *Water Works and Sewerage.*

CANADA

Municipal Utilities. 1950–   .

GREAT BRITAIN

Journal of Hygiene, The. 1901–   .
Journal of the Institution of Sanitary Engineers. 1905–   .
Journal of the Royal Sanitary Institute. 1876–   . Collective index, 1876–1900.
Water and Water Engineering. 1899–   .

GERMANY

Archiv für Hygiene und Bakteriologie. 1883–   .
Literaturberichte über Wasser, Abwasser, Luft und Boden. 1950–
Wasser und Abwasser. 1909–1943. Apparently discontinued.

15. Agricultural Chemistry

The number of agricultural journals is very large. Many of them contain at least an occasional article of chemical interest. Only journals of special chemical interest are listed below. The following journals have not been divided into two groups (Soils and Fertilizers and Pesticides and Crop-control Agents) because several of the more important ones cover all four subjects.

UNITED STATES

Agricultural Chemicals. 1946– .
Agronomy Journal. 1907– .
Commercial Fertilizer. 1910– .
Farm Chemicals. 1894– .
Journal of Agricultural and Food Chemistry. 1953– . It is devoted to the publication of papers of new research. Published by the American Chemical Society.
Journal of the Association of Official Agricultural Chemists. 1915– . In addition to original papers, this journal contains committee reports on changes in and additions to the official and tentative methods of analysis.
Journal of Economic Entomoloy. 1908– .
Pest Control. 1933– .
Soil Science. 1916– . This journal is devoted to publishing papers on the chemistry, physics and microbiology of the soil. Collective index, Vols. 1–25.

GERMANY

Zeitschrift für Pflanzenernährung Dungung Bodenkunde. 1922– . This is a continuation of *Bodenkunde und Pflanzenernährung.*
Wasser und Boden. 1949– .

GREAT BRITAIN

Journal of Agricultural Science, The. 1905– . This journal publishes many papers of interest to chemists. Collective index, Vols. 1–20.
Journal of the Science of Food and Agriculture. 1950– . This journal of the Society of Chemical Industry puts emphasis on the publication of chemical research work.
Journal of Soil Science. 1950– .
Soil and Fertilizers, Commonwealth Bureau of Soil Science. 1938– . This includes a large number of abstracts.

HOLLAND

Plant and Soil. 1948– . *International Journal of Plant Nutrition, Plant Chemistry, Soil Microbiology and Soil-borne Plant Diseases.*

16. Fermentation Industries

There are few journals of chemical value in this field. Much of the research in this field is published in journals devoted to bio-chemistry, bacteriology, or microbiology, and some is widely scattered. The specialized journals that do exist cover only a portion of the field—alcoholic beverages and industrial alcohol for the most part.

108   PERIODICALS

UNITED STATES

American Brewer. 1868–   .
American Society of Brewing Chemists, Proceedings. 1940–   .
Brewers Digest. 1934–   . A trade publication that includes abstracts.
Wallerstein Laboratories Communications. 1937–   . The laboratories
specialize in alcoholic beverages and industrial alcohol. The abstract
section of this publication is useful.

GERMANY

Branntweinwirtschaft, Die. 1947–   .

GREAT BRITAIN

Journal of the Institute of Brewing. 1895–   . Abstracts are included.
Collective indexes, 1895–1934.

JAPAN

Journal of Fermentation Technology (Hakkô Kôgaku Zasshi). 1923–   .

17. Pharmaceuticals, Cosmetics, Perfumes

Many pharmaceutical journals occasionally publish a paper of
interest to chemists, but only those are included below that publish
such papers frequently.

UNITED STATES

American Journal of Pharmacy. 1830–   .
American Perfumer and Aromatics. 1906–   . Formerly the *American
Perfumer and Essential Oil Review.* This journal also covers soaps,
cosmetics, and flavors. It includes a few abstracts.
Antibiotics and Chemotherapy. 1951–   .
Ciba Review. 1937–   . There are two editions, one published in the United
States and the other in Switzerland; they do not always contain the
same articles on pharmaceuticals.
Current Researches in Anesthesia and Analgesia. 1922–   .
Drug and Cosmetic Industry. 1926–   . A useful trade journal that in-
cludes some abstracts.
Journal of the American Pharmaceutical Association. 1912–   . There
have been two editions since 1940, the scientific edition in which papers
of chemical interest appear and the practical pharmacy edition.
Journal of Pharmacology and Experimental Therapeutics. 1909–   . Collective indexes, 1909–1930.
Journal of the Society of Cosmetic Chemists. 1947–   .
Merck Report, The. 1892–   . This report is published in the interest of
pharmacy and medicine.

ARGENTINA

Anales de farmacia y bioquímica. 1930–   .

BELGIUM

Journal de pharmacie de Belgique. 1919– .

BRAZIL

Revista de química e farmacia do Rio de Janeiro. 1935– .

DENMARK

Archiv för Pharmaci og Chemi. 1844– .
Acta Pharmaceutica Internationalia. 1950– .

FRANCE

Annales pharmaceutiques françaises. 1943– . This journal was formed by combining the *Journal de pharmacie et de chimie* and *Bulletin des sciences pharmacologiques.* The present journal includes abstracts.
Journal de pharmacie et de chimie. 1815–1942. See *Annales pharmaceutiques françaises,* above.
Industries de la parfumerie. 1946– .
Parfumerie moderne, La. 1908– .

GERMANY

Archiv der Pharmazie und Berichte der deutschen pharmazeutischen Gesellschaft. 1822– . The name of this journal from 1835 to 1923 was *Archiv der Pharmacie;* 1832–1834, *Annalen der Pharmacie;* 1822–1832, *Archiv des Apotheker Vereins im nördlichen Teutschland.* Collective indexes, 1822–1857; 1858–1873.
Arzneimittel-Forschung. 1951– .
Pharmazie, Die. 1946– .
Pharmazeutische Zentralhälle für Deutschland. 1859– .

GREAT BRITAIN

British Journal of Pharmacology and Chemotherapy. 1946– .
International Perfumer, The. 1951– . A review of progress and research. Printed in English, French, or German.
Journal of Pharmacy and Pharmacology. 1949– . Formerly the *Quarterly Journal of Pharmacy and Pharmacology,* 1928–1948. Abstracts are included.
Manufacturing Chemist and Pharmaceutical and Fine Chemical Trade Journal. Incorporating *Manufacturing Perfumer.* 1930– . This is a trade journal that includes abstracts and lists of patents.
Perfumery and Essential Oil Record, The. 1910– .
Pharmaceutical Journal, The. 1841– . Collective indexes, 1841–1878, in 3 volumes.
Soap, Perfumery and Cosmetics. 1928– . A trade publication that includes abstracts and patents.

HOLLAND

Chemische en pharmaceutische techniek. 1946– .
Pharmaceutisch Weekblad. 1866– .

ITALY

Bolletino chimico-farmaceutico. 1861– .

JAPAN

Journal of the Pharmaceutical Society of Japan (Yakugaku Zasshi). 1881–
. Published in Japanese with English or German summaries.
Pharmaceutical Bulletin. 1953– . Printed in English, French, or German.

SWEDEN

Svensk Farmaceutisk Tidsskrift. 1897– .

SWITZERLAND

Pharmaceutica Acta Helvetiae. 1929– . This is the scientific supplement to *Schweizerische Apotheker Zeitung.*
Schweizerische Apotheker Zeitung. 1863– .

18. Acids, Alkalies, Salts, and Other Heavy Chemicals

There are no journals devoted exclusively to these fields. The
journals under section 13, General Industrial Chemistry, publish
most of the papers.

19. Glass, Clay Products, Refractories, and Enameled Metals

UNITED STATES

American Ceramic Society Bulletin, The. 1922– . This has been a
separate publication since 1946 when it was removed from the *Journal
of the American Ceramic Society* of which it was one section. A valuable
publication.
Ceramic Age. 1921– .
Ceramic Industry. 1923– .
Enamelist Bulletin. 1924– . A continuation of *The Enamelist.*
Glass Industry, The. 1920– . A good trade journal that includes
abstracts.
Journal of the American Ceramic Society. Includes *Ceramic Abstracts.*
1918– . A valuable journal both for original papers and its very
large abstract section. Formerly the *Transactions of the American
Ceramic Society,* an annual publication, 1899–1917.

BELGIUM

Silicates industriels. 1929– . Verre, Céramique, Email, Ciment, Terre
cuite-Produits refractaires. Formerly *Verre et silicates industriels.* Includes abstracts.

FRANCE

Céramique, La. 1898–1940. Suspended publication in 1940.
Industrie céramique, L'. 1947–   . Some abstracts are included.
Verres et refractaires. 1947–   . Some abstracts are included.

GERMANY

Berichte der deutschen keramischen Gesellschaft e.v. und des Vereins deutscher Emailfachleute e.v. 1920–   . Some abstracts were included from 1920 to 1930.
Glastechnische Berichte. 1923–   . Includes abstracts.
Keramische Rundschau. 1893–1942.
Keramische Zeitschrift. 1949–   . Abstracts and patents are included.
Sprechsaal für Keramik-Glas-Email. Fach und Wirtschaftsblatt für die Silikat-Industrien. 1868–   . The name of this journal has varied. It includes lists of patents and abstracts.
Tonindustrie Zeitung. 1876–1944.
Tonindustrie-Zeitung und Keramische Rundschau. 1949–   . Formed by the merger of *Keramische Rundschau,* 1893–1942, and *Tonindustrie Zeitung,* 1876–1944.

GREAT BRITAIN

British Clayworker. 1893–   . Abstracts are included.
Journal of the Society of Glass Technology. 1917–   . Publishes many important original papers in addition to having an extensive abstract section.
Refractories Journal. 1925–   . Includes abstracts. Collective indexes, 1925–1934.
Transactions of the British Ceramic Society. 1901–   . This journal publishes original papers and has a very large abstract section, now called "British Ceramic Abstracts." The name of this journal has changed several times: Present title since 1939; 1917–1938, *Transactions of the Ceramic Society;* 1904–1916, *Transactions of the English Ceramic Society;* 1900–1903, *Transactions of the North Staffordshire Ceramic Society.*

JAPAN

Journal of the Ceramic Association (Yogyo Kyokai Shi). 1893–   . Printed in Japanese with English summaries.

USSR (SOVIET UNION)

Steklo i Keramika (Glass and Ceramic Industry). 1944–   .

20. Cement, Concrete, and Other Building Materials

A large part of the research in this field is published in journals of general industrial chemistry or in engineering journals.

UNITED STATES

Concrete. 1904– . A "Cement Mill" edition of *Concrete* was issued, 1912–1946.
Journal of the American Concrete Institute. 1929– .
Pit and Quarry. 1916– .
Proceedings of the American Concrete Institute. 1905–1930. The proceedings are now published in the *Journal of the American Concrete Institute.*
Proceedings of the American Wood-Preservers' Association. 1905– . Collective indexes, 1905–1929.
Rock Products. 1902– .
Wood Preserving News. 1923– .

FRANCE

Revue des matériaux de construction et de travaux publics. 1905– .

GERMANY

Zement. 1911–1944.
Zement-Kalk-Gips. 1948– . Formerly *Zement.*

GREAT BRITAIN

Cement and Lime Manufacture. 1928– . Formerly *Cement and Concrete Manufacture.*
Magazine of Concrete Research. 1949– .
Mine and Quarry Engineering. 1931– . Includes some abstracts.

USSR (SOVIET UNION)

Tsement (Cement). 1933– .

21. Fuels and Carbonization Products

A considerable part of the research work in this field appears in journals of general industrial chemistry.

UNITED STATES

Coal Age. 1911– .
Gas Age. 1921– . Its name was *Gas Age Record,* 1921–1937.

FRANCE

Chaleur et industrie. 1920– . A very useful journal that includes abstracts at the present time.
Journal des usines à gaz. 1877– .

GERMANY

Brennstoff-Chemie. 1920– . A very good journal for fuel chemistry. It includes patents, but the abstract section was discontinued in 1939.

Erdöl und Kohle. 1948– . This journal also covers synthetic mineral oils.

Gas und Wasserfach, Das. 1858– . Current numbers carry a few abstracts.

GREAT BRITAIN

Bulletin of the British Coal Utilization Research Association. 1936– .

Fuel. A Journal of Fuel Science. 1922– . Formerly *Fuel in Science and Practice.* Name changed in 1948. An excellent journal that includes abstracts.

Gas Journal (London). 1849– .

Gas World, The. 1884– . It includes a monthly coking section, an industrial gas supplement, and an annual review number.

Journal of the Institute of Fuel (London). 1926– . Many good papers of chemical interest appear here and abstracts are included in current numbers.

22. Petroleum, Lubricants and Asphalt

The number of trade journals devoted to this field is very large and most of them publish few papers of chemical interest. Much of the scientific work on petroleum and its products is published in journals of general industrial chemistry; some appears in geological and engineering journals. Some of the research work relating to the manufacture of organic compounds from petroleum appears in journals of organic chemistry and general chemistry.

UNITED STATES

Bulletin of the American Association of Petroleum Geologists. 1917– . Publishes some papers of chemical interest.

Geophysics. 1930– .

Industrial and Engineering Chemistry. 1909– . A large proportion of the chemical research work on petroleum and its products that is done in the United States is published here.

Journal of Petroleum Technology. 1949– . This is a good scientific journal, not a trade journal, and publishes many papers of chemical interest.

Lubrication Engineering. 1945– . Publishes some papers of chemical interest.

Oil and Gas Journal, The. 1902– . This is a useful trade journal that also publishes research on petroleum, much of which is of chemical interest.

Petroleum Engineer, The. 1929– . Most of the papers in this excellent journal are devoted to the chemistry of petroleum and its products.

Petroleum Processing. 1946– . It is primarily a trade and news publication that covers the processing of crude petroleum and natural gas for fuels, lubricants, and chemicals. It was formerly the monthly technical section of *National Petroleum News.* It includes lists of patents.

Petroleum Refiner. 1922–   . Formerly *Refiner and Natural Gasoline Manufacturer.* This journal publishes many papers of chemical interest and includes some abstracts and lists of patents.

World Oil. 1916–   . Formerly *The Oil Weekly.* This is a good trade journal for news and general information, part of which is of chemical interest.

FRANCE

Revue de l'institut français du pétrole et Annales des combustibles liquides. 1946–   . This journal publishes some papers on petroleum chemistry and includes some abstracts.

GERMANY

Bitumen, Teere, Asphalte, Peche und verwandte Stoffe. 1950–   .

Erdöl und Kohle. 1948–   . This journal publishes many papers on the chemistry of petroleum and its products. It is a continuation of several journals that were discontinued during World War II, the most important of which was *Petroleum Zeitschrift* (see below). *Erdöl und Kohle* includes some abstracts.

Petroleum, Zeitschrift für die gesamten Interessen der Erdöl-Industrie und des Mineralöl-Handels. 1905–1939. This journal published many papers of chemical interest and many abstracts.

GREAT BRITAIN

Institute of Petroleum Review. 1947–   . This is primarily a review journal for petroleum, part of which is of chemical interest.

Journal of the Institute of Petroleum. 1914–   . Its name was *Journal of the Institution of Petroleum Technologists,* 1914–1938. This is an indispensable journal in a library for petroleum chemistry, both for research papers and for its abstract section.

USSR (SOVIET UNION)

Trudy Instituta Nefti Akademiya Nauk SSSR. 1949–   . This journal of the petroleum institute publishes many papers of chemical interest.

Much of the work on the chemistry of petroleum that is done in Russia is published in: *Zhurnal Prikladnoi Khimii* (see under General Industrial Chemistry); and *Izvestiya Akademii Nauk SSSR* (see under General Science).

23. Cellulose and Paper

Many of the journals in this field are trade journals that publish little or nothing of chemical interest. The journals given below cover most of the scientific and technical work in this field that does not appear in journals of general industrial chemistry.

UNITED STATES

Bulletin of the Institute of Paper Chemistry, 1930–   . Very little of the research work of the Institute is published here, but this is valuable for

its "Library Notes," a very extensive and comprehensive abstract section.
Journal of the Forest Products Research Society. 1951– .
Paper Mill News. 1876– . Good for news, some of which is of chemical interest.
Paper Industry. 1919– . The name was *Paper Industry and Paper World*, 1938–1950. It often publishes papers of chemical interest and includes some abstracts and patents.
Paper Trade Journal. 1872– . It often publishes papers of chemical interest. It had a very extensive abstract section that covered both papers and patents from 1920 to 1930. Since then it has published only abstracts of patents.
Pulp and Paper. 1927– . Formerly *Pulp and Paper Industry.*
Southern Pulp and Paper Manufacturer. 1938– . Formerly *Southern Pulp and Paper Journal.* It often publishes papers of chemical interest.
TAPPI. 1918– . Successor to *Technical Association Papers.* The *Technical Association Papers*, 1918–1948, were not as valuable as TAPPI because most of the papers appeared previously in the *Paper Trade Journal* (see above). TAPPI, published by the Technical Association of the Pulp and Paper Industry, is an invaluable journal for cellulose and paper chemistry. It includes abstracts of United States patents on paper and pulp.

CANADA

Canadian Pulp and Paper. 1948– . Publishes some papers of chemical interest.
Pulp and Paper Magazine of Canada. 1903– . Publishes a large number of papers of chemical interest.

FINLAND

Paperi ja Puu (Papper och Trä; Paper and Timber). 1919– . This journal publishes many papers of chemical interest. The text is in English, Finnish or Swedish.

FRANCE

Association technique de l'industrie papetière, Bulletin. 1947– . It publishes a good many papers of chemical interest and is the most important scientific publication devoted to paper in France.
Papeterie, La. 1878– . A trade publication that publishes some papers of chemical interest and includes some abstracts.
Papier, Le. 1898–1944. Published many papers of chemical interest.

GERMANY

Allgemeine Papier-Rundschau, Fachblatt für Papier-Industrie, graphisches Gewerbe, Schreibwaren, und Bürobedarf. 1949– . Successor to *Papier Zeitung.* It publishes many papers of chemical interest.
Cellulosechemie. 1920–1936, 1940–1944. This was a supplement to *Der Papier-Fabrikant* up to Vol. 11, no. 12 (1930), when it became a separate journal.

116 PERIODICALS

Nitrocellulose. 1929–   . It suspended publication from 1943 (Vol. 14) to 1952 (Vol. 15).

Papier, Das. Zeitschrift für die Erzeugung von Holzstoff, Zellstoff, Papier, und Pappe. Chemische Technologie der Cellulose. 1947–   . This is the most important of the current German journals devoted to paper and cellulose. It publishes many papers of chemical interest.

Papier und Druch. 1952–   . A few papers of chemical interest appear here, and some abstracts are included.

Papier-Fabrikant, Der. 1903–1943. Many papers of chemical interest were published.

Wochenblatt für Papierfabrikation. 1870–   . Frequently publishes papers of chemical interest.

Zellstoff und Papier, 1921–1941.

GREAT BRITAIN

British Paper and Board Maker's Association, Proceedings of the Technical Section. 1921–   . Formerly the *Paper Maker's Association of Great Britain and Ireland, Proceedings of the Technical Section.* This journal publishes many papers of chemical interest.

Paper Maker (London) and British Paper Trade Journal. 1891–   . It publishes a number of papers of chemical interest and includes some abstracts.

World's Paper Trade Review, The. 1879–   . It is a useful trade paper for general information, some of which is of chemical interest. It includes patents, trademarks and market information.

NORWAY

Norsk Skogindustrie (Journal of the Norwegian Paper, Pulp, Timber and Wallboard Industries). 1947–   . Publishes many papers of chemical interest.

SWEDEN

Svensk Papperstidning (Svensk Pappersförädlingstidskrift; Swedish Paper Journal). 1898–   . Publishes many papers of chemical interest.

USSR (SOVIET UNION)

Bumazhnaya Promyshlennost (Proizvodstvenno-tekhnicheskii Zhurnal) (Paper Industry). 1926–   . Publishes many papers of chemical interest.

24. Explosives and Explosions

There are few journals in this field and some of these publish little of chemical interest. Most of the reports of new work in this field are widely scattered in a variety of journals.

UNITED STATES

Explosives Engineer, The. 1923–   . Publishes little of chemical interest. It includes some abstracts.

Ordnance. Formerly *Army Ordnance.* 1920– . Publishes little of chemical interest.

FRANCE

Mémorial des poudres. 1882– . This is issued about once a year and includes much of chemical interest.

GERMANY

Sprengtechnik. Zeitschrift für die Wissenschaft, Technik und Wirtschaft der Sprengstoffe und Zündmittel. 1952– . This is a continuation of *Zeitschrift für das gesamte Schiess- und Sprengstoffwesen* (see below) and it has not published much of chemical interest so far, but it may do so later.
Zeitschrift für das gesamte Schiess- und Sprengstoffwesen. 1906–1944. The most valuable journal in the field of explosives has been continued under another name, *Sprengtechnik* (see above). Collective indexes, Vols. 1–30.

25. Dyes and Textile Chemistry

Much of the research work in dye and textile chemistry is published in the specialized journals given below, but part of it is widely scattered in a great variety of journals. Also, there are many journals devoted to textiles which publish little or nothing of chemical interest.

UNITED STATES

American Dyestuff Reporter. 1917– . The "Proceedings of the American Association of Textile Chemists and Colorists" are included in this journal. Many original papers on textiles, dyes, and dyeing appear in this journal. It has excellent abstract and patent sections.
Rayon and Synthetic Textiles. 1925– . A useful trade journal that publishes some work of chemical interest. Includes some abstracts and patents. There have been frequent changes in its name: 1937–1948, *Rayon Textile Monthly;* 1934–1936, *Rayon and Melliand Textile Monthly;* 1930–1933, *Rayon and Rayon Journal;* 1925–1930, *Rayon.*
Textile Industries, 1899– . Formerly *Cotton, Atlanta.* Until recently, this trade journal was of no interest to chemists.
Textile Research Journal. 1930– . This is the outstanding American journal for textile research of chemical interest. Its name was *Textile Research,* 1930–1945, and it included a bound copy of the abstracts from the *Journal of the Textile Institute* (England) until 1951.
Textile World. 1888– . Very useful for trade information of many kinds. Its original title was the *Textile World Journal,* which was formed by combining the *Textile World Record* and the *Textile Manufacturers Journal.*

DENMARK

Tidsskrift for Textilteknik. 1943– .

France

Bulletin de l'institut textile de France. 1947–   . This is the most important of the French textile journals for the chemist. It publishes many abstracts.

Rayonne et fibres synthétique. 1945–   .

Revue générale des matières colorantes de la teinture, de l'impression, du blanchiment et des apprêts. 1896–1940.

Teintex. 1936–   . This journal, of the same type and coverage as the preceding one, carries some abstracts.

Germany

Melliand Textilberichte. 1920–   . This is an excellent journal for all phases of textile chemistry. It publishes a large amount of original work. It carries some abstracts.

Reyon, Zellwolle, und andere Chemiefasern. 1919–   . Former titles of this journal are: 1951, *Reyon, Synthetica, Zellwolle;* 1937–1950, *Kunstseide und Zellwolle;* 1925–1936, *Kunstseide;* 1919-1924, *Deutsche Fasterstoffe und Spinnpflanzen.*

Great Britain

Dyer, Textile Printer, Bleacher and Finisher. 1879–   . Includes some abstracts.

Empire Cotton Growing Review. 1920–   . This now consists entirely of abstracts.

Journal of the Society of Dyers and Colourists. 1884–   . This is an excellent dye journal. Many good original papers are published. The abstract section is very large and covers both papers and patents.

Journal of the Textile Institute, The. 1910–   . This is an excellent journal that publishes many original papers on textile chemistry. It has a very extensive abstract section. The journal was divided into two monthly issues beginning with Vol. 40 (1949); one is entitled *Journal of the Textile Institute, Proceedings and Abstracts,* and the other, *Journal of the Textile Institute, Transactions.*

Textile Manufacturer. 1875–   . A trade journal.

India

Indian Textile Journal. 1890–   .

Japan

Journal of the Society of Textile and Cellulose Industry (Sen-i Gakkaishi). 1946–   . Printed in Japanese with translated tables of contents.

Journal of Sericulture Science of Japan, The (Nippon Sanshi-Gaken Zasshi). 1930–   . Formerly *The Bulletin of Sericulture and Silk Industry.*

Switzerland

Textil-Rundschau. 1946–   . A useful trade publication.

USSR (SOVIET UNION)

Tekstil'naya Promyshlennost (Textile Industry). 1941–   .

26. Paints, Varnishes, Lacquers, Ink

UNITED STATES

American Ink-maker. 1923–   .
American Paint Journal. 1916–   .
Modern Lithography. 1934–   .
Organic Finishing. Devoted exclusively to industrial coating. 1939–   .
Includes some abstracts and patents. Up to 1950, this journal was a
section of *Metal Finishing*, see page 94.
Oil, Paint, and Drug Reporter. 1871–   . Good for statistics and trade
information.
Paint Industry Magazine, The. 1885–   . Formerly *Drugs, Oil, Paints.*
(1893–1939).
Paint, Oil and Chemical Review. 1883–   . Includes abstracts.
Paint and Varnish Production. 1911–   . Formerly *Paint and Varnish
Production Manager.* Includes some abstracts.

FRANCE

Peintures, pigments, vernis. 1924–   .

GERMANY

Deutsche Farben-Zeitschrift. 1947–   .
Farbe und Lack. 1895–   .
Farben-Zeitung. 1895–1943.
Nitrocellulose. 1929–   .

GREAT BRITAIN

Journal of the Oil and Colour Chemists' Association. 1918–   . It includes
abstracts. Collective index, Vols. 1–28 (1918–1945).
Paint. Colour, Oil, Printing Ink, Varnish, Lacquer. 1931–   . Incor-
porating *Paint Manufacture.* Includes information about patents.
Paint, Oil and Colour Journal. 1879–   . Includes abstracts.
Paint Technology. 1936–   . Incorporating Synthetic and Applied Fin-
ishes. Includes abstracts and patents.
*Review of Current Literature Relating to the Paint, Colour, Varnish, and
Allied Industries.* 1928–   . Reviews and abstracts.

27. Fats, Fatty Oils, Waxes, and Detergents

UNITED STATES

Journal of the American Oil Chemists Society. 1924–   . Formerly *Oil
and Soap.* This is a very useful journal that has an extensive abstract

section. It also includes a comprehensive annual review of the literature on fats, oils, and soaps.

Soap and Chemical Specialties. 1925–   . Formerly *Soap and Sanitary Chemicals.* Includes some abstracts and patents. Collective index, Vols. 10–15 (1934–1939).

FRANCE

Oléagineux. Revue générale des corps gras et dérivés. 1946–   . It includes a number of abstracts.

GERMANY

Fette und Seifen einschliesslich der Anstrichmittel. 1891–   . This is a useful journal that includes some abstracts. There have been several changes in title: present title since 1936; 1933–1936, *Fettchemische Umschau;* 1916–1932, *Chemische Umschau auf dem Gebiete der Fette, Oele, Wachse und Harze;* 1894–1915, *Chemische Revue über die Fett- und Harz-Industrie.*

Seifen-Öle-Fette-Wachse. Kosmetik. 1874–   . This is a new title for *Seifensieder-Zeitung;* the change was made in 1948.

GREAT BRITAIN

Journal of Detergents and Collective Chemistry. 1952–   . This journal publishes research papers and includes abstracts and patents.

Soap, Perfumery and Cosmetics. 1928–   . Includes some abstracts. There have been several title changes.

28. Sugar, Starch, Gums

UNITED STATES

Sugar (Including *Facts About Sugar,* and the *Planter and Sugar Manufacturer*). 1914–   . Publishes a large number of papers on sugar chemistry and includes a good abstract section.

BELGIUM

Sucrerie belge, La. 1872–   . Includes some abstracts.

CZECHOSLOVAKIA

Listy Cukrovarnické. 1882–   . A number of papers on sugar chemistry appear here.

FRANCE

Sucrerie française. 1860–   . Formerly called *Journal des fabricants de sucre.*

GERMANY

Korrespondenzbriefe für Zuckerfabriken. 1951–   .

Stärke, Die. 1949–   . Apparently the only journal devoted to starch and its chemistry.

Zeitschrift für die Zuckerindustrie (Berlin). 1951–   . Publishes a number of papers on sugar chemistry.
Zucker. 1948–   . Publishes many papers on sugar chemistry.

GREAT BRITAIN

International Sugar Journal, The. 1899–   . Publishes valuable papers on sugar chemistry and includes a good abstract section.

USSR (SOVIET UNION)

Sakharnaya Promyshlennost (Sugar Industry). 1928–   . A large amount of work on sugar chemistry is published here.

29. Leather and Glue

UNITED STATES

Journal of the American Leather Chemists' Association. 1906–   . This valuable journal publishes original papers and includes a comprehensive abstract section. Collective indexes, 1906–1915, 1916–1925.

FRANCE

Revue technique des industries du cuir. 1908–   . Formerly *Le Cuir technique.* Includes some abstracts.

GERMANY

Collegium. 1902–1944. Published many good papers on leather chemistry.
Leder, Das. 1950–   . Publishes many good papers on the chemistry of leather and tanning.

GREAT BRITAIN

Journal of the Society of Leather Trades' Chemists. 1917–   . This is an excellent journal, both for original papers and for its abstract section. Its title was *Journal of the International Society of Leather Trades' Chemists,* 1925–1947.

30. Rubber and Other Elastomers

Much of the research in this field is widely scattered; a considerable part of it appears in journals of general industrial chemistry.

UNITED STATES

India Rubber World. 1889–   . This is a good trade journal that publishes many research papers. It includes an abstract section.
Rubber Age (New York). 1917–   . A useful trade journal.
Rubber Chemistry and Technology. 1928–   . Contains translations from Russian and other journals. A very good quarterly journal. Collective index, Vols. 1–10 (1928–1937).

FRANCE

Revue générale du caoutchouc. 1924–   . Publishes many research papers and includes abstracts.

GERMANY

Gummi und Asbest. 1948–   .

Kautschuk und Gummi. 1948–   . Of the two current journals in Germany, this one publishes the most research on rubber. It also includes abstracts.

GREAT BRITAIN

India Rubber Journal, The. 1884–   . A good trade journal that includes some abstracts. Collective index, Vols. 1–10.

Journal of Rubber Research. 1932–1951. Formerly *Journal of the Research Association of British Rubber Manufacturers.* Valuable papers were published in this journal and it had an extensive abstract section.

Rubber Age and Synthetics, The. 1920–   . Formerly *Rubber Age* (London). A useful trade journal.

Transactions of the Institution of the Rubber Industry. 1925–   . An excellent journal that publishes valuable papers. Collective index, Vols. 1–20 (1925–1945).

JAPAN

Journal of the Society of Rubber Industry of Japan (Nippon Gomu Kyokai Shi). 1928–   .

Malaya (Federation of Malaya)

Journal of the Rubber Research Institute of Malaya. 1929–   . Research on natural rubber was resumed after World War II.

REPUBLIC OF INDONESIA

Archives of Rubber Cultivation. 1917–   . A continuation of *Archief voor de Rubbercultuur in Nederlandsch-Indie.* Research on natural rubber was resumed after World War II.

31. Synthetic Resins and Plastics

UNITED STATES

Journal of Polymer Science. 1946–   . An excellent journal that publishes many valuable papers on synthetic resins, plastics, and rubber, and on basic science in the polymer field.

Modern Plastics. 1925–   . A useful trade journal that includes some abstracts.

Plastics Industry. 1943–   .

AUSTRALIA

Australian Plastics Journal. 1945–   .

FRANCE

Industrie des plastiques modernes (Paris). 1945– .
Revue générale des matières plastiques. 1928– .

GERMANY

Kunststoffe. 1911– .
Makromolekulare Chemie, Die. 1947– . Many papers on synthetic resins, plastics, and rubber appear in this journal. The basic science of polymerization receives considerable attention.

GREAT BRITAIN

British Plastics. 1929– .
Plastics (London). 1937– .
Plastics Institute, The, Transactions and Journal (London). 1932– .

HOLLAND

Plastica. 1948– .

JAPAN

Chemistry of High Polymers (*Kobunshi Kagaku*). Printed in Japanese with English translations of titles.

ABSTRACT JOURNALS

The importance of published abstracts, indeed their absolute necessity, needs no emphasis to the chemist. Without the abstract journals a literature search would be a hopeless task. The value of an abstract service was early recognized in chemistry and the chemist has had abstracts available for many years. Other sciences have followed suit so that now most of the natural sciences have one or more sources of abstracts; these are often of interest to chemists.

Abstracts are essentially unorganized. Even though carefully classified in abstract journals and correlated with other related abstracts by references and well indexed, the purpose of the scientist interested in a subject in a general way is not served as well by abstracts as by critical reviews.

Abstract journals are invaluable, but it should be pointed out that they are guides to the literature, not primary sources of information. It is not wise for the research chemist to depend too much on the information given in them. In some circumstances an abstract is enough. If a paper located by use of an abstract journal has important bearing on a problem, it is usually advisable to get the full paper, not so much to verify the accuracy of the abstract (partly for this purpose, however) as to get the point of view of the author and important details.

Before attempting to describe the various sets of abstracts of interest to chemists, the general characteristics of an efficient abstract service and the history of abstract journals will be discussed. It is hoped that such information will be helpful in evaluating the various journals and in the use of the abstracts.

An Efficient Abstract Service

The production of the modern chemical abstract journal requires an organized group, trained in the work, and backed by a large scientific organization, in order systematically to examine current literature, to prepare abstracts of the papers and patents of chemical interest that appear throughout the world, to classify the abstracts for convenient use, and to publish them and to furnish all indexes needed to make the published record available. As a result, the individual, who could not hope to do so otherwise, can keep abreast of chemical advances in his field or search out information on any subject that may engage his interest. *Chemical Abstracts*, for example, is the product of the work of an editor, 19 associate editors and 35 assistant editors and advisors, aided by the part-time work of 50 section editors and about 1,500 abstractors with the backing of the approximately 75,000 members of the American Chemical Society.

The ideal abstract journal (1) covers its field completely, (2) publishes good annual and collective indexes, (3) maintains a high quality in its abstracts, and (4) keeps its service prompt. All are important but completeness and the publication of good indexes are of the most consequence. Completeness depends to some extent on the quality of the abstracts. An abstract journal may report every paper that appears in its field and still will not be complete if individual abstracts are inadequate. An index to serve as a thorough guide to the literature must be based on abstracts that are complete from the indexing point of view. Proper indexing is a factor in completeness. If completeness is attempted and safeguarded by an abstract journal, it can be used with a feeling of reasonable assurance that the search has been thorough. It is well to remember that the user of an abstract journal must contribute his part in a thorough search by effective use of its indexes.

The quality of abstracts depends largely on the ability of the abstractor to understand the significance of the paper being covered and his skill as a maker of abstracts. The making of good brief abstracts is an art that must be learned by experience. Some abstract journals employ professional abstractors; others have their work done by a larger number of abstractors who are engaged in other scientific work and do abstracting in their spare time to help out a good cause. By the latter method it is possible for most of the abstracts to be made by scientists who are specialists in the subjects involved and who are therefore particularly well equipped to discover and report significant points in a paper. The abstracting skill of professional abstractors is likely to be greater, and abstracts can be obtained more promptly. The authors of this book consider the best method of obtaining abstracts to be one that involves the assigning of papers to be abstracted to specialists (active in other chemical work) who have acquired abstracting skill and who are willing to devote a part of their spare time to this work.

A good chemical abstract begins with a statement of the author's purpose in the work reported if this is not apparent from the title. It indicates fully the scope of the paper and reports or makes specific reference to all new material of chemical interest contained therein. Since a complete and permanent record is the object, it is very important that the abstract should contain specific reference to all of the information in a paper that is suitable to be indexed. This should include every measurement, observation, method, apparatus, suggestion, and theory that is presented as new and of value in itself. All new compounds and all elements, compounds, and other substances for which new data are given should be entered in the abstract.

Adequate precision is important when data are given. E.g., it is usually not sufficient to refer to "steel" if "3% chromium steel" is specified and it is not satisfactory to omit temperature, pressure, and similar variations if these are significant. The author's conclusions from his work should be reported in the abstract. Some journals have an auxiliary-publication plan whereby the journal publishes the paper in abbreviated form and the complete paper is deposited with a suitable organization from which a photoprint or microfilm is available; specific reference to this should be made in the abstract. The ideal abstract is informative, not merely descriptive; that is to say, the more important actual results are reproduced in the abstract instead of a statement being made as to what one may expect to find by turning to the original paper.

Good abstracts have other desirable characteristics. They are reasonably brief. The length of the abstract should be affected by the degree of availability of the paper being covered. The abstract should be longer if the paper appears in a rare journal or is written in a language that is read by few chemists served by the abstract journal. Abstracts should be written in full sentences for clearness and easy reading. If an abstract is a part of a series of abstracts on a given subject, its value is increased if reference is made to previous abstracts in the same journal or to the papers themselves. Good nomenclature should be used in the abstracts. Word abbreviations used in abstracts should follow a definite system for each journal and a key should be provided for users. See Appendix 2 for abbreviations frequently used.

The indexes, so important in an abstract journal, will be considered in Chapter 8.

Promptness in the publication of abstracts is important. Research workers in rapidly developing fields of science and in industry, in particular, are anxious for new information at the earliest possible time. Some abstract journals are more prompt in their publication of abstracts than others; the difference is likely to depend on the method of obtaining abstracts. If a large enough staff of professional abstractors is available, abstracts can be prepared more quickly than when part-time abstractors, who are actively working as specialists with the subjects involved, are asked to decide what is new and worth reporting and to make the abstracts. Unless the professional abstractors are also subject matter specialists, they can only make descriptive abstracts (sometimes just annotations) and the quality of such abstracts is low. Since the greatest value of a set of well indexed abstracts is as a permanent record and key to the literature, it is questionable policy to sacrifice the quality of the abstracts to speed in preparing them.

When world-wide coverage of a field is undertaken by an abstract journal, some abstracts will be late or appear to be late for special reasons. If for some reason a paper or patent has been missed, the abstract will be late because completeness is put ahead of a reputation for speed.

There are certain time lags that are unavoidable: (1) periodicals sometimes get behind in their printing schedules and appear later than the dates on their covers indicate, (2) some periodicals from remote parts of the world cannot be obtained quickly, (3) occasionally an abstract is held up because of some unclear point in a paper that led to correspondence between the author and the abstractor, and

(4) at times, budgetary limitations have forced abstract journals to hold up the printing of certain abstracts for a while.

An abstract journal is fortunate if it can assign, obtain, check, and edit an abstract within a month's time and it usually takes about a month for an abstract to go through the printing mill. If an abstract appears within two months after the original paper was published, the abstract journal is doing well. The average for abstract journals varies someplace between two months and a year. A lag of a year in publishing an abstract is undesirable.

History of Abstract Journals

No distinct line can be drawn between journals publishing full papers and those publishing abstracts. Many journals publish a limited number of abstracts along with full papers; only a few are devoted exclusively to abstracts. The general tendency has been to segregate abstracts into special journals. Many journals that formerly published abstracts have given up the practice with the development of the modern abstract journal.

The development of chemical abstract journals may be divided into two periods from the standpoint of making literature searches: the period before 1907, and that after 1907, the date when *Chemical Abstracts* was started.

Before 1907 there was no one journal that provided abstracts for all of chemistry. In making a thorough search of the earlier chemical literature one has to examine all of the chemical journals of the period that published abstracts and even then one can hardly expect to get results as satisfactory as those gained by the use of a single, modern, comprehensive, and well indexed journal. There was no attempt at comprehensiveness, no uniformity, and little system in the early abstract services. The situation gradually improved as abstract services provided by the major chemical societies were established and developed. The French Chemical Society started to publish abstracts in the *Bulletin de la société chimique de France* in 1858. The German Chemical Society published abstracts in *Berichte der deutschen chemischen Gesellschaft* from 1868 through 1896 and then took over *Chemisches Zentralblatt* in 1897. In Great Britain the Chemical Society and the Society of Chemical Industry started publishing abstracts in the *Journal of the Chemical Society* in 1871 and in the *Journal of the Society of Chemical Industry* in 1882. The American Chemical Society published abstracts in the *Journal of the American Chemical Society* from 1897 through 1906, after which

Chemical Abstracts was established. An examination of the classified list of abstract journals that follows will show that the number of journals that published abstracts had grown from one in 1778 (*Crell's Chemisches Journal*) to over sixty by 1907. However, none of these earlier abstract journals attempted world-wide coverage of either pure or applied chemistry.

For the period 1885 to 1907 an examination of all of these six abstract journals (*Chemisches Zentralblatt, Angewandte Chemie, Journal of the Chemical Society* (London), *Journal of the Society of Chemical Industry, Bulletin de la société chimique de France,* and *Chemiker-Zeitung*) will locate a very large percentage of the papers on a given topic in many cases. To make a thorough search during this period, all journals publishing abstracts on a given topic must be consulted.

Before 1907 it is not possible to locate all of the papers on a given topic in chemistry by the use of abstract journals alone. Index publications should be used too (see pages 279–285).

After 1907 abstract services became more centralized and there are several comprehensive abstract journals that attempt to cover all of chemistry. The first to appear and to approach complete coverage is *Chemical Abstracts,* published by the American Chemical Society (1907–   ). *Chemisches Zentralblatt* was expanded in 1919 to cover applied chemistry as well as pure chemistry. *British Abstracts* (1926–1953) gives comprehensive coverage for chemistry and, after 1938, for some fields of biology. *Referativnyi Zhurnal, Khimiya* started publication in 1953 and is gaining headway as a comprehensive journal. For literature searches after 1907, *Chemical Abstracts* is the best starting point and for many purposes it is the only abstract journal which one needs to use.

The more useful individual abstract journals available for use by the chemist will now be briefly described. The first group includes those of general chemical interest and the second those devoted to specific branches of chemistry.

The most important sources of abstracts of chemical interest are given in this chapter. Some other current sources of abstracts may be found by consulting these publications.

Lederman, L. F., "Abstracting and Indexing Periodicals of Chemical Interest Published in the United States," *J. Chem. Educ.* **29,** 396–400 (1952).
List of Periodicals and Bulletins Containing Abstracts Published in Great Britain. 2nd ed. Issued by the Royal Society, London, Cambridge Univ.

Press, 1950, 95 pp. The appendix gives a partial list for the British Commonwealth.

Index Bibliographicus. Vol. I, *Science and Technology,* compiled by Theodore Besterman, 3rd ed., 52 pp. Paris, UNESCO, and The Hague, International Federation of Documentation, 1952. This is an international directory of current periodical abstracts and bibliographies (indexes). Vol. 1 of the 3rd edition of *Index Bibliographicus* replaces the *List of Current Specialized Abstracting and Indexing Services* (FID publication no. 235) prepared by the International Federation for Documentation for the International Conference on Science Abstracting convened by UNESCO in Paris in June 1949. FID considered the 1949 list a temporary one.

Bibliography of Engineering and Abstracting Services (S.L.A. Bibliography no. 9), New York, Special Libraries Association, 1955.

Abstracts of General Chemical Interest

The journals of general chemical interest are those that publish abstracts devoted to the whole of chemistry, or to pure or to applied chemistry, respectively. These journals are divided into two groups, based on their general importance; the most important ones are described individually and the others are listed.

There are only three chemical abstract journals currently appearing that are devoted to the whole of chemistry: *Chemical Abstracts, Chemisches Zentralblatt,* and *Referativnyi Zhurnal, Khimiya. Bulletin signalétique* is an abstract journal for all of the sciences.

CHEMICAL ABSTRACTS (1907–   )

Chemical Abstracts, published by the American Chemical Society, is the most comprehensive of the chemical abstract journals. From the beginning the editors have placed special emphasis on complete coverage of the world's chemical literature. It was the first abstract journal to attempt to cover thoroughly both pure and applied chemistry and was the only journal doing this up to 1919, when *Chemisches Zentralblatt* took over the abstract section of *Angewandte Chemie. Chemical Abstracts* was the only abstract journal published in English with such a policy until *British Chemical Abstracts* was established in 1926. *Chemical Abstracts* is published semimonthly and the abstracts are reasonably prompt.

Coverage. The completeness of *Chemical Abstracts* is based on several factors: the number and kind of publications that are examined regularly, the broad interpretation of the scope of the interest of chemists, the inclusion in each abstract of all of the new material of interest to chemists, systematic checking to find and correct omissions, and finally thorough indexing.

The number of periodicals regularly examined for papers suitable to abstract for *Chemical Abstracts* has grown steadily and is now over 7,000. This list includes, in addition to the scientific and technical journals devoted to chemistry, many journals of the other sciences and the trade journals of many industries that are dependent, at least in part, on chemistry. Some house organs are included if there are papers in them that contain new information which does not have an advertising slant. The term periodical is applied in a broad sense, too, so that the reports of scientific congresses and conferences of chemical interest are included in the list, particularly since 1926. A large number of annual publications are also included; among these are reviews, reports on scientific progress, proceedings or transactions of scientific meetings, and, in recent years, a number of publications of the nature of *Organic Synthesis* and the *National Nuclear Energy Series*. *Chemical Abstracts* covers suitable serials issued at irregular intervals and a considerable number of government publications; these include published miscellaneous bulletins and circulars but does not include mimeographed, or otherwise processed, unpublished reports and documents of governmental or other origin.

From 1907 to date, *Chemical Abstracts* has endeavored to abstract all United States chemical patents. This journal has also included, 1907–   , abstracts of the chemical patents of a large number of foreign countries, but it has not always been possible to cover all of the foreign patent literature as completely as that of the United States. More information on patent coverage will be found in the chapter on Patents, page 172. Patent abstracts are thoroughly indexed along with the papers in the subject, author, and formula indexes and in addition are provided with a patent number index.

Books rarely report the results of new experimental work for the first time so that very few are abstracted by *Chemical Abstracts*. But the titles of new and revised books of chemical interest are entered in the appropriate sections of *Chemical Abstracts* with references to published reviews whenever these are located since 1919. Bibliographies published as separate items are included among the books. New scientific periodicals are also reported with the books. New books and periodicals are indexed by author names and by subjects. There were 1,926 new books and 50 new journals reported in 1954.

Broad interpretation of the scope of the interests of chemists adds to the completeness of *Chemical Abstracts* in several ways. Considerable information that is not strictly chemical but is useful to the chemist in his work is included by briefly abstracting papers that are only in small part of chemical interest.

Chemical Abstracts always has gone further than other chemical abstract journals in its coverage of many fields in order to insure a full chemical record; nuclear and electronic phenomena, mineralogical and geological chemistry, metallurgy and metallography, biochemistry, water, sewage and sanitation, agricultural chemistry, and fields represented by basic industries are in this category. In the case of papers that are on the borderline between chemistry and the other sciences, the general policy is to abstract them if there is doubt as to their chemical nature.

Except in a few special cases, each abstract in *Chemical Abstracts* is made by a specialist in the field involved. Quality is further safeguarded by the editorial supervision of men of high standing in their branches of chemistry who serve as editors for the various sections of *Chemical Abstracts*. The abstracts usually give specific information; they are not merely descriptive or indicative. Abstracts from the less accessible publications average longer than those from readily available journals.

The policy of complete coverage is reflected in the requirement that abstracts be written so as to be complete from the indexing point of view, followed by thorough indexing.

Omission of abstracts of papers is prevented by the editors of *Chemical Abstracts* by several methods. If a periodical is not available currently, the abstracts are prepared and included at a later date. Of course, a certain amount of this catching up goes on all the time, but it was most frequent after World Wars I and II. *Chemical Abstracts* succeeded remarkably well in currently covering the periodicals published during World War II. When the British blockade stopped the flow of German and other central European journals from coming to America, *Chemical Abstracts* organized a staff of 75 abstractors in Switzerland where these journals were available. Abstracts made in French or German were sent to America by clipper plane and published in *Chemical Abstracts* after translation. The American Army of Occupation of Japan organized a staff of Japanese abstractors which supplied *Chemical Abstracts* with abstracts of the Japanese literature for the war years during several years while Japan was cut off from the rest of the world.

In addition to the combing process that is applied to the many periodicals on the official list of *Chemical Abstracts*, the editors check other sets of abstracts against *Chemical Abstracts* indexes. When it is found that another abstract journal has covered a paper of chemical interest that has so far been missed by *Chemical Abstracts*, steps are taken at once to obtain an abstract. An abstract is usually obtained for *Chemical Abstracts* from the original paper if it can be obtained; if the other abstract is used, due credit is given.

Classification of Abstracts and Use of Abbreviations. Abstracts published in abstract journals are usually classified more or less systematically. For example, *Chemical Abstracts* classifies its abstracts in 33 sections and runs a table of contents listing these sections. The users of abstract journals usually get accustomed to where to look for abstracts of interest to them. Cross references, usually provided, help. In this connection it should be borne in mind that there are some related sections, such as one devoted to foods and another to nutrition, that are so close in general subject matter as to mean that just about every abstract could be cross referred from one section to the other and vice versa. It is the custom of abstract journals to expect readers to look into such sections instead of providing cross references. Within each of the sections of a journal there is usually a rough classification of abstracts to which the reader can helpfully become accustomed.

The key for the abbreviations used in the text of the abstracts is published annually, usually at the end of the volume in the last index number. The full titles of journals to which *Chemical Abstracts* refers in abbreviated form are found in the *List of Periodicals Abstracted by Chemical Abstracts*, published at five-year intervals.

Indexes to *Chemical Abstracts*. The individual numbers of *Chemical Abstracts* carry author indexes, but the other types of indexes appear only at annual and ten-year intervals. *Chemical Abstracts* is planning to publish subject indexes at monthly intervals as soon as the necessary staff can be obtained and trained.

The annual indexes are: author (1907–   ), subject (1907–   ), formula (1920–   ), numerical patent (1935–   ), and ring-system, which is a part of the introduction to the annual subject index (1916–   ).

The collective indexes are: decennial author and subject indexes for the periods 1907–1916, 1917–1926, 1927–1936, 1937–1946; 27-year collective formula index (1920–1946); the numerical patent index (1907–1936, see below); and the numerical patent index (1937–1946). All of the indexes are published by the American Chemical Society, except the numerical patent index (1907–1936), which was compiled by the Special Libraries Association, with the permission of the Society, and published by J. W. Edwards, Ann Arbor, Michigan. The present policy is to provide collective indexes for authors, subjects, formulas, and patent numbers at regular intervals, probably ten years, though five-year indexes are under consideration. The formula indexes cover both organic and inorganic compounds.

The Subject Indexes. *Chemical Abstracts* places strong emphasis on the publication of good indexes, subject indexes in particular. About half of the effort that goes into the production of *Chemical Abstracts* is devoted to indexing. For every thousand words of abstract material approximately 700 words of index are published and the indexing is all done by highly trained and experienced indexers.

CHEMISCHES ZENTRALBLATT (1830–   )

This important German abstract journal has value because of its early appearance, almost continuous publication, and good abstracts. There have been several changes of name, the original one being *Pharmaceutisches Centralblatt* (1830–1850). This was followed by *Chemisches-Pharmaceutisches Centralblatt* (1850–1856) and *Chemisches Zentralblatt* (1856–   ). *Zentralblatt* was spelled *Centralblatt* from 1856 to 1897. The Deutsche Chemische Gesellschaft published it from 1897 to 1945. Publication was suspended for a short time in 1945. Then two editions were issued in parallel from 1945 through 1950, one from the Eastern and the other from the Western Zone of Germany; the two editions were combined in 1951 to form a journal sponsored jointly by several scientific societies in each zone. It appears weekly. The usual form of reference to it is *Chem. Zentr.* or *Chem. Centr.*

Coverage. Up to 1919, *Chemisches Zentralblatt* was not a comprehensive abstract journal because it limited its abstracts to papers dealing directly or indirectly with pure chemistry, and it covered German chemical work more thoroughly than that of other countries. In 1919 the abstract section of *Angewandte Chemie* (then called *Zeitschrift für angewandte Chemie*) was made a part of *Chemisches Zentralblatt* and ever since it has endeavored to cover the world's periodical literature thoroughly for both pure and applied chemistry, though with some delays and omissions as an effect of World War II.

Before 1919 only German patents were abstracted by *Chemisches Zentralblatt*, and then only part of them, the leaning being toward patents on organic chemical substances. From 1919 to date *Chemisches Zentralblatt* has covered the world's chemical patents quite thoroughly. Throughout the years its patent coverage has not always been the same as that of *Chemical Abstracts* because the two journals have not made abstracts from the patents of all of the same countries. For example, *Chemisches Zentralblatt* does not make abstracts of Japanese patents whereas *Chemical Abstracts* has done so since 1917, and *Chemical Abstracts* has not always covered Russian patents, even in part. Because neither journal attempts to abstract all of the chemical patents of the world, the two sets of abstracts supplement each other in this respect.

Since 1926 new books have been announced by title in each of the divisions of the abstracts, usually at the beginning of the division or subdivision, but *Chemisches Zentralblatt* does not abstract or review books. The total number announced each year is much smaller than reported in *Chemical Abstracts*.

Chemisches Zentralblatt's coverage of the world's chemical literature was adversely affected by World War II and its aftermath, from 1939 through 1951. By 1952 it was making abstracts from papers in 4,925 periodicals. It is now approaching its prewar standard and the abstracts are reasonably prompt. Abstracts of some papers originating in the USSR and its satellite countries appear sooner in *Chemisches Zentralblatt* than in *Chemical Abstracts*.

It is very unusual to find an abstract of a paper in *Chemisches Zentralblatt* that is not also in *Chemical Abstracts* from 1907 on because of the care that the editors of the latter use to prevent omissions. If it does occur, it is not likely to represent a paper of major chemical importance but rather one of little chemical interest in a borderline field between chemistry and another science.

Classification of the Abstracts and Use of Abbreviations. To use current numbers of *Chemisches Zentralblatt*, it is necessary to become familiar with the system of classification of the abstracts because there is no subject index for each number; an outline of the system appears at the beginning of the volume and, in condensed form, on the cover of each number. It differs from the *Chemical Abstracts* classification in several ways, the most marked one being greater distinction between pure and applied chemistry. At present the abstracts are divided into eight groups, one of which (H) has 24 subdivisions and covers most of the applied chemistry, including patents.

Many abbreviations occur in the text of the abstracts, but a key is provided in the front of the index volumes; currently this key is in the annual author and patent index. For the full names of journals referred to in the abstracts see *Periodica Chemica* which is *Chemisches*

Zentralblatt's list of periodicals abstracted. These name abbreviations differ from those used by *Chemical Abstracts*.

Indexes. Each number, author only; semiannual, author and numerical patent number (1897–1950), subject (1889–1924); annual, subject, and organic formula (1925–   ), author and numerical patent number (1951–   ). Collective author and subject (1870–1881); author, subject, and patent at 5-year intervals (1897–1924); author, subject, patent, and organic formula at 5-year intervals (1925–   ); general index (1922–1934). A new collective index (author, subject, patent, and formula) for 1925 through 1938 has been announced. For a description of the indexes see Chapter 8, Indexes. The annual subject index is slow in appearing at present.

CHEMIKER-ZEITUNG (ABSTRACTS, 1882–   )

This journal was never devoted to abstracts only, but it needs to be considered in relation to abstract journals because its abstract section supplemented *Chemisches Zentralblatt* by covering industrial and applied chemistry before 1919. It was started in 1877 and its name was changed to *Chemiker-Zeitung mit Chemie Börse* in 1951. The extensive abstract section covers both papers and patents; this section was called *Chemisches Repertorium* (1882–1915) and *Chemisch-technische Übersicht* (1916–1945). There are annual subject and author indexes, but no collective indexes for this journal. The annual subject indexes through 1944 are divided into separate alphabetical arrangements of entries for each of the sections of the abstracts (over 30), which makes them inconvenient to use. Publication of *Chemiker-Zeitung* was suspended from March 1945 to 1951 and few abstracts have been published in this periodical since 1951.

ANGEWANDTE CHEMIE (ABSTRACTS, 1887–1918)

This is another German journal that was never devoted entirely to abstracts. This journal of applied chemistry had an extensive abstract section (1887–1918) that was made a part of *Chemisches Zentralblatt* in 1919. Its title was *Zeitschrift für angewandte Chemie* up to 1932. These abstracts cover both papers and patents and are needed to supplement *Chemisches Zentralblatt* before 1919. Collective author, subject, and patent indexes for 1887–1907 and 1908–1927.

BRITISH ABSTRACTS (1926–1953)

Both the Chemical Society (London) and the Society of Chemical Industry (London) published abstracts in their respective journals, the *Journal of the Chemical Society* (London) and the *Journal of the Society of Chemical Industry*, until the end of 1925 (see below). In 1926 the two societies combined their abstracting activities and founded *British Chemical Abstracts*, which continued under this name through 1937. In 1938 *Physiological Abstracts* was merged with *British Chemical Abstracts* and the name was changed to *British Chemical and Physiological Abstracts*. In 1939 a section on anatomy was added. The name was changed again in 1946, *British Abstracts* becoming the new name.

Coverage. Up to 1938, as its history would lead one to expect, *British Abstracts* covered only the chemical field with considerable thoroughness, but after that date it became something more than a chemical abstract journal, with anatomy and nonchemical phases of physiology as the principle additional fields of coverage. The coverage of chemistry was extensive but not as comprehensive as that of *Chemical Abstracts* for the same period, 1926–1953. Applied as well as pure chemistry was abstracted, and many patents were covered. The excellent, promptly appearing abstracts, once informative, tended to become descriptive about the time of World War II.

Classification of Abstracts. From 1926 through 1944 there are two parts, A (Pure Chemistry) and B (Applied Chemistry). From 1944 through 1953 there are three parts: A, B, and C (Analysis and Apparatus). The parts have been subdivided in somewhat different ways at different times; they were issued and bound separately.

Indexes. Annual indexes cover subjects, authors, and patents. Collective indexes for parts A and B (1923–1932 and 1933–1937) cover authors and subjects. The 1923–1932 index includes abstracts that were published in the *Journal of the Chemical Society* (London) and in *The Journal of the Society of Chemical Industry* (1923–1925). The subject indexes are somewhat less extensive than those of *Chemisches Zentralblatt* and of *Chemical Abstracts*.

JOURNAL OF THE CHEMICAL SOCIETY (LONDON)
(ABSTRACTS, 1871–1925)

Part of this journal was once devoted to abstracts that covered pure chemistry as published in all of the more important scientific journals. Some sources of new information of chemical interest were not covered, but this is the most comprehensive set of abstracts in English before 1907. A few patent abstracts are included, most of which are in the field of organic chemistry. After 1878 the abstracts were paged separately from the papers (*Transactions*) and given a separate volume number so that they could be bound separately. There are annual subject indexes. A collective index covers the period, 1841–1873, and decennial indexes were issued thereafter. The excellent abstracts are better than are the indexes.

JOURNAL OF THE SOCIETY OF CHEMICAL INDUSTRY (ABSTRACTS, 1882–1925)

Part of this journal was devoted to abstracts that covered all phases of applied chemistry. The abstracts are very good. English, German, French, and United States patents are covered. There are annual author, subject, and patent number indexes; the decennial indexes cover authors and subjects. These abstracts together with those in the *Journal of the Chemical Society* give a good, but not complete, coverage of both pure and applied chemistry that is particularly useful before 1907.

BULLETIN DE LA SOCIÉTÉ CHIMIQUE DE FRANCE (ABSTRACTS, 1858–1947)

Part of this journal was devoted to abstracts in pure chemistry. The abstracts are fairly comprehensive up to 1939. Until 1933 every second volume was devoted to abstracts. From 1933 through 1945 the *Bulletin* was divided into two separate parts: *Bulletin de la société chimique de France, Memoires* (Papers); and *Bulletin de la société chimique de France, Documentation* (Abstracts). A few abstracts were published in 1946 and 1947. Again, the abstracts for the period before 1907 are particularly useful. There are annual author and subject indexes and collective indexes for the period 1858–1926. The subject indexes are rather inadequate.

CHIMIE ET INDUSTRIE (1918–)

From 1918 to 1939 a considerable part of this French journal was devoted to abstracts that covered the literature of applied chemistry with considerable thoroughness. Since then the number of abstracts has been rather small. This journal is particularly useful for abstracts of French patents.

BULLETIN SIGNALÉTIQUE (1940–)

The full title of this abstract journal is *Bulletin signalétique du centre national de la recherche scientifique*. It was begun in 1940 but did not become an important journal until after World War II. This journal represents the effort that is being made in France to centralize scientific abstracting services and to publish abstracts that cover all of the sciences in one journal. It endeavors to abstract the scientific periodicals of the world and to review the scientific books of the world. It covers both pure and applied sciences but does not cover agriculture, engineering, or medicine, except for phases that are related to the basic sciences. Dissertations and theses from French universities are abstracted and also the reports of many scientific meetings and congresses, those meeting in Europe for the most part. *Bulletin signalétique* publishes very brief abstracts, often little more than descriptive annotations. The service is prompt and subscribers may quickly and inexpensively obtain microfilm copies of papers abstracted. This journal was called *Bulletin analytique* up to 1956.

The journal is published in two parts and is issued monthly. Part one covers the physical sciences, including chemistry and chemical technology. Part two covers the biological sciences, including all phases of biochemistry and the chemistry of foods. There is an annual author index but no subject index. The lack of a subject index makes this journal of value mostly for keeping up with current scientific research and with new books.

REFERATIVNYI ZHURNAL, KHIMIYA (1953–   )

This chemical abstract journal started publication in October, 1953. It is issued by the Soviet Institute of Scientific Information (Institut Nauchnoĭ Informatsii, Akademiya Nauk SSSR, Moscow). It appears twice a month. Each issue has an author index, names of non-Russian authors being given in both the Russian and the Latin alphabet. Only the Russian language is used in the abstracts, but for non-Russian papers the title and the author's name are also given in the original language (named in parentheses). Annual indexes cover authors and subjects. The 1954 indexes include the numbers issued in 1953.

This journal was announced as one that would cover all of the world's chemical literature, both pure and applied. Good progress towards this goal is being made. Dissertations are abstracted, books are reviewed and some newspaper articles are abstracted, an unusual feature. *Referativnyi Zhurnal, Khimiya* is one of a series of abstract journals that the Soviet Institute of Scientific Information is publishing. Some abstracts of chemical interest appear in other journals of the series. Biochemistry is being covered in a separate abstract journal.

The journal is designed for Soviet chemists but it will be a very valuable journal for others as it develops comprehensive coverage of chemical research and patents in the USSR and countries under its domination.

OTHER SOURCES OF ABSTRACTS OF GENERAL CHEMICAL INTEREST

1778–1781. *Crell's Chemisches Journal* (Germany).
1781–1786. *Crell's Entdeckungen in der Chemie* (Germany).
1784–1803. *Crell's Chemisches Annalen* (Germany).
1789–1870. *Annales de chimie et de physique* (France).
1790–1796. *Elwert's Repertorium für Chemie* (Germany).
1820–1931. *Dingler's Polytechnisches Journal* (Germany).
1822–1847. *Berzelius' Jahresbericht der Chemie* (Germany).
1832–1860. *Annalen der Chemie* (Germany).
1834–1873. *Journal für praktische Chemie* (Germany).
1835–1875. *Polytechnisches Centralblatt* (Germany).
1840–1858. *The Chemist* (England).
1846–1875. *Chemisch-Technische Mittheilungen* (Germany).
1857–1926. *Moniteur scientifique* (France).
1868–1896. *Berichte der deutschen chemischen Gesellschaft* (Germany).
1877–1945. *Zeitschrift für Krystallographie* (Germany).
1881–1886. *Appendice alla gazzetta chimica italiana.*
1892–   . *Zeitschrift für anorganische Chemie* (Germany). Vols. 1–37 only.
1897–1906. *Journal of the American Chemical Society.*
1898–   . *La revue des produits chimiques* (France).
1901–1918. *Répertoire général de chimie pure et appliquée.* Supplement to *Revue générale de chimie pure et appliquée* (France).
1919–1935. *Giornale di chimica industriale ed applicata* (Italy).
1912–   . *Anales de la sociedad española de fisica y química* (Spain).
1922–   . *Australian Science Abstracts.* Published in the Australian Journal of Science.
1922–1929. *Japanese Journal of Chemistry.*
1927–   . *Complete Abstracts of Japanese Chemical Literature* (Nippon Kagaku Soran).
1935–   . *Indian Science Abstracts* (Calcutta).
1935–   . *La chimica e l'industria* (Italy).
1954–   . *Journal of Applied Chemistry* (England).

Abstracts for Specific Branches of Chemistry

The above descriptions and list cover the more important journals publishing comprehensive abstracts devoted to the whole of chemistry or to pure or to applied chemistry, respectively, and a few devoted to natural sciences. The following journals are devoted in whole or in considerable part to abstracts relating to specific branches of chemistry or to sister sciences. Many of the abstracts in journals devoted

140   PERIODICALS

to other sciences are of chemical interest. The journals that publish abstracts only are so marked and described briefly here; the others are listed and, for the current ones, additional information may be found in the descriptions of journals on the classified list. These journals which include abstracts are classified in accordance with the classification system used for abstracts in *Chemical Abstracts* except that journals covering physical chemistry and electronic and nuclear phenomena are all in one group and journals on agricultural chemistry are not subdivided.

It should be emphasized that the general chemical abstract journals, as *Chemical Abstracts, Chemisches Zentralblatt,* and *British Abstracts* provide a more satisfactory abstract service for the various branches of chemistry, as far as the chemical side of things is concerned, than do the sets of abstracts devoted exclusively to definite branches. The exceptions to this general rule are rare.

The value of abstracts devoted exclusively to definite branches is mostly to supplement those in general chemical abstract journals after 1907 when *Chemical Abstracts,* the first comprehensive journal, was started. These specialized abstracts, in many cases, cover useful nonchemical information; they may be longer or give more specific details; and they may appear more promptly. They are particularly useful for topics on the borderline between chemistry and other sciences. Of course, those that existed before 1907 are necessary in a comprehensive search, not supplementary.

2a–3a. PHYSICAL CHEMISTRY, ELECTRONIC AND
NUCLEAR PHENOMENA

1872–1920. *Journal de physique théorique et appliquée* (France).
1877–1919. *Beiblätter zu den Annalen der Physik* (Germany). Abstracts only.
1889–1904. *Zeitschrift für physikalische Chemie* (Germany).
1896–1906. *Journal of Physical Chemistry* (United States).
1898– . *Science Abstracts* (England). Abstracts only. This excellent journal was split into two sections, A and B, in 1903. Section A, Physics, covers much of interest to physical chemists and is decidedly useful for nuclear and electronic phenomena. Section B, Electrical Engineering, is seldom of interest to chemists. The indexes are poor.
1903–1912. *Journal de chimie physique* (France).
1908– . *Zeitschrift für wissenschaftliche Photographie, Photophysik und Photochemie* (Germany).
1904–1909. *Physikalisch-chemisches Centralblatt* (Germany).
1904–1919. *Le radium* (France). Abstracts on radioactivity, radiation, and gaseous ionization.

1906– . *Kolloid-Zeitschrift* (Germany). A large number of abstracts on pure and applied colloid chemistry.
1920– . *Physikalische Berichte* (Germany). Abstracts only.
1922– . *Journal de physique et Le radium* (France). A large abstract section.
1922–1940. *Japanese Journal of Physics.* Abstracts of Japanese literature in English and German.
1923–1930. *Revue générale des colloides et de leurs applications industrielles* (France).
1947– . *Journal de chimie physique et de physicochimie biologique* (France). A large number of abstracts now appear in this journal.
1948– . *Nuclear Science Abstracts.* Abstracts only. These abstracts, which are a publication of the United States Atomic Energy Commission, cover atomic energy literature in chemistry, biology, physics, engineering, and medicine. There are subject, author, and nuclide indexes. Vol. III, no. 12 is a collective index for Vols. I–III. These abstracts are issued promptly and do not materially duplicate *Chemical Abstracts. Nuclear Science Abstracts* is a very useful journal.

4. ELECTROCHEMISTRY

There is no comprehensive set of abstracts for this field outside of the general chemical abstracting journals.

1894–1907. *Zeitschrift für Elektrochemie und angewandte physikalische Chemie* (Germany).
1898– . *Science Abstracts* (England). Electrochemistry is covered in Section B, Electrical Engineering.
1948– . *Electroplating and Metal Finishing* (England). This journal has a large abstract section.

5. PHOTOGRAPHY

1865– . *British Journal of Photography.* Patent abstracts.
1893–1930. *Bulletin de la société française de photographie.* A limited number of abstracts.
1902–1943. *Photographische Industrie* (Germany). Abstracts of German patents.
1915– . Eastman Kodak Company. *Kodak Research Laboratories' Monthly Abstract Bulletin* (United States). Complete coverage of all phases of the chemistry of photography as well as general aspects. An excellent journal.
1921– . *Photographic Abstracts* (England). These are very comprehensive abstracts. Abstracts only.
1921– . *Science et industries photographiques* (France). This journal has a very large and comprehensive abstract section.

6. INORGANIC CHEMISTRY

There are no abstracts in this field outside of the general chemical abstracting journals.

7. ANALYTICAL CHEMISTRY

1862–1935. *Zeitschrift für analytische Chemie* (Germany).
1877– . *Analyst, The* (England). A comprehensive abstract section up to 1950.
1880–1915. *School of Mines Quarterly, The* (United States).
1896– . *Chimie analytique* (France).
1908– . *Annals des falsifications et des fraudes* (France).
1954– . *Analytical Abstracts* (England). Abstracts only. This journal of the Society for Analytical Chemistry (London) covers all fields of analytical chemistry.

8. MINERALOGICAL AND GEOLOGICAL CHEMISTRY

1807–1950. *Neues Jahrbüch für Mineralogie, Geologie und Palaontologie* (Germany).
1916– . *American Mineralogist.* A few abstracts.
1920– . *Mineralogical Abstracts.* Abstracts only. This appears quarterly in the *Mineralogical Magazine and Journal* of the Mineralogical Society (England). It attempts to cover the world's mineralogical literature.
1920–1940. *Revue de géologie et des sciences connexes* (Belgium). There are a number of mistakes in the abstracts published in this journal.
1922– . *Japanese Journal of Geology and Geography.* Abstracts of Japanese literature in English and German.
1950– . *Geophysical Abstracts* (United States Bureau of Mines). Abstracts only.

9. METALLURGY AND METALLOGRAPHY

1855–1920. *Bulletin de la société de l'industrie minérale* (France).
1857– . *Revue universelle des mines* (Belgium).
1865– . *Glückauf, Bergmannische Zeitschrift* (Germany).
1869– . *Journal of the Iron and Steel Institute* (England). There has always been a large abstract section in this journal and in recent years there have been about 4,000 abstracts per year on the iron, steel, and allied industries.
1898– . *Journal of the Chemical, Metallurgical, and Mining Society of South Africa.*
1904–1911. *Metallurgie* (Germany).
1904– . *Revue de metallurgie* (France). Earlier volumes contain more abstracts than do the current ones.
1909– . *Journal of the Institute of Metals and Metallurgical Abstracts* (England). These abstracts cover general and nonferrous metallurgy. There are currently about 6,000 abstracts per

year. The abstract section of the journal became *Metallurgical Abstracts* in 1931.

1911–1918. *Internationale Zeitschrift für Metallographie* (Germany).

1919– . *Zeitschrift für Metallkunde* (Germany). Earlier volumes contained a number of abstracts, but there have been few since 1930.

1921– . *Revue de l'industrie minérale* (France).

1923– . *Bulletin and Foundry Abstracts of the British Cast Iron Research Association.*

1928– . *Metals Review* (United States). This contains the *American Society for Metals Review of Metal Literature*, which is very comprehensive. The entries are more like annotations than abstracts.

1952– . *Crerar Metals Abstracts.* Abstracts only. Crerar Library, 86 E. Randolph Street, Chicago, Ill. These abstracts cover ferrous alloys, vanadium, titanium, zirconium, hafnium, rare earths, and molybdenum.

10. ORGANIC CHEMISTRY

Abstracts in this field appear only in the general chemical abstracting journals.

11. BIOLOGICAL CHEMISTRY

1902–1909. *Biochemisches Zentralblatt* (Germany).

1909–1918. *Zentralblatt für Biochemie und Biophysik* (Germany).

1918– . *Berichte über die gesamte Physiologie und experimentelle Pharmakologie* (Germany). (Abt. B of *Berichte über die gesamte Biologie.*) This and the two preceding entries are really the same journal. This is the most extensive set of abstracts for the earlier years.

1915– . *Endocrinology* (United States). Publishes a considerable number of abstracts on hormones and studies of the glands of internal secretion.

1916–1926. *Abstracts of Bacteriology* (United States). Abstracts only. Many abstracts of chemical interest. Merged in *Biological Abstracts* in 1926.

1919–1937. *Physiological Abstracts* (England). Abstracts only. Excludes medical aspects of physiology but covers the physiology and biochemistry of both plants and animals. Merged with *British Abstracts* in 1937.

1919–1926. *Botanical Abstracts* (United States). Abstracts only. Plant biochemistry is included. Collective index, Vols. 1–10. Merged in *Biological Abstracts* in 1926.

1922–1948. *Japanese Journal of Botany.* Abstracts of Japanese literature in English or German.

1922–1941. *Japanese Journal of Medical Sciences.* Abstracts of Japanese literature in English, French, or German. Includes biochemistry and biophysics.

1926–   . *Biological Abstracts* (United States). Abstracts only. This is a very useful journal for biochemists. It endeavors (as completely as funds permit) to cover the biological literature of the world and is now publishing more than 30,000 abstracts per year. Since 1939 *Biological Abstracts* has been issued in sections, and a subscriber may obtain all or part of them (Section A, General Biology; B, Basic Medical Sciences; C, Microbiology, Immunology and Parasitology; D, Plant Sciences; and E, Animal Sciences). Additional sections (F, G, H, and J) were added, 1942–1947, by further subdividing the topics covered in A–E, but Sections F and G were discontinued at the end of 1953 and these topics were returned to A–E. There are annual subject, author, systematic (phyla, genera, class, order), and geographical indexes.

1926–   . *Berichte über die wissenschaftliche Biologie* (Abt. A. of *Berichte über die gesamte Biologie*, Germany). Publishes a large number of abstracts, some of chemical interest.

1931–   . *Nutrition Abstracts and Reviews* (Great Britain). A large part of this journal is devoted to abstracts.

1932–   . *Internationale Zeitschrift für Vitaminforschung* (Switzerland). Includes a large number of abstracts.

1947–   . *Abstracts of World Medicine* (England). These are not as useful for chemists as *Excerpta Medica*.

1948–   . *Excerpta Medica* (Holland). Abstracts only. This journal is issued in 15 sections which are sold separately. Sections II and III, which cover physiology, biochemistry, pharmacology, and endrocrinology, are most frequently of interest to chemists. *Excerpta Medica* abstracts the world's medical literature. The abstracts are printed in English. The indexes have been delayed.

1949–   . *Journal de physiologie* (France). Includes a large number of abstracts, many of which are of chemical interest.

12. Foods

1882–1890. *Vierteljahresschrift der Chemie der Nahrungs- und Genussmittel* (Germany).

1891–1925. *Zeitschrift für Untersuchung der Nahrungs- und Genussmittel sowie der Gebrauchsgegenstände* (Germany).

1926–   . *Zietschrift für Untersuchung der Lebensmittel-Untersuchung und -Forschung* (Germany).

1889–1946. *Experiment Station Record*. See Section 15, p. 146.

1891–1922. *Hygienische Rundschau* (Germany).

1891–1944. *Zeitschrift für Fleisch- und Milchhygiene* (Germany).

1908–   . *Annales des falsifications et des fraudes* (France).

1929–   . *Food Science Abstracts* (England). This journal, started in 1929, is an enlargement and continuation of the *Index to the Literature of Food Investigation*, Department of Scientific and Industrial Research (British Government).

1939–   . *Dairy Science Abstracts* (Great Britain).
1947–   . *Food Technology* (United States). Some abstracts are included.

13. GENERAL INDUSTRIAL CHEMISTRY

There is no current comprehensive set of abstracts in this field out-side of the general chemical abstracting journals. For abstracts of the older industrial chemical work, the first three journals listed below must be used because *Chemisches Zentralblatt* did not cover industrial chemistry until 1919 and *Chemical Abstracts* did not appear until 1907.

1882–   . *Chemiker Zeitung* (Germany). A very extensive abstract section that covers both papers and patents. The number of abstracts is small after 1945.
1882–1925. *Journal of the Society of Chemical Industry* (England). A very extensive abstract section that covers both papers and patents.
1887–1918. *Zeitschrift für angewandte Chemie* (Germany). A very extensive abstract section that covers both papers and patents.
1918–   . *Chimie et industrie* (France). Published a large number of abstracts until 1939 that covered both papers and patents. Since 1939 few abstracts have been included.
1935–   . *La chimica e l'industria* (Italy). A very large number of abstracts.
1946–   . *U. S. Government Research Reports.* Formerly the *Bibliography of Technical Reports* and before that the *Bibliography of Scientific and Industrial Reports*. This is really a combination index and annotated bibliography of declassified U. S. Government research reports and of declassified reports of research work that was sponsored by the U. S. Government. Some reports from foreign governments are included, particularly in the earlier volumes. Issued by the Office of Technical Services, U. S. Department of Commerce. Some of the reports are of chemical interest.
1951–   . *Technische Zentralblatt* (Germany). Abstracts only.
1950–   . *Chemical Market Abstracts.* Published by F. D. Snell, Inc. New York, N. Y.
1954–   . *Journal of Applied Chemistry* (London). A large abstract section was started after *British Abstracts* ceased publication in 1953.

14. WATER, SEWAGE, SANITATION

1909–1943. *Wasser und Abwasser* (Germany).
1919–   . *Journal of the American Water Works Association.* The non-chemical phases of water supply are covered more fully than in *Chemical Abstracts*.
1920–1949. *Journal of Industrial Hygiene and Toxicology* (United States). A number of abstracts.

1921– . *Public Health Engineering Abstracts.* These are issued by the United States Public Health Service.

1928– . *Water Pollution Abstracts.* These are issued by the Department of Scientific and Industrial Research (British Government).

1950– . *Archives of Industrial Hygiene and Occupational Medicine* (United States). A number of abstracts.

15. AGRICULTURAL CHEMISTRY

1803–1818. *Archiv der Agrikulturchemie (Hermbstaedts)* (Germany).

1872–1936. *Zentralblatt für Agrikulturchemie (Biedermann)* (Germany). Abstracts only. Collective indexes, Vols. 1–55 (1872–1926).

1889–1946. *Experiment Station Record.* This was published by the United States Department of Agriculture. Abstracts only. After the first few years, the *Experiment Station Record* gave almost international coverage of periodicals, bulletins, and reports on agriculture in addition to abstracting the publications of the U. S. experiment stations and the Federal Department of Agriculture. Collective indexes for Vols. 1–12, 13–25, 26–40, 41–50, 51–60, 61–70 (1887–1934). These abstracts are useful for both food and agricultural chemistry.

1910–1946. *International Review of Agriculture.* Formerly the *International Review of the Science and Practice of Agriculture.* Mostly abstracts. Issued by the International Institute of Agriculture (Rome). The coverage was not complete and errors in the abstracts are not infrequent.

1912– . *Review of Applied Entomology.* Some abstracts on insecticides.

16. FERMENTATION INDUSTRIES

There are no systematic abstracts devoted exclusively to this field, but some abstracts are found in the *Journal of the Institute of Brewing* and in *Wallerstein Laboratory Communications.*

17. PHARMACEUTICALS, COSMETICS, PERFUMES

1785–1787. *Elwert's Magazin fuer Apotheker* (Germany).

1809–1814. *Bulletin de pharmacie et de chimie* (France).

1815–1876. *Gehlen's Repertorium der Pharmacie* (Germany).

1815–1942. *Journal de pharmacie et de chimie* (France).

1830– . *American Journal of Pharmacy.* A few abstracts.

1841– . *Pharmaceutical Journal* (England). Published a number of abstracts up to 1939.

1842–1859. *Chemical Gazette.*

1844–1926. *Répertoire de pharmacie* (France).

1852–1911. *Proceedings of the American Pharmaceutical Association.*

1859– . *Pharmazeutische Zentralhalle für Deutschland.*

1912–1934. *Yearbook of the American Pharmaceutical Association.*

1920–1938. *Pharmaceutische Monatschefte* (Austria).

ABSTRACT JOURNALS

147

1925–1952. *Squibb Abstract Bulletin, The* (United States). Abstracts only. Most of these abstracts are of interest to pharmaceutical chemists.

1928– . *Soap, Perfumery and Cosmetics* (England). A number of abstracts appear here.

1930– . *Manufacturing Chemist and Pharmaceutical and Fine Chemical Trade Journal Incorporating Manufacturing Perfumer* (England). A number of abstracts appear here.

1935–1948. *Pharmaceutical Abstracts.* These appeared in the *Journal of the American Pharmaceutical Association.*

1943– . *Annales pharmaceutiques françaises.* A number of abstracts appear here.

1946– . *Produits pharmaceutiques* (France).

18. ACIDS, ALKALIES, SALTS, AND OTHER HEAVY CHEMICALS

There are no abstracts for this field outside of those in the general chemical abstracting journals.

19. GLASS, CLAY PRODUCTS, REFRACTORIES,
AND ENAMELED METALS

1908– . *Transactions of the British Ceramic Society.* There is a very large and comprehensive abstract section, now called *British Ceramic Abstracts.*

1917– . *Journal of the Society of Glass Technology* (England). There is a very large and comprehensive abstract section.

1919– . *Journal of the American Ceramic Society.* A very large and extensive abstract section called *Ceramic Abstracts* is included.

20. CONCRETE, CEMENT, AND OTHER BUILDING MATERIALS

1928– . *Building Science Abstracts.* Abstracts only. These are issued by the Department of Scientific and Industrial Research (British Government).

1934– . *Road Abstracts.* Abstracts only. These are issued by the Department of Scientific and Industrial Research (British Government).

21. FUELS AND CARBONIZATION PRODUCTS

1890–1930. *American Gas Association, Bulletin of Abstracts.* These were issued in loose-leaf form.

1908–1926. *Journal of the American Peat Society.*

1920–1939. *Brennstoff-Chemie* (Germany). The periodical is current, but its excellent and comprehensive abstract section was discontinued in 1939.

1923– . *Fuel. A Journal of Fuel Science* (England). Formerly called *Fuel in Science and Practice.*

1945– . *Fuel Abstracts.* Abstracts only. These are issued by the Department of Scientific and Industrial Research (British Government).

1945– . *Gas Abstracts* (United States). These abstracts are comprehensive for gas and partially for petroleum and coal.

1950– . *Synthetic Liquid Fuel Abstracts.* These are issued by the United States Bureau of Mines.

22. PETROLEUM, LUBRICANTS, AND ASPHALT

1905–1939. *Petroleum. Zeitschrift für die gesamte Interessen der Erdöl-Industrie und des Mineralöl-Handels.* A considerable number of abstracts were published here.

1914– . *Journal of the Institute of Petroleum* (England). Formerly *Journal of the Institution of Petroleum Technologists.* The abstract section is very large and comprehensive. Outside of the general chemical abstracting journals, this is the most valuable set of abstracts for petroleum chemistry and technology.

1934– . *Road Abstracts.* See section 20, p. 147. A number of abstracts on asphalt appear here.

1946– . *Revue de l'institut français du pétrole et Annales des combustibles liquides.* A limited number of abstracts.

1948– . *Erdöl und Kohle* (Germany). A few abstracts.

23. CELLULOSE AND PAPER

1920–1930. *Paper Trade Journal* (United States). Published a comprehensive set of abstracts that were prepared by a committee of the Technical Association of the Pulp and Paper Industry.

1930– . *Bulletin of the Institute of Paper Chemistry* (United States). "Library Notes," which comprise most of this journal, give a very comprehensive abstract service for pulp and paper research and technology. These "Notes" are more like annotated bibliography entries than abstracts.

24. EXPLOSIVES AND EXPLOSIONS

There are almost no abstracts in this field outside of the general chemical abstract journals and not a great many there.

1882–1897. *Proceedings of the United States Naval Institute.* Notes on the literature of explosives.

1924– . *Explosives Engineer* (United States).

25. DYES AND TEXTILE CHEMISTRY

See the section on journals in this field for others that carry some abstracts. Each publication given below publishes a large number.

1879–1948. *Textile Colorist and Converter* (United States). Formerly *Textile Colorist.* Abstracts of U. S. patents.

1884– . *Journal of the Society of Dyers and Colourists* (Great Britain). Publishes a large number of abstracts that cover both papers and patents.

1910– . *Journal of the Textile Institute* (England). A large number of abstracts. Since 1949 there have been two monthly issues, only one of which carries abstracts. (*J. Textile Inst., Proc. and Abstr.*)

1917– . *American Dyestuff Reporter*. The abstracts cover both papers and patents on dyes and textiles.

1930– . *Bulletin de l'institut textile de France.*

1944– . *Natural and Synthetic Fibers*. A loose-leaf abstracting service of Interscience Publishers, Inc., New York.

1944– . *Textile Technology Digest*. Institute of Textile Technology. Charlottesville, Va.

26. Paints, Varnishes, Lacquers, Inks

Abstract Review. Scientific Section. National Paint, Varnish, and Lacquer Association, Washington, D. C. A large number of abstracts.

Review of Current Literature Relating to the Paint, Colour, Varnish and Allied Industries (England). 1928– . A very large number of abstracts are published.

27. Fats, Fatty Oils, Waxes, and Detergents

1932– . *Journal of the American Oil Chemists Society*. A very large abstract section that covers fats, oils, soaps, detergents, and waxes.

1944– . *Fats–Oils–Detergents*. This is a loose-leaf abstracting service of Interscience Publishers, New York.

28. Sugar, Starch, and Gums

1908– . *International Sugar Journal* (England). A good abstract section.

1923–1941. *Facts About Sugar* (United States).

1941– . *Sugar* (United States).

1872– . *Sucrerie belge, La* (Belgium). Current numbers include a number of abstracts.

1941– . *Sugar Industry Abstracts*. Tate and Lyle Research Laboratories, Keston, Kent, England.

29. Leather and Glue

1906– . *Journal of the American Leather Chemists Association*. A comprehensive abstract section.

1912–1944. *Collegium* (Germany).

1917– . *Journal of the Society Leather Trades' Chemists* (England). A comprehensive abstract section.

30. RUBBER AND OTHER ELASTOMERS

1932–1951. *Summary of Current Literature.* The Research Association of British Rubber Manufactures. It was also published in the *Journal of Rubber Research* (England) from 1932 through 1951. This summary covers both papers and patents.

1952– . *Rubber Abstracts* (England).

31. SYNTHETIC RESINS AND PLASTICS

1942– . *Resins–Rubber–Plastics.* A loose-leaf abstracting service of papers and patents that is published by the Interscience Publishers, New York.

1945– . *British Plastics Federation Abstracts.* The British Plastics Federation, 47–48 Piccadilly, London, W.1., England. These abstracts cover practically all of the papers and patents in the field.

NOTES ON THE USE OF PERIODICALS

Literature Searches

The question continually arises as to how far back one should go in using the journal literature in a literature search. This depends entirely on the nature of the subject and on the object of the search, as discussed in the chapter on Procedure in Literature Searches. Some searchers consider that it is usually safe to assume that everything of value in the periodical literature has been made a part of the book literature after a period of about twenty years, or has been carried over into the journal literature of later date. The older literature is not always valueless by any means and books cannot be depended upon to glean everything of lasting value.

Determining the Existence of a Periodical

Frequently one wishes to ascertain the existence of a periodical that covers a particular field of chemistry. An effort has been made to include the most important current ones in the lists in this chapter. For current periodicals that appeared after the latest edition of the *List of Periodicals Abstracted by Chemical Abstracts* see the discussion on new periodicals, page 66; for other current ones the examination of the *List of Periodicals Abstracted by Chemical Abstracts* is not very satisfactory because the list is not classified and the names of periodicals frequently do not effectively indicate their fields of coverage. Neither the *World List of Scientific Periodicals* nor *Periodica Chimica,* which is the name for *Chemisches Zentralblatt's* list of periodicals abstracted, is any more helpful than the *Chemical Abstracts* list for the same reasons. Published lists of current periodicals devoted to a specific field of chemistry are difficult to locate and are frequently unrewarding when found because they are not very comprehensive. The lists in Appendix 4 of this book will be helpful in some cases. The National Science Foundation, Washington, D. C., made a grant, in 1953, for the compilation of lists of scientific and technical serial publications that will be of interest to chemists when completed.

Large scientific libraries or highly specialized scientific libraries can often give helpful information. Sometimes the quickest way to get the information is to examine the appropriate section of *Chemical Abstracts* for a year or two and note the journals to which reference is made in the abstracts. Sometimes *Ulrich's Periodicals Directory*, 7th ed. (Eileen C. Graves, ed., New York, Bowker & Co., 1954) is useful. Ulrich includes a large number of scientific periodicals that are classified; it shows where each periodical is abstracted or indexed and whether the periodical includes abstracts, patent information, or trade information; it also gives the collective indexes that exist in most cases.

Locating Periodicals in Libraries

If one wishes to consult a periodical that is not available in his local library, the nearest library in the United States or Canada that does have it can be learned by consulting the following:

1. *List of Periodicals Abstracted by Chemical Abstracts*, found in December 10, 1956, issue of *Chemical Abstracts*. Also available as a reprint from the American Chemical Society. This list is revised every five years. The list contains a "Key to Library Files."
2. *Union List of Serials in Libraries of United States and Canada*, New York, Wilson Co., 2nd ed., 1943; first supplement to 2nd ed., 1945; second supplement to 2nd ed., 1954. This publication and its supplements cover library holdings through December 31, 1949.
3. *New Serial Titles*, 1953–   . This is a monthly journal issued by the Library of Congress, Washington, D. C., which covers periodicals that began publication after January 1, 1950, and are received by the Library of Congress and cooperating libraries. It also includes titles that are new for each cooperating library after December 31, 1949. This journal serves as a continuing supplement to the *Union List of Serials*.
4. *Union List of Technical Periodicals*, 3rd ed. (1947), New York, Special Libraries Association. This covers 200 libraries maintained by industries or manufacturers of chemicals. Many of these libraries are not covered by the publications mentioned above.

5. For other publications occasionally useful to chemists see Appendix 4 of this book.

It should be noted that sources (1) and (3) mentioned above cover only periodicals which the libraries received at the time the list was compiled; they do not show the extent of the holdings. Sources (2) and (4) show both current reception and the extent of all periodical holdings, including the completeness of each set. If the library is too far away for one to examine the periodical, his local librarian may be able to arrange an interlibrary loan. See Chapter 9, Libraries, for more information on this point.

Obtaining a Copy of a Paper

If one wants to obtain a paper to which he has found a reference or of which he has read an abstract, and if the periodical is not available in libraries near enough to be visited, it is usually better to send to an appropriate library for a photoprint or a microfilm copy than to try to borrow a volume of the journal. Most of the larger libraries provide photoprints and many of them provide microfilm copies that are cheaper for long papers. The American Chemical Society's photocopying service saves a lot of time-consuming and expensive shopping around, but it is limited to members of the American Chemical Society and to current subscribers to *Chemical Abstracts;* it will provide a photoprint or microfilm of any chemical paper covered by *Chemical Abstracts* if that paper is available any place in the United States. To obtain this service it is necessary for those eligible to purchase special coupons from the Secretary of the American Chemical Society at 1155 16th Street, N.W., Washington, D. C., and to send the coupon (properly filled out) to the U. S. Department of Agriculture Library, Washington 25, D. C., where the work is done. For additional details of this special ACS service, one should consult any current issue of *Chemical Abstracts,* where it is described in the front of the journal.

Many of the libraries on the location list published in the *List of Periodicals Abstracted by Chemical Abstracts* provide microfilm or photocopying services; reference to this list and to Appendix 3 of this book is recommended.

It is often worth while to get a photoprint of a paper or a portion of it even when it is in a library to which one has access to save time and prevent error in copying material.

Sometimes a copy of a paper can be obtained by asking the author for a reprint. Authors' addresses are usually given in abstract journals such as *Chemical Abstracts*.

Obtaining Translations of Papers

Before one has a translation made to order it is well to check the sources given below to find out if the paper has been translated and how to obtain a copy of the translation.

1. Scientific Translations Center, Science Division, Library of Congress, Washington 25, D. C. (established by the U. S. National Science Foundation in 1953). The Library of Congress is publishing a monthly list of translations from Russian newly received at the Center and of translations that are available from commercial agencies. The Library of Congress supplies photocopies of translations on file at the Center. Translations from **Russian only** are available.
2. Special Libraries Association Translation Pool, John Crerar Library, 86 East Randolph Street, Chicago 1, Illinois. These are all technical translations and include translations from all languages **except Russian.**

For translations that are made to order, again see libraries that are on the list printed in the *List of Periodicals Abstracted by Chemical Abstracts* for those which provide this service. The Special Libraries Association Translations Pool also maintains a file of reliable translators for many languages and will furnish names upon request, as will some libraries.

References to the Literature

Difficulty is often encountered in locating a paper to which reference has been made in a bibliography or a footnote of a paper because journals and books vary greatly in their methods of citing references to the periodical literature. Some of the same problems arise too in using abstract journals because they vary in their methods of showing the location of papers in the original journals. Sometimes the abbreviations used for the names of journals cause trouble; sometimes the method of designating the place in the journal where a given paper is to be found is the stumbling block.

Journal names as used in references are usually abbreviated, but the abbreviations do not follow an internationally accepted system. At the present time, as a matter of fact, there is seldom uniformity in journal-name abbreviations even on a national basis. But the situation has improved greatly within the last 35 years; the very high degree of individualism exhibited by authors and editors of chemical papers and books in the matter of journal-name abbreviations up to approximately 1920 has gradually yielded to system. The rapidly growing periodical literature has actually forced editors and authors to pay attention to systematic journal-name abbreviations, and in recent years a good deal of effort has been devoted to standardizing them. At the suggestion of UNESCO, the International Organization for Standardization (the successor, in 1946, to the International Federation of National Standardizing Associations, founded in 1926, which suspended its activities during World War II) is working on the problem, and published a draft of a recommended international code for the abbreviation of the titles of periodicals in 1954.[7]

However, there are three different systems of journal-name abbreviations that have greatly influenced the usage; these are (1) the *Chemical Abstracts* abbreviations for journal names, (2) the *Chemisches Zentralblatt* abbreviations for journal names, and (3) those used in the *World List of Scientific Periodicals*. Reference to the list of periodicals abstracted by each of these journals, which gives the abbreviations of the journal names, and to the *World List of Scientific Periodicals* will clear up many difficulties in identifying journals from the abbreviations used for their names.

Chemical Abstracts has had international circulation for many years and its *List of Periodicals Abstracted* is widely distributed (issued at about five-year intervals in the annual index beginning with 1911); consequently its journal-name abbreviations have been adopted by many for use. Also, the International Union of Pure and Applied Chemistry adopted them in 1922 as an international standard for chemistry; this encouraged the use of the journal-name abbreviations used by *Chemical Abstracts* but has not resulted in universal acceptance of them.

It is difficult to assess the influence that the *Chemisches Zentralblatt* system of journal-name abbreviations has had on general usage, but it is considerable. The list of journals abstracted by *Chemisches Zentralblatt* (*Periodica Chimica*) has not been issued frequently and has not been as widely distributed as the *Chemical Abstracts* list because the *Zentralblatt* list has been issued separately in book form. But *Chemisches Zentralblatt* has also enjoyed international circulation for a long time and chemists who have used it have carried over its methods of citing references to the journals into their own papers and books.

The *World List of Scientific Periodicals* system of journal-name abbreviation has not influenced usage among chemists and scientists in general as much as the *Chemical Abstracts* and the *Zentralblatt* systems have because it has not been as generally used by scientists as the two abstract journals. But the *World List of Scientific Periodicals* is the most comprehensive list available. There is great similarity between the journal-name abbreviations used in the *World List of Scientific Periodicals* and in *Chemisches Zentralblatt* because both systems are based upon one recommended by the International Institute of Intellectual Cooperation. The *World List* is a standard reference list, now in the third edition, and is available in many libraries that do not receive *Chemisches Zentralblatt*.

The farther back one goes in the chemical literature the more difficult it becomes to identify journals from the abbreviations used for their names. To add to the confusion that resulted from a lack of system and standards, it was once a rather common custom to refer to a journal by the name of its current editor. So the older literature references to what seem to be different journals turn out to be a number of references to the same journal edited by different men through a period of time.

Methods of citation, leaving variations in journal names out of the question, also lack standardization and the farther back in the literature one goes the more problems arise. Again the bulk of the scientific literature has forced editors to pay more attention to the problem and an effort is being made to standardize methods of citation. The International Organization for Standardization is also working on this problem and published a draft of an international standard for bibliographic citation and reference in 1954.[7]

The methods that *Chemical Abstracts* and *Chemisches Zentralblatt* use to cite references to the journal literature have had a certain standardizing effect because chemists locate a large part of their information through these abstract journals and have carried over the methods of citation into their own papers and books when compiling bibliographies.

The following examples of variation in methods of citation (variation in journal-name abbreviations not shown) illustrate much of the current and past usage:

1. *Am. J. Sci.* **(5) 3, no. 6,** 378–381 (June 1922), which is series 5, Volume 3, issue number 6, pages 378–381, issued in June 1922.
2. *Am. J. Sci.* **(5) III (6),** 378–381 (1922), which is also series 5, Vol. 3, issue number 6, pages 378–381.
3. *Am. J. Sci.* **3,** 378–381 (1922), which is the volume, pages, and year.
4. *Am. J. Sci.* 1922, **3,** 378–381, which is year, volume, and pages.
5. *Am. J. Sci.* 1922, 378–381, which is year and pages.

The method of citation in example (3) or (4) above is sufficient if the pagination of the journal involved is not started anew with each number as is sometimes the case. Some journals do not have a volume number, the year being used instead. Some journals have more than one series of pages, as the R (Reviews), T (Transactions), and A (Abstracts) series formerly published in the *Journal of the Society of Chemical Industry.* Some periodicals have more than one volume per year. If difficulty is experienced in locating a paper this may be the source of the trouble. With volume and year both given it is usually comparatively easy to find a paper even when a mistake has been made someplace in the reference. There are a few publications that give synchronistic tables for the year and volume of a limited number of chemical periodicals; the most extensive ones being those given by D. H. Horowitz in the *Journal of the Patent Office Society,* Vol. 32, 243–257 (1950), for 38 of the most important chemical journals from 1880 through 1949, and by Dyson [8] whose table covers 68 journals from 1800 to 1951.

ABBREVIATIONS USED IN ABSTRACT JOURNALS

Many abstract journals use a number of word abbreviations in the text of the abstracts. There is usually a key to the system in the annual index of the publication. Also see Appendix 2 of this book.

INDEXES OF JOURNALS

Most journals have annual subject and author indexes. If a year's issue is bound in several parts, the index is usually found in the last part. Some periodicals publish collective indexes. Sometimes collective indexes for a periodical are not purchased by a library, and libraries seldom have a record of existing collective indexes that they do not own. There are two comprehensive, published sources of information on existing periodical indexes:

Ulrich's Periodicals Directory (see p. 151).
Haskell, D. C., *A Check List of Cumulative Indexes to Individual Periodicals in the New York Public Library,* New York, The N. Y. Public Library, 1942, 370 pp.

For more information on indexes and their use see the chapter on Indexes in this book.

LITERATURE CITED

(1) Davis, Watson, *American Documentation* **2**, 7, 8, 11 (1951).
(2) Lamb, A. B., *Chem. Eng. News* **27**, 2841–2844, 2876 (1949).
(3) Peiss, Reuben, *Chem. Eng. News* **28**, 1364–1366 (1950).
(4) Noyes, W. A., *J. Am. Chem. Soc.* **42**, 2101 (1920).
(5) Sosman, J., *Wash. Acad. Sci.* **11**, 80 (1921).
(6) Crane, E. J., *Chem. Eng. News* **31**, 864 (1953).
(7) *Standardization in Documentation,* The Hague, International Organization for Standardization, 1954, 60 pp.
(8) Dyson, G. M., *A Short Guide to Chemical Literature,* London, Longmans, Green, 1951, Appendix III.

CHAPTER 4

PATENTS

||||||||||||||||||||||||||||||||||||||||||||||||||||||

Patents make up an important part of the literature of applied chemistry. They are primary sources of information because an invention must cover new and really useful information to be patentable. Much of the chemical work done in industrial laboratories and a great many of the products of chemists of inventive ability are reported and described in patent form only. Few chemical literature searches with an industrial aspect are complete without examination of this immense field. Effort and money spent in working out processes already covered by patents are obviously wasted, and infringement difficulties are to be avoided. Patents are also frequently the object of search by chemical firms for legal information.

Patents are the major source of information regarding technological advances in chemistry. Keeping up with this literature as patents are issued is the best way to learn the state of modern applied chemistry and the trends in its development. The patent literature is a better source of information on many phases of chemical technology than are either reference books (soon outdated) or papers in scientific and technical journals. It is only occasionally that a book or a paper appears that includes a thorough survey of the existing patent literature of a specific phase of chemistry.

There is a tendency on the part of some to underestimate the value of patents as a source of chemical information. Industrial chemists as a rule understand their importance and do not neglect them. The investigator in pure chemistry cannot afford to neglect the patent literature; it frequently provides useful information that is not available elsewhere.

In this chapter an attempt will be made to answer the questions: Just what kind of information and how much can one expect to get from patents? Where should one look for it? What is the best way to obtain it?

NATURE AND SCOPE OF THE PATENT LITERATURE

The word "patent" is frequently used in a general, descriptive sense without regard to the scope or extent of protected rights. It is usually so used here. In its legal sense the word refers to the grant by some government to the patentee of certain exclusive rights in the invention covered. It is really a contract between the public and the inventor. The terms of the contract are that for a **full disclosure of the invention to the public** the government gives the inventor a monopoly for a limited period, which varies in the different countries (17 years in the United States). The basis for the United States patent system was laid in the Constitution as originally adopted in 1787, which provided that: "The Congress shall have the power . . . **to promote the progress of science and useful arts,** by securing for limited times to authors and inventors the exclusive right to their respective writings and discoveries." The early disclosure of inventions in patents and the stimulation of invention by patent protection are the salient points in "the promotion of the progress of science and useful arts" by the patent system. The boldface type in this paragraph has been used with the purpose of emphasizing the fact that patents are granted primarily for the benefit of the public.

Patent disclosures are supposed to be so full, clear, and exact as to enable anyone skilled in the art to which the invention pertains to make, compound, and use the same. Unfortunately they do not always measure up to this standard. Even though it may properly be considered that a patent is addressed to skilled individuals and is not intended to be a complete statement for the benefit of the general public, which might require a long treatise on the whole science surrounding an invention to understand it, it is still possible to say that disclosures are sometimes inadequate and sometimes misleading. This is the greatest weakness of patents as a part of the chemical literature. Often experimental details are not given sufficiently to enable even the skilled chemist to duplicate patented processes when the patent has expired, at least not without excessive investigation. A patent application sometimes intentionally has the real essence of the invention hidden away in a single inconspicuous paragraph. When a citizen of one country takes out a patent in another, not with the intention of working it in the foreign country but with the object of preventing citizens of that country from manufacturing the patented product, there is a strong temptation to conceal the real invention if possible. Often patents, worded by lawyers, are written in a form that is difficult to strip of legal terminology to get down to facts.

Not infrequently unexpired patents contain disclosures that are not claimed and are therefore public property.

Patents are supposed to be practical. They may be based merely on empirical observations without the underlying principles being understood. The underlying principles are not as such patentable. Patents are continually being issued on subject matter the real nature of which is not understood. Scientific theory or understanding may have little or nothing to do with a case; patent validity is not dependent on them. This constitutes a significant difference between patents in general and the average journal article as sources of chemical information.

On the other hand patents are taken out at times on mere speculation by individuals who wish to pre-empt without the delay or expense of test something that they think will be practical and useful. Such patents are valid only if what they propose actually turns out to be capable of actual use or operation as they allege. Statements in the technical journal literature can more safely be presumed to be based on experiment or experience.

Patents are the source of new and useful information because novelty and utility (seeming utility at least) are essential in the obtaining of a patent on any process or product. The statutes provide that "any person who has invented or discovered any new and useful art, machine, manufacture, or composition of matter, or any new and useful improvement thereof, may obtain a patent therefor." A great many chemical patents are of the "composition of matter" type and accordingly it is pointed out that this phrase, as used in the statutes, covers all compositions of two or more elements or substances, including "all composite articles, whether they be results of chemical union, or of mechanical mixture, or whether they be gases, fluids (liquids), powders or solids." The legal interpretation, as far as patents are concerned, of "invention," "novelty," "utility," "manufacture," etc., requires pages to be stated clearly; it is hardly within the scope of this book to attempt that here. A sufficiently definite notion of just what kind of information one can expect to get from patents is conveyed, it is hoped, without that.

For information on the meaning of chemical patents on "composition of matter" and similar terms mentioned in the paragraph above, see the books on patent law that are listed further on in this chapter.

Chemistry students, for whom this chapter may be an introduction to patents, may get a good idea of the great variety of information that can be obtained from patents by looking at the patent abstracts in recent issues of *Chemical Abstracts*. Patent abstracts are to be found in nearly all of the thirty-three sections.

Like the journal literature the **patent literature is voluminous** and is growing rapidly. Almost every country with any degree of industrial development issues patents and some of them have been issuing them for many years. Chemical patents are increasing in the percentage of the whole number taken out. Fleischer [1] has made a study of the growth of chemical patents and reports that in the United States the chemical patents were 3.2% of the total number issued in 1907–1909, 10% in 1925–1929, and 20.2% in 1945–1948. His study shows a similar growth in other countries. The United States had issued over 2,730,000 patents by January 1, 1956. The British Government has been granting patents since 1617. Among the countries which issue patents, according to White and Ravenscroft,[2] are:

Afghanistan	Ecuador	Israel
Albania	Egypt	Italy
Argentina		
Australia	Federation of	Japan
Austria	Malay States	Jordan
	Finland	
Belgium	France	Lebanon
Bolivia		Liberia
Brazil	Germany (German	Luxemburg
Bulgaria	Federal Republic)	
	Great Britain	Mexico
Canada	Greece	
Ceylon	Guatemala	New Zealand
Chile		Nicaragua
China	Haiti	Norway
Colombia	Holland	
Costa Rica	Honduras	Pakistan
Cuba	Hungary	Panama
Czechoslovakia		Paraguay
	India	Persia (Iran)
Denmark	Iraq	Peru
Dominican Republic	Ireland	Philippines

162 PATENTS

Poland	South West Africa	United States
Portugal	Spain	Uruguay
	Sweden	
Rhodesia	Switzerland	Venezuela
Rumania	Syria	Vietnam
Salvador, El	Turkey	Yugoslavia
South African Union		

For a complete listing see White and Ravenscroft's book, which is loose-leaf and is kept up to date by issuing new pages.

Russia still has a patent law but all inventions that are made by employees of the state are excluded. Consequently, Russia seldom issues a patent now. Russian scientists may obtain a certificate of invention. For a discussion of the Soviet patent law see Tolpin [3] and Prince. [4]

Patents of the same invention are frequently taken out in more than one country. It is pretty safe to assume that a citizen of any patent-issuing country will apply for a patent in his own country first, but issuance more promptly in another may mean that the disclosure will be made there at an earlier date. Most inventions of practical value patented in the lesser industrial countries are later patented also in one or more of the major countries (United States, Great Britain, Germany, or France). More inventions are made in the United States, Great Britain, Germany, France, Switzerland, and Japan than in all of the other countries put together.

Internationalization of patents has been proposed on several occasions, but the only accomplishment that has even approached that in nature is the agreement known as the International Convention for the Protection of Industrial Property, which has been entered into by most of the industrially important countries. According to it, if more than one application for the same invention is made in a given country, preference is given to the one with earliest filing date in any of the subscribing countries, provided the first application was not more than a year old at the time of the later application.

THE SOURCES OF PATENT INFORMATION

These may be classified as follows:

(1) The original specifications.
(2) Official patent office publications.
(3) Scientific and technical journals.
(4) Patent digests and lists.

(5) Court records.
(6) Publications on patent law and practice.
(7) Periodicals devoted to patents.
(8) Miscellaneous.

Original Specifications

The standard form of patent specifications, both domestic and foreign, is: (1) the heading, which includes the name and address of the patentee or patentees, the assignee and the address thereof, the patent number, the date of application, the serial number, and the title of the invention, (2) a brief statement of the general nature or objects of the invention, (3) an explanation of the drawings reproduced, if any, (4) a specific, detailed description of one or more ways of embodying and carrying out the invention, and (5) one or more claims that define concisely and comprehensively the invention covered by the patent.

It is to be noted that patent titles often fail to indicate the content of the patents in a precise manner. They are often too general, as "Electrolysis" when the patent is on a means of electroplating with nickel, and sometimes they are misleading.

In examining a patent for chemical information the description (4), including the examples, is the section to be read carefully; it gives the new technical information.

The countries listed below issue printed copies of complete patent specifications.

Australia	Germany	Pakistan
Austria	Great Britain	Philippines
Belgium	Holland	Russia
Canada	Hungary	Sweden
Czechoslovakia	Ireland	Switzerland
Denmark	Italy	United States
Egypt	Japan	Yugoslavia
Finland	Mexico	
France	Norway	

Canada has provided printed patents only since January 1, 1949, and Belgium since January 1, 1950. Copies of patents issued in Canada and Belgium before these dates may be obtained as photoprints. Many of the other countries that issue patents will supply photoprint copies, the charge for which varies considerably.

In addition to the full specifications it is possible at the United States Patent Office in Washington, D. C., to examine, in the case of U. S. patents, files of the various Patent Office proceedings leading up to patent grants, including the original application papers and amendments thereto, and the official communications of the examiners in which reference is made to prior patents and published statements considered relevant by the examiners. Records of interference proceedings in which U. S. patents may have been involved are likewise available at the Patent Office. In these proceedings one may find lists of prior patents and published statements relating to the same subject matter as the patent under investigation, and at times testimony of interest. If desired, copies of foreign patent applications can usually be obtained from the patent offices of the principal countries.

Since 1947 the full specifications of a United States patent include the references cited in the file of the patent (this file is made in the patent office during the proceedings that lead up to a patent grant); these references are to U. S. and foreign patents, to books, and to papers in periodicals and correspond to the literature cited at the ends of papers in periodicals.

In certain countries, of which Germany is a noteworthy example, patent applications are thrown open to inspection by the public for a certain period before a patent is actually granted upon them for the purpose of offering an opportunity for any interested parties to file an "opposition" proceeding, in which the opponent is privileged to call to the attention of the Patent Office any reasons that he may regard as constituting a proper and legal bar to the issuance of a patent as sought in the application. This is in contrast to the practice in the United States, where patent applications are, as a general rule, maintained in secrecy by the Patent Office up to the time the patent is actually issued.

A number of libraries in the United States maintain complete files of United States patents. In most cases the specifications are found in order of patent numbers. Other libraries have substantially complete sets of United States patents. The libraries named below have complete sets.

California: Public Library, Los Angeles.
Colorado: Public Library, Denver.
Georgia: Georgia Institute of Technology, Atlanta.
Illinois: Public Library, Chicago.
Massachusetts: Public Library, Boston.
Michigan: Public Library, Detroit.
Minnesota: Public Library, Minneapolis.

Missouri:
  Linda Hall Library, Kansas City.
  Public Library, St. Louis.
New Jersey: Public Library, Newark.
New York:
  University of State of New York, Albany.
  Grosvenor Library, Buffalo.
  Public Library, New York City.
Ohio:
  Public Library, Cincinnati.
  Public Library, Cleveland.
  Public Library, Toledo.
  The Ohio State University Library, Columbus.
Pennsylvania:
  Carnegie Library, Pittsburgh.
  Franklin Institute, Philadelphia.
Rhode Island: Public Library, Providence.
Wisconsin:
  State Historical Society of Wisconsin, Madison.
  Public Library, Milwaukee.

Some of the larger libraries have sets of the patents of certain of the more industrially important foreign countries. The collection at the New York Public Library, New York City, is outstanding; it is the second best in the United States and is excelled only by that of the library of the U. S. Patent Office.

The United States Patent Office, Washington, D. C., is the place in our country where patent searching facilities are best. In fact, it has the only library in the United States where it is practical to attempt a thorough search of foreign patents. Fleischer [5] gives much useful information on the foreign patents available there and on the aids provided for searching foreign patents. There, in addition to U. S. patents, files of complete patent specifications are maintained for the following countries at the present time:

Australia	Germany	Norway
Austria	Great Britain	Philippines
Belgium	Holland (Netherlands)	Poland
Czechoslovakia	Hungary	Russia (up to 1927)
Canada	Italy	Sweden
Denmark	India	Switzerland
Finland	Ireland	Yugoslavia
France	Japan	

The patents in these sets are arranged numerically. Duplicate sets are available with the patents classified in accordance with the official systems of the respective countries for Austrian, British, Danish, French, German, Norwegian, Swedish, and Swiss patents.

Abstracts of patents are received at the Patent Office from Belgium, Canada, Finland, and New Zealand.

Anyone interested in the files of foreign patents that are maintained at the U. S. Patent Office Library should consult the book by Severance[6] for further information. He gives very complete information up to 1935. The *Official Gazette of the United States Patent Office* now gives (quarterly) a list of the names of the countries from which the Library receives patents together with the highest number of the patents received from each.

To facilitate searches patents are classified. The classification systems of the various countries differ in most cases. The United States, British, French, German, and Swiss classifications differ greatly from one another. Swedish, Norwegian, and Danish patents are classified according to the German system, which is regarded as excellent. The Austrian classification is only slightly different from the German. All classification systems naturally have limitations. The field covered is broad and different kinds of patent searches involve different points of view. The French classification is considered the least satisfactory.

The classification system for U. S. patents is outlined in the U. S. Patent Office *Manual of Classification of Patents and Index to Classification;* the 1949 edition of this is in loose-leaf form and is kept up to date by replacement pages that are issued to subscribers. A new edition of this manual is published occasionally. The system of classification has been undergoing revision continuously ever since 1898. It is necessary to use the *Definitions of Revised Classes and Subclasses* and the *Classification Bulletins of the U. S. Patent Office* in conjunction with the *Manual.* These are all sold by the Superintendent of Documents, Government Printing Office, Washington, D. C.

For U. S. patents there are 70 examining divisions, over 300 classes, and over 45,000 subclasses. About 30 of the divisions include chemical patents. From the point of view of the chemist the U. S. patent classification is far from satisfactory.

The U. S. Patent Office has translated the outline[7] of the 2nd edition (1910) of the German patent classification, which is now in the 6th edition (1949); *Gruppeneinteilung der Patentklassen,* 6th ed., Berlin, Albert Nauk. This office also has a copy of the *Official Classification of the British Patent Office* (London, H.M. Stationery Office, 1927–1932), and one of *Key to the Classifications of Patent Specifications of France, Germany, Austria, Netherlands, Norway,*

SOURCES OF PATENT INFORMATION   167

Denmark, Sweden, and Switzerland, which was published by the
British Patent Office (2nd ed., 1905, 3rd ed., 1915).

U. S. patent specifications are available at the Patent Office (1) in
the Search Room, arranged according to the official classification
(with cross references), (2) in the adjacent hall, arranged numerically,
and (3) in the examining divisions (by permission), arranged in
general according to the official classification but with departures in
the form of unofficial reclassifications made in some instances by the
examiners for classes of patents never officially reclassified and the
official system for which is unsatisfactory, and in the form of further
subdivision of official classes. The examiners also have introduced
cross references and have made digests of patents and other literature along the lines of their work. The examining divisions also
have sets of various foreign patents relating to their subjects classified in the same way as their U. S. patents. For more information
on the facilities for searching both domestic and foreign patents at
the U. S. Patent Office, see Fleischer's papers [5, 8] and Lindenmeyer's
paper.[14]

Official Patent Office Publications

The patent offices of most of the countries publish official journals
in which the patents and trade marks issued are reported in brief
form. Sometimes the patents and trade marks are reported in separate publications. The following list, originally compiled by Julian
F. Smith [9] and here brought up to date, gives those publications that
are current. With very few exceptions they give abstracts of patent
specifications.

Argentina:	*Patentes de Invención y Marcas de Fábrica, Co-mercio y Agricultura.* 1904– .
Australia:	*Australian Official Journal of Patents, Trade Marks and Designs.* 1899– .
Austria:	*Oesterreichisches Patentblatt.* 1899– .
Belgium:	*Recueil des brevets d'invention.* 1854– .
Bolivia:	*Boletin departmental,* which was continued after 1939 by *Revista industrial.*
Brazil:	*Diario Official.*
Canada:	*Canadian Patent Office Record and Register of Copyrights and Trade Marks.* 1873– .
Chile:	*Industria (Santiago), Boletin de la Sociedad de Fomento Fabril.*
Cuba:	*Boletin oficial de la propiedad industrial.*
Czechoslovakia:	*Patentri Vestnik.*
Denmark:	*Dansk Patenttidende.* 1894– .

168 PATENTS

Egypt:	*Recueil égyptien périodique de la propriété industrielle.*
Finland:	*Suomen patenttireksteri.*
France:	*Bulletin official de la propriété industrielle et commerciale.* 1828– .
Germany:	*Patentblatte.* 1880– . *Aüszüge aus den Patentschriften.* 1887– .
Great Britain:	*Abridgments of Specifications* (1617–) and *Official Journal (Patents).* 1854– .
Greece:	*Episēmon deltion biomechanikes idioktēsias (Official bulletin of industrial property).*
Hungary:	*Szabadalmi közlöny es központi vedjigirtesitö.*
India:	*Patent Office Journal* and the *Gazette of India.*
Ireland:	*Official Journal of Industrial and Commercial Property.*
Italy:.	*Bolletino dei brevetti per invenzione, modelli e marchi* and *Il Monitore industrial.*
Japan:	*Tokkyo Koho (Official Patent Reports).*
Mexico:	*Gaceta de la propiedad industrial.*
Netherlands:	*Octrooiraad Nederland* and *Bijblad bij industrieele eigendom.*
New Zealand:	*Patent Office Journal.*
Norway:	*Norske Tidende for det industrielle Rettsvern.*
Pakistan:	*Gazette of Pakistan.*
Peru:	*Registro Official de Fomento.*
Poland:	*Wiadomości Urzedu patentowego.*
Portugal:	*Boletin da propriedade industrial, Appendice ao Diário do Governo.*
Russia:	*Byulleten Byuro Ekspertizy i Registratsü Izobretenii Gosplana* SSSR.
Spain:	*Boletin oficial de la propiedad industrial* and *Nucleo* (Madrid).
Sweden:	*Svensk Tidskrift för Industriellt Rättsskydd.*
Switzerland:	*Patent-liste.* 1890– .
Turkey:	*Resmi sinai mulkiyet gazeteu (Official gazette of industrial property).*
Union of South Africa:	*Official Journal of Patents, Trade Marks, Designs and Copyrights.*
United States:	*Official Gazette.* 1872– .
Venezuela:	*Boletin de la propiedad industrial y comercial.*

The New York Public Library, New York City, published (1954) a booklet, *Patent and Trade Mark Publications,* which is an annotated list of these publications in their extensive collection. The library of the United States Patent Office receives all of the patent office journals; the New York Public Library collection is the second best; and a number of other libraries in the United States receive some of them. For addresses of the various patent offices, see the latest January 10th issue of *Chemical Abstracts* (in the front under the heading "Patents") and White and Ravenscroft,[2] which is a looseleaf book and is kept up to date; no information on subscription rates is given here. Patent office journals can be obtained by subscription in most cases, either directly from the respective patent offices or through dealers in periodicals.

The *Official Gazette of the United States Patent Office*, which has been issued weekly since the beginning of 1872, is devoted mostly to brief reports on patents issued, the patent heading being followed by one or more typical claims and a selected figure if the patent is accompanied by drawings. The heading includes the class and subclass number. The *Official Gazette* also contains reports on trade marks, designs, labels and prints, and selected decisions rendered in patent, trade mark, etc. cases by the Commissioner of Patents, the Court of Appeals of the District of Columbia, the United States Supreme and other courts, and occasional opinions of the Attorney-General concerning such cases. In each number there is an alphabetical list of patentees and a "list of inventions arranged in accordance with the first significant character or word of the name" (title); also, a numerical list of patents arranged by classes and subclasses is given. In recent years the *Official Gazette* has published brief descriptions of patent applications for which patents are not to be granted; *Chemical Abstracts* publishes abstracts of these and sometimes they contain useful information. Since July 1, 1952, the brief reports on patents issued have been classified into three groups: (1) General and Mechanical, (2) Chemical, and (3) Electrical. This makes it easier and quicker to use the *Gazette*. The Superintendent of Documents, Government Printing Office, Washington, D. C., handles the subscriptions. The *Gazette* is widely distributed. There is a large free list, including, by act of Congress in 1895, "one copy to eight such public libraries having over 1,000 volumes, exclusive of Government publications, as shall be designated by each Senator, Representative, and Delegate in Congress."

There is an annual index of U. S. patents, formerly published as the larger part of the *Annual Report of the Commissioner of Patents*, but starting with 1920 issued separately under the title "Index of Patents," which contains entries, arranged separately, for patentees (assignees are included) and for subjects, similar to those mentioned in the preceding paragraph as occurring in the individual numbers of the *Gazette*. The so-called "alphabetical list of inventions," being based entirely on patent titles, and being compiled merely by the

selection of the word considered most prominent, does not serve as
a satisfactory subject index. The "Index" is supplied without extra
charge to those who receive the *Gazette*.

The United States Patent Office, Washington 25, D. C., issues a
free pamphlet called *General Information Concerning Patents*. It is
very useful and, among other information, lists all of the publications
of the Patent Office. There are a number of these publications that
are needed by those who are concerned with patent law, rules of
practice of the U. S. Patent Office, a roster of attorneys and agents
registered to practice before the U. S. Patent Office, and other matters
that are beyond the scope of this book.

The Official Journal (Patents), published weekly by the British
Patent Office, contains good abstracts, often with illustrations, of all
British patents together with lists of applications filed and of patents
granted. The patent abridgments are arranged numerically. This
journal is obtainable from the Patent Office, London. There is an
annual *Index to Names of Applicants*, a *Quarterly Subject-Matter
Index of Accepted Complete Specifications*, and an annual subject
index (both annual indexes have appeared since 1853).

The searching of British patents is very greatly facilitated by
reason of the fact that the British Patent Office has published carefully classified abridgments of all patents granted since the British
patent system was started in 1617. In separate volumes one will
find all of the patents for a considerable period of years on the subjects of each of the many classes. For example, the abridgments
of all British patents issued between 1622 and 1866 relating to "acids,
alkalis, oxides, and salts" are in a single volume. The system of
classified abridgments was changed in 1855, and for the period 1855
to 1908 there are 146 volumes (because of that many classes) for each
of nine consecutive periods. Starting with 1909 the abridgments
have been classified in 271 volumes for the periods 1909–1915 and
1916–1930. Abridgments are now arranged in 40 groups. Completed
volumes are to be had for some of these, and any that are not complete, as well as future volumes, can be obtained sheet by sheet as
ready for distribution from the British Patent Office. These classes
are not subdivided but each class is provided with periodic sets of
"index headings," under which there are entries for kindred patents
from a wide variety of bases of similarity.

There have been published for British patents an index of names
for the period 1617–1852, a subject index for the same period, a

numerical index for each of the years from 1901 to 1916, and a list of patents in force annually from 1917 to date.

A 50-year subject index of British patents for the period 1861 to 1910 in 271 volumes corresponds to the *Illustrated Abridgment Classes.* A subject index of British patent specifications for the period 1939–1953 was made on microfilm by the British Patent Office in 1953. See *Nature* **172,** 103 (1953) for more information.

The German *Patentblatt,* a weekly, has a supplement, *Auszüge aus den Patentschriften,* which contains illustrated abstracts of German patents similar to those in the U. S. and British publications except that they are arranged according to the German classification instead of by numbers. The only index in the *Auszüge* is the chronological list of classes and subclasses, the patents in each in the number involved being noted. The annual index (*Verzeichnis erteilten Patente*) is divided into five sections, as follows: (1) a chronological list of patent numbers, which shows the class in which each patent has been placed; (2) a chronological list of classes and subclasses, which shows the distribution of the patents; (3) an alphabetical index of patentees; (4) an alphabetical subject index; and (5) an index of patents in effect at the time, arranged (*a*) according to classes and (*b*) according to numbers. The *Patentblatt* suspended publication from 1945 to 1950, and *Auszüge aus den Patentschriften* was suspended from 1945 to 1953.

German patents are frequently referred to in the literature as D.R.P., which is an abbreviation for Deutsches Reichs-Patent.

A description of the other official patent office journals would be close to a repetition of the preceding paragraphs with names changed. The best source of information on the publications of foreign patent offices and how to use them is Severance's *Manual.*[6]

Scientific and Technical Journals

The chemical journals provide a large amount of information on patents. Most of the abstract journals in the chemical field publish abstracts of patents; some of them endeavor to cover the patent literature as fully as the journal literature. The journals that do not have abstract sections, particularly those dealing with applied chemistry, often publish lists of patent applications or of patents issued. Some of these journals publish both abstracts and lists; *Chimie et industrie* (France) is one of them.

Of the journals publishing abstracts of chemical patents the following deserve special comment.

Chemical Abstracts has abstracted the chemical patents of the principal industrial countries of the world ever since it started publication in 1907. It now abstracts the chemical patents of these countries: Australia, Austria, Belgium, Canada, Denmark, France, Germany, Great Britain, Hungary, India, Italy, Japan, Netherlands, Norway, Spain, Sweden, Switzerland, and the United States. Many of these have been covered ever since 1907; others were added to the list as their chemical industries developed. Japan was added in 1917 and *Chemical Abstracts* is the only abstract journal that covers Japanese patents.

Chemical manufacturers or citizens of countries that are not on the *Chemical Abstracts* list frequently take out patents in the United States, Great Britain, Germany, or France in addition to their own countries. Consequently, *Chemical Abstracts* coverage is wider than it appears on the surface because it has always tried to abstract all of the chemical patents issued in these four countries.

The thoroughness with which *Chemical Abstracts* has covered foreign patents varied a little during the earlier years of this journal. All French, German, and Swiss patents that were issued during and immediately after World War I were not abstracted. Part of those missed during this period are covered by *Chemisches Zentralblatt*. A few times financial limitations made it necessary to curtail patent abstracting for foreign countries. Many Russian patents were abstracted but these could not always be obtained. However, Fleischer,[1] a patent specialist who has made a study of the completeness of the coverage of chemical patents of the world by the major abstract journals for the period 1907–1948, concludes that while *Chemical Abstracts* is "not ideal," it has the best coverage to be found anywhere. He also states that *"Chemical Abstracts* has provided remarkably thorough and reliable coverage of United States chemical patents ever since 1907."

Chemical Abstracts indicates whether a patent is equivalent to to one issued and abstracted previously; this saves much time in patent searches in the case of an invention that is patented in several different countries. It does this by giving the patent number and title and a reference to a previous abstract. Beginning with 1945, the abstracts of chemical patents in *Chemical Abstracts* give more detail than earlier and are prepared, for the most part, by chemists who are specialists in the given field. *Chemical Abstracts* has given the class numbers of German and Swiss patents in recent years because locating the complete specifications in libraries is difficult without this help. The subject indexing has received special attention, and there are annual and collective patent number indexes that are classified by country. Those who use *Chemical Abstracts* to locate patents should read the comments on patents at the beginning of the latest January 10th issue.

Chemisches Zentralblatt, 1830–   , has published abstracts of German patents for a long time, but did not cover these completely up to 1919. Before 1919 mostly German patents on organic compounds, medicinals, and dyes were abstracted. Since 1919, when the expansion of *Chemisches Zentralblatt* to cover industrial chemistry occurred, it has endeavored to abstract the chemical patents of the principal countries of the world. It has not always abstracted patents from the same countries as *Chemical Abstracts* has done, or with the same degree of thoroughness. The two sets of abstracts sometimes supplement each other to some extent.

The numerical patent indexes of *Chemisches Zentralblatt*, published since 1897, give tables of equivalent patents up to 1945. Since then reference to equivalent patents is made in the abstracts.

Zeitschrift für angewandte Chemie, 1887–   , published abstracts of patents and patent applications, mainly German, until its abstract section was discontinued at the end of 1918, this applied chemistry abstract service being taken over by *Chemisches Zentralblatt* at that time. The abstracts were unusually long in the earlier volumes. Starting with 1890 the German patents have been indexed by numbers and the patent applications listed in accordance with the official German patent classification system.

Chemiker-Zeitung has published abstracts of the patents of the principal countries of the world ever since 1882, but only German chemical patents are covered with any approach to completeness. All of the patent abstracts have been indexed numerically since 1908.

Jahresbericht über die Leistungen der chemischen Technologie publishes an annual numerical index of the German patents which it has covered from 1887 to date.

The Journal of Applied Chemistry, 1954–   , publishes a large number of patent abstracts in its abstract section. It covers the chemical patents of the principal industrial countries, including Great Britain. It is published by the *Society of Chemical Industry* (London) and continues the patent coverage that was formerly provided by *British Abstracts* (see below).

British Abstracts (1926–1953) undertook to abstract the chemical patents of the principal industrial countries of the world and did so with considerable thoroughness. *British Abstracts* did not always abstract patents from the same countries as did *Chemical Abstracts*, so it supplements *Chemical Abstracts* during 1926–1953. There are numerical patent indexes.

The Journal of the Society of Chemical Industry is a particularly good source of chemical patent information for the period 1882–1925. The abstracts are good and comparatively full. The field was covered with considerable thoroughness. The countries whose patents were covered are: England, United States, France, and Germany. Names of assignees as well as those of patentees are given and also application dates as well as dates of issue. Annual patent number indexes of British patents were published from 1901 to 1925 and of the abstracted patents of the other countries from 1916 to 1925. In this and the other journals the patent abstracts are of course covered by the author and subject indexes, the letter "P" being used in some journals following entries to denote "Patent." The publication of abstracts in the *Journal of the Society of Chemical Industry* was discontinued when *British Abstracts* was started in 1926.

The Journal of the Chemical Society (London) published a limited number of abstracts of patents, mainly in the field of organic chemistry, from 1871 to 1925. The abstracts are very good. Numerical indexes were first published in 1913.

Chimie et industrie, 1919–   , publishes good abstracts of patents. The countries whose chemical patents are covered with considerable thoroughness are France, United States, Great Britain, Germany, Norway, and Sweden. This journal is recommended for abstracts of French patents in particular. There are no numerical patent indexes and the subject indexes are not very full.

Moniteur scientifique de Docteur Quesneville has an abstract section devoted to patents. The patents of various countries have been covered. This journal is not recommended for patent searching except that it may be used, as a last resort, as a source of information regarding French patents. It was combined with *Revue de chimie industrielle* in 1927.

Referativnyi Zhurnal, Khimiya, the new chemical abstract journal of the USSR, is abstracting the chemical patents of several countries. What its coverage will be remains to be seen.

The journals that are devoted to specific branches of chemistry or to specific chemical industries and that publish abstracts or have abstract sections frequently include abstracts of patents. These specialized abstracts often cover patents that are not strictly chemical, but are useful in the industry. They often give a fuller abstract than is found in the general abstract journals. These specialized abstract services cover their fields with varying degrees of thoroughness and, on the whole, should be regarded as supplements to the major abstract journals which endeavor to cover the chemical patents of the world as thoroughly as possible. See "Abstracts for Specific Branches of Chemistry," pages 140–150. See also the bibliography of periodicals and books by von Hohenhoff [10] and the paper by Fleischer [5] for more information on these patent abstracts. Some of the journals which provide such abstracts in special fields are:

American Dyestuff Reporter.
British Journal of Photography.
Eastman Kodak Co. Monthly Abstract Journal.
International Sugar Journal (England).
Journal of the American Ceramic Society.
Journal of the American Leather Chemists Association.
Journal of the Institute of Petroleum (England).
Journal of the Society of Dyers and Colourists (England).
Journal of the Society of Glass Technology (England).
Journal of the Textile Institute (England).
Kolloid Zeitschrift (Germany).
Petroleum Refiner (United States).
Transactions of the Ceramic Society (England).
Zeitschrift für Metallkunde (Germany).

Patent Digests and Lists

The number of digests of patents on specific subjects and of other patent compilations calculated to be helpful in patent searches is small. Many of them are German publications and are often based on German patents only. When these German works include patents of other countries they are often less thorough. Several of these patent digests and other sources of lists of patents are given below:

Bräuer, A., and D'Ans, J. (eds.), *Fortschritte in der anorganisch-chemischen Industrie an Hand der deutschen Reichspatente dargestellt*, 5 vols., Berlin, Springer 1921–1939. This covers inorganic chemistry for the period 1877 to 1938.

Doyle's Digest of Patents Relating to Coal Tar Dyes and Allied Compounds, New York, Chemical Pub. Co., 1926, covers all patents on dyestuffs and intermediates issued up to 1924. The patents are classified in 24 groups. Useful indexes are included.

Faust, O., *Celluloseverbindungen*, 2 vols., Berlin, Springer, 1935. Includes patents of many countries.

Friedländer, P., *Fortschritte der Teerfarbenfabrikation und verwandter Industriezweige*, Berlin, Springer, 1888–1942. Twenty-six volumes of this work, which covers the patent literature from 1877 to about 1940, have appeared. H. E. Fierz-David compiled the last few volumes. This publication covers German patents thoroughly and some of those of other countries (mostly French, British, and United States) in the field of synthetic coal tar chemistry, including intermediates, dyes, medicinal compounds, and perfumes. The patents are classified and after a general discussion of each class the full text of accepted patents and the claims of patent applications are reproduced. References to foreign patents are numerous. Each volume includes numerical, patentee, and subject indexes. The patent applications have a separate number list. Beginning with Vol. IV (1894–1897) the numerical index to the accepted patents is cumulative in each volume. Beginning with Vol. V (1897–1900) the cumulative numerical index is followed by number lists of French, British and United States patents cited.

Houben, J., *Fortschritte der Heilstoffchemie*, Berlin, de Gruyter, 1926–1939. The first division of this work (six volumes) covers the German patent literature on medicinal and pharmaceutical chemistry for the period 1877 to 1928. The second division of the work is an index to journal literature.

Lange's *Die Zwischenprodukte der Teerfarbenfabrikation*, Leipzig, 1920, contains a brief summary of the patented methods (German patents only) for making aromatic intermediates. The arrangement is systematic.

A digest of old United States patents of chemical interest was published in the Census Bulletin No. 210, published in 1902. This same list of chemical patents granted prior to 1902 was also published as an appendix to *Census Reports*, Vol. 10, Twelfth Census of the United States, Manufacturers, Part 4, Special Reports on Selected Industries.

Loesche, A., *Patentregister der Jahresberichte über die Leistungen der chemischen Technologie*, Leipzig, Johann Ambrosius Barth, is a collective index to the patents recorded in the *Jahresberichte* for the period 1877 (the year in which the German Patent Office was founded) to 1924.

Reference works often include a number of patents among their citations of the literature. Among those reference works described in Chapter 2, these are useful to those interested in patents:

Abegg and Auerbach's *Handbuch der anorganischen Chemie*.
Beilstein's *Handbuch der organischen Chemie*.
Elsevier's *Encyclopaedia of Organic Chemistry*.
Frémy's *Encyclopédie chimique*.
Gmelin's *Handbuch der anorganischen Chemie*.
Kirk and Othmer's *Encyclopedia of Chemical Technology*.
Mellor's *Treatise on Inorganic and Theoretical Chemistry*.
Pascal's *Traité de chimie minérale*.
Thorpe's *Dictionary of Applied Chemistry*.
Ullmann's *Enzykopaedie der technischen Chemie*.
Watt's *Dictionary of Chemistry*.
Watt's translation of Gmelin's *Handbook of Inorganic Chemistry*.
Wurtz's *Dictionnaire de chimie pure et appliquée*.

Repertorium der technischen Journal-Literatur, 1823–1909, was an official publication of the German Patent Office from 1877 to 1909, when it was taken over by a private organization and published for a few years under the name *Fortschritte der Technik*. See page 285 for a description.

The unofficial examiner's lists of patents at the United States Patent Office are helpful in searches. These are available only at the Patent Office.

Winther, A., *Zusammenstellung der Patente auf dem Gebeite der organischen Chemie*, 3 vols., Giessen, Germany, Topelmann, 1908–1910. The first volume contains digests, classified by subjects, of the German patents and patent applications of the period 1877 to 1905 that relate to organic compounds other than dyes. The second volume covers German patents on dyes for the same period, the abstracts being classified according to dye classes. The third volume is the index volume and it contains (1) a numerical list of German patents relating to organic chemistry, with the corresponding U. S., British, French, Austrian, and Russian patent numbers, if any; (2) separate lists of U. S., British, French, Austrian, and Russian patents relating to organic chemistry for the period 1895 to 1908, in which are given the number, date, name of patentee, and subject of the corresponding German patents, if any; (3) and index of patentees; (4) a subject index; and (5) a useful list of trade names with information as to the chemical composition of the products and the manufacturer, as well as patent or other literature citations.

Worden, E. C., *Chemical Patents Index*, New York, Chemical Catalog Co., 5 vols. This work covers United States patents for the period 1915–1924 inclusive. Over 390,000 patents are covered.

Many books on specific subjects in chemistry give patents among their references, and occasionally one covers the patent literature very thoroughly. Some of them will be found in the bibliography of Fleischer's paper [5] and a large number of the older books will be found in von Hohenhoff's bibliography.[10] Locating a book that gives a large number of patent references is often very time consuming; sometimes the publishers' catalogs give information on this point and book reviews often mention it.

Court Records

Information of value may also be obtained at times from court records of patent cases. Extensive searches are usually made when such litigation is being conducted and the pertinent findings are made a part of the case record. The *Official Gazette* of the United States Patent Office gives brief reports on selected decisions rendered in patent cases by the Commissioner of Patents, the Court of Appeals of the District of Columbia, the United States Supreme Court and other courts, and occasional opinions of the Attorney-General concerning such cases. Some useful sources of legal decisions on patents are:

Court of Customs and Patent Appeals, Reports of the Patent Section, Washington, D. C.
Decisions of the Commissioner of Patents, Government Printing Office, Washington, D. C.
The Federal Reporter, published monthly by The West Publishing Co., St. Paul, Minn. Series F (1) and Series F (2).
U. S. Supreme Court, Law Edition, published by the Lawyer's Cooperative Publishing Co., Rochester, New York.
U. S. Supreme Court (*Reports for Patent, Copyright and Trade Mark Cases*), Banks Law Publishing Co., New York, N. Y.
U. S. Patent Quarterly, published by the Bureau of National Affairs, Inc., Washington, D. C.

Publications on Patent Law and Practice

These books and papers may often supply information needed by chemists:

(1) Amudur, L. H., *Patent Office Rules and Practice*, New York, Clark Boardman, 1949 (looseleaf and kept up to date).
(2) Biesterfeld, C. H., *Patent Law for Lawyers, Students, Chemists, and Engineers*, New York, Wiley, 1949, 2nd ed.
(3) Calvert, Robert, *Patent Practice and Management for Investors and Executives*, New York, Reinhold, 1950, 371 pp. See also Calvert's article in the *Encyclopedia of Chemical Technology*, Vol. 5, 868–890 pp.
(4) Deller, A. W., *Walker on Patents*, New York, Baker Voorhis & Co., 1934. Annual cumulative supplements keep it up to date.

(5) Hill, S. B., Select List of Works on Patent, Trade-mark and Copyright Law, *Record* **3:** 158–165, April 1948 (a publication of the Association of the Bar of New York City).

(6) Hoar, R. S., *Patent Tactics and Law*, New York, Ronald Press, 1950.

(7) Norwig, E. A., "Bibliography of Articles on Patent Law," *J. Patent Office Soc.* **21,** 463–484 (1939); **32,** 44–69 (1950). These cover the period 1929–1948.

(8) Patterson, R. J., "Inventions in the Chemical Field," *J. Patent Office Soc.* **37,** 8–37 (1955).

(9) Payne, N. M., "Patent Terms in Some Languages Other Than English," *J. Chem. Educ.* **25,** 389–390 (1948).

(10) Rhodes, F. H., *Elements of Patent Law*, Ithaca, Cornell Univ. Press, 1949.

(11) Rivise, C. W., and Caesar, A. D., *Patentability and Validity*, Charlottesville, Va., Michie, 1936.

(12) Rossman, J., *Law of Patents for Chemists*, 2nd ed., Washington, D. C., Inventors Pub. Co., 1934.

(13) Severance, B., *Manual of Foreign Patents*, Washington, D. C., Patent Office Society, 1935.

(14) Stringham, E., *Outline of Patent Law and Guide to Digests*, Madison, Wisc., Pacot Pub., 1937.

(15) Thomas, E., *Chemical Inventions and Chemical Patents*, New York, Clark Boardman, 1950.

(16) Toulmin, H. A., *Patent Law for the Executive and Engineer*, 2nd ed., Dayton, Ohio, Research Press, 1948.

(17a) *United States Patent Office, Patent Laws*, new editions issued frequently.

(17b) *United States Patent Office Rules of Practice*, new editions issued frequently.

(17c) *United States Patent Office Manual of Patent Examining Procedure*, 1949. All three of these publications are distributed by the U. S. Government Printing Office, Washington, D. C.

(18) Vojacek, J., *Survey of the Principal National Patent Systems*, New York, Prentice-Hall, 1936.

(19) White, W. W., and Ravenscroft, B. G., *Patents Throughout the World*, New York, Trade Activities, 1948, 2nd ed. (looseleaf, kept up to date by issue of replacement sheets). This is a very useful publication that gives brief digests of the patent laws of all of the countries of the world.

(20) Wise, J. K., *Patent Law in the Research Laboratory*, New York, Reinhold, 1955, 155 pp.

Periodicals Devoted to Patents

There are several periodicals that deal wholly or in part with patents. Three such journals published in the United States are:

Journal of the Patent Office Society (Washington, D. C.).

Patent and Trade-Mark Review (New York).

Research, Patents, and Trade Marks (New York).

The Journal of the Patent Office Society is a monthly and was started in September, 1918. It is controlled and published by employees of the technical examining force of the Patent Office. It consists mainly of articles of legal, scientific, and historical interest with reference to patents and trade-marks, and contains current information concerning Patent Office and court procedure. It also lists and reviews books on patents and patent law.

Patent and Trade-Mark Review is also a "monthly authority on foreign patent and trade-mark law." It has been appearing since 1902.

Research, Patents, and Trade Marks (formerly the *International Bulletin of Industrial Property*), 1947– , has international coverage and gives more detailed information than does the *Patent and Trade-Mark Review.*

Of interest because of international coverage are: *Dessins et modèles internationaux,* which is published by the International Bureau for the Protection of Industrial Property, Bern, Switzerland, and *Revue internationale de la propriété industrielle et artistique,* which is published in Paris.

The Index to Legal Periodicals, 1908– , is published by Wilson Co., New York. It is good for locating papers on patents and patent law.

Miscellaneous

Fleischer's papers [5,8] contain much useful information on patents and patent searching. A useful discussion of patents and patent literature from the British point of view is found in Roberts' book.[11] Those who are inexperienced in understanding patents will find the comments in Fleischer's paper [8] and in those by Hill [12] and by Frankel [13] particularly helpful.

SCIENTIFIC LIBRARY OF THE UNITED STATES PATENT OFFICE

In addition to the facilities as to patent specifications and publications mentioned above, the Patent Office library contains a very large number of scientific and technical books and bound volumes of periodicals devoted to science and technology. The number of foreign patents available totals millions of copies. Assistants are provided to help those interested in locating publications. A translator and an assistant translator are connected with the library. Four editions of catalogs of the Patent Office Library have been published as follows: Catalog of Library of Patent Office, 1878; catalog of additions, May 1, 1878–May 1, 1883; catalog of books in law library of Patent Office, 1883; catalog of additions, 1883–1888. The catalog now being carried on cards has not been printed since 1888. Lindenmeyer [14] gives rather detailed information about this library.

For a discussion of procedure in patent searching, see Chapter 10, Procedure in Literature Searches.

HOW TO OBTAIN PATENTS

Copies of U. S. patents can be obtained for 25 cents apiece from the Patent Office, Washington 25, D. C. For convenience in ordering patents and in paying for them, coupons are sold by the Patent Office in pads of 20 and books of 100. These coupons are printed so that one merely has to fill in the necessary patent data and his name and address and send the coupon off to the Patent Office when a U. S. patent is wanted.

If the supply of printed U. S. patents is temporarily exhausted it is possible to obtain photoprint copies from the Patent Office at a rate of 30 cents per print. Such copies can also be obtained from libraries which have files of U. S. patents.

While it costs a little more as a rule, it is convenient and time-saving to obtain copies of foreign patents by taking advantage of the fact that the U. S. Patent Office will supply a photoprint of any available patent at 30 cents per print. The countries whose patents are regularly received at the Patent Office are listed in the section on "Original Specifications" (page 165). Certain libraries have a like service but are more or less limited in the number of foreign patents on file. An estimate of the cost of any particular patent (depending on its length) or of any series of patents can be obtained in advance from the Patent Office. A convenient plan, when copies of foreign patents are frequently ordered, is to make a deposit of $25 and have copies, as needed, charged against the deposit account.

It should be mentioned incidentally that photoprints of any other literature available in the Scientific Library at the Patent Office can also be obtained at the same rate.

In ordering a copy of a patent, the number of the patent, the date, the name of the patentee, and the subject of the invention should all be stated if possible.

To obtain copies of foreign patents directly from foreign patent offices, see the latest January 10th issue of *Chemical Abstracts* for the rates, addresses of the patent offices, and other details; this list includes the patents of all of the countries that *Chemical Abstracts* covers. For the addresses of other patent offices, see White and Ravenscroft's book *Patents Throughout the World;* [2] this gives no information on prices but this information can be obtained by writing to the Patent Office.

LITERATURE CITED

(1) Fleischer, Joseph, "The Growth of Chemical Patents," *Chem. Eng. News* **30**, 239–241 (1952).

(2) White, W. W., and Ravenscroft, B. G., *Patents Throughout the World,* New York, Trade Activities, 1948, 2nd ed. This is looseleaf and is kept up to date.

(3) Tolpin, J. G., "Patents in the USSR," *Chem. Eng. News* **25**, 434 (1947).

(4) Prince, Charles, "The New Soviet Patent Law," *J. Patent Office Soc.* **28**, 261, 367 (1946).

(5) Fleischer, Joseph, "Exploring Foreign Chemical Patent Literature," in *Searching the Chemical Literature,* no. 4 in *Advances in Chemistry Series,* Washington, D. C., American Chemical Society, 1951.

(6) Severance, B., *Manual of Foreign Patents,* Washington, D. C. The Patent Office Society, 1935.

(7) Lovett, G. A., *Manual of Classification of the German Patent Office,* Washington, D. C., U. S. Government Printing Office, 1911.

(8) Fleischer, Joseph, "Exploring United States Chemical Patent Literature," in *Searching the Chemical Literature,* no. 4 in *Advances in Chemistry Series,* Washington, D. C., American Chemical Society, 1951.

(9) Smith, J. F., *Ind. Eng. Chem.* **16**, 527 (1924).

(10) von Hohenhoff, E., "Bibliography of Journals, Books and Compilations (American and Foreign) which List and Abstract Patents," *J. Patent Office Soc.* **17**, 808–825, 971–992 (1935); **18**, 49–67, 139–150 (1936). Also a reprint, Baltimore, The Special Libraries Assoc., 1936, 70 pp.

(11) Roberts, A. D., *Guide to Technical Literature,* London, Grafton, 1939, pp. 28–34.

(12) Hill, W. S., "The Chemist and the Patent," *J. Chem. Educ.* **21**, 225–227 (1944).

(13) Frankel, R., "Chemists Should Read Patents," *Ind. Eng. Chem. News Edition* **19**, 1399 (1941).

(14) Lindenmeyer, H. F., *J. Patent Office Soc.* **36**, 463–481 (1954).

CHAPTER 5

GOVERNMENT
PUBLICATIONS

||||||||||||||||||||||||||||||||||||||||||||||||||||||||||||||||||||||||||||||||||||||

Government publications are now an important source of scientific information. Patents were considered in Chapter 4. The governments of many countries now maintain one or more research laboratories and the number is growing. India alone has established eleven national laboratories since 1947, one of which is a chemical laboratory. An interesting account of this, "India Turns to Science," is Mrs. McBain's paper.[1] A large quantity of valuable scientific work is done in these government laboratories, often in areas that are not covered or only partially covered by industrial and university laboratories. Government laboratories are established for the welfare of the country as a whole and are in a position to do certain types of work that both university and industrial laboratories consider outside their realm of responsibility or interest.

The reports of much of this scientific research appear only in government publications. The reports that appear in scientific periodicals (either sponsored by governments or other publishers) and are covered by the abstract journals and the indexing serials present no problems when it comes to locating them. It is the large quantity of material issued as separate items at irregular times that makes government publications difficult to keep up with and to locate when needed. Government publications include much valuable chemical information. They appear as bulletins, technical papers, pamphlets, leaflets, and books; they are printed or processed (mimeographed or duplicated in some similar form); and their number is legion.

The government publications of the United States are discussed here the most fully because they are probably the most numerous

183

and because Americans use this material more frequently. Also, there are many similarities in the work of the government laboratories and agencies concerned with science. This should not be interpreted to mean that the scientific publications of the United States government are necessarily the most important. Many exceedingly valuable reports are issued by other governments.

UNITED STATES

Federal Government

A number of government laboratories have been doing research work in chemistry for many years and publishing the results either in government publications of various kinds or, to a much smaller extent, in periodicals that are not government publications. Before World War II, the quantity of chemical research carried out by the government agencies was relatively small in proportion to that done in private industry and the universities. However, much valuable work was done in government laboratories before World War II. These laboratories are concerned with the public welfare and with the development of industry as a whole. Consequently, they often do research work that concerns an entire industry and they publish it; privately operated industrial laboratories are under no such obligation. The research in the National Bureau of Standards, for example, is in the area of the public welfare and produces such chemical and scientific information that is not available from other sources.

During World War II a great expansion in government scientific research occurred and now it is a major activity. An editorial in *Chemical and Engineering News* **30,** 3077 (1952) entitled "Uncle Sam—Researcher" cites a study made by Paul B. Beal who states that 22 government agencies were responsible for the expenditure of $1.6 billion in 1952 for scientifiic research and that, in addition to work in government laboratories, much of this research is done under contract with about 1,500 industrial organizations and about 150 colleges and universities. Also, according to Beal, it is extremely difficult to estimate how much of the total is earmarked for national defense and military purposes, and how much for nonmilitary projects. The National Science Foundation was created by act of Congress on May 10, 1950; one of the functions of this federal agency is to develop a national policy for the promotion of basic research and education in the sciences. Other developments could be pointed out but these are sufficient to emphasize the fact that chemical research work that originates in government agencies is a much larger part of the total than it used to be.

Exactly how important the government publications and the unpublished government documents are as sources of chemical information, in comparison with books, periodicals, and patents, is difficult to determine. Some results of government research are classified, at least temporarily, which prevents publication. When declassified the information is often published in journals. Some is reported in government bulletins, circulars, reports, and papers, and some remains unpublished, in the usual sense of the word, as a typewritten or mimeographed document of which photoprint or microfilm copies can often be obtained. When a thorough search of the chemical literature is made, these government sources must be taken into consideration.

Aside from the results of chemical research, the government publishes much information that is important to chemists. This includes bibliographies, compilations of physical and chemical data, standards for chemicals, equipment, and apparatus, information on the safe handling and storage of chemicals, and many other kinds too numerous to mention. Much of this information is not available elsewhere.

The government also publishes large quantities of information on natural resources, trade statistics, and other business information that is invaluable to the chemical industries. In many cases this information can be obtained only from these government sources for use in business operations and in chemical market research.

The quantity and multiplicity of these publications make it difficult to locate information. The United States government is said to be the greatest publisher in the world, at least judging by the quantity of its products. Even with a great deal of watchfulness, it is easily possible to miss government documents of interest and value.

Space does not permit a lengthy discussion of all the various government publications. The notes that follow are only intended to give some idea of the kind of information available from the various government agencies and to help the chemist locate those publications in which he is interested.

These notes cover only the agencies which most frequently publish material of interest to chemists or to chemical industries. A list of sources of information about their publications will follow. The agencies are arranged according to the present government plan of organization.

U. S. DEPARTMENT OF AGRICULTURE

The various agencies within the Department of Agriculture publish much of chemical interest and considerable statistical material. The research work covers all phases of agricultural chemistry, the use of agricultural products in industry, food processing, nutrition, and other fields. Some of the agencies are:

Bureau of Agricultural Economics. This bureau publishes all types of statistical information and economic surveys.

Bureau of Industrial and Agricultural Chemistry. The primary emphasis here is on chemical research to find outlets for agricultural products (both for foods and industrial uses).

Bureau of Animal Industry. Much work of a chemical nature is published dealing with meats, leather, furs, animal nutrition, and similar topics.

Bureau of the Dairy Industry. A considerable number of chemical publications dealing with the nutrition of dairy cattle, milk, and milk products originate here.

Bureau of Entomology and Plant Quarantine. Much chemical research work is done in this bureau on discovering and developing insecticides and fungicides.

Forest Products Laboratory. This laboratory, maintained at Madison, Wisconsin, issues many technical bulletins dealing with the chemistry of wood, paper, cellulose, and other wood products such as turpentine and rosin.

Bureau of Human Nutrition and Home Economics. The chemical research work of this bureau deals with nutrition, the composition of foods, and textiles.

Bureau of Plant Industry, Soils, and Agricultural Engineering. This bureau issues much information on the chemistry of soils and fertilizers.

The Department of Agriculture has laboratories all over the United States, but most of the Bureaus have a laboratory at the Agricultural Research Center at Beltsville, Maryland, where much of the basic research is done.

U. S. DEPARTMENT OF COMMERCE

The agencies within this department also provide both chemical and business information.

Bureau of the Census. The facts and statistics collected and published are invaluable to the chemical industries in their business and market research studies. The census of agriculture, the census of business, the census of manufactures, and the census of mineral industries are all of great value. There are other special compilations in addition to the census of the population. The census of manufactures shows, among other things, the number and kind of chemical manufacturing plants, and the quantity and value of many chemical products (rayon, drugs, paints, etc.).

The *Facts for Industry Reports* are issued monthly, quarterly, and annually to provide current data. These cover many chemicals and products which use chemicals in their manufacture.

Foreign trade statistics are now published in the Census Bureau; these were transferred from the Bureau of Foreign and Domestic Commerce in 1941. The *Foreign Trade Reports* provide current information; these are issued monthly. These trade statistics are invaluable and have wide coverage.

Bureau of Foreign and Domestic Commerce. The publications of this bureau together with those of the Census Bureau are the basis of a chemical business library. The publications and services of the Bureau of Foreign and Domestic Commerce are numerous; its work of gathering and distributing information covering business conditions at home and abroad is very broad. Much of its work and many of its publications deal directly with chemicals and chemical industries.

National Bureau of Standards. This bureau does much chemical work and publishes useful information on analytical chemistry, organic chemistry, physical chemistry, and inorganic chemistry, in addition to various phases of industrial chemistry. It determines and provides much information on physical constants and properties of materials. It is also the source of information on standards of many kinds.

The Patent Office. This agency has been discussed in the chapter on Patents.

Office of Technical Services. The principal function of the Office of Technical Services is to make available all of the declassified research reports that originate in the Army, Navy, and Air Force laboratories, and in private organizations that do research financed by the federal government. The guide to this material is an index called U. S. Government Reports (see page 145). The Office of Technical Services also serves as an information center on technical data in the possession of the government.

U. S. DEPARTMENT OF DEFENSE

Department of the Army. The Chemical Corps (often called the Chemical Warfare Service) and some of the Army's other agencies do some chemical work. A lot of work is done by private organizations under contract with the Army.

Department of the Navy. The Office of Naval Research does a considerable amount of work in chemistry. Work is also done for the Navy by private organizations under contract.

Department of the Air Force. Some of the research work done by the Air Force or for it by contractors is of chemical interest.

U. S. DEPARTMENT OF HEALTH, EDUCATION AND WELFARE

This department includes the agencies of the former Federal Security Agency.

The Public Health Service. Much chemical work, including biochemistry, organic chemistry, pharmaceutical chemistry, and many other fields is carried on at the National Institutes of Health.

Food and Drug Administration. Most of the work of this agency is concerned with enforcing the food and drug laws. It does a lot of analytical work and formulates and publishes standards and methods of analysis for foods and drugs.

U. S. DEPARTMENT OF THE INTERIOR

The Geological Survey. The Survey's Geological Branch does much work in geochemistry. It analyzes rocks and minerals and studies the distribution and reserves of mineral deposits, including petroleum.

The Water Resources Branch studies the distribution, quantity, quality, and mineral content of both the surface and underground water of the United States. The publications of the branch are very valuable sources of information on water for domestic, agricultural, and industrial uses.

Bureau of Mines. This bureau does a large quantity of work on the utilization of minerals, the preparation and utilization of metals and nonmetals, metallurgy, coal, gas, and petroleum, explosives (both for mining and military use), and explosions. Much of this research is of chemical interest.

The bureau also has an Economics and Statistics Branch that collects, analyzes, and publishes information on metals, minerals, petroleum, and coal. This branch also collects and supplies information on foreign mineral resources, supplies, trade, and other items.

The most valuable single publication of the Bureau of Mines is the *Minerals Yearbook*.

U. S. DEPARTMENT OF THE TREASURY

The material published here is largely statistical. The Bureau of Internal Revenue statistics of income show returns by industry and by industrial groups, the chemical industries among them. The bureau also collects useful data on industrial alcohol. Other bureaus publish statistics of use to chemical industries.

INDEPENDENT ESTABLISHMENTS

Atomic Energy Commission. The Commission publishes a large number of papers after the information has been declassified from secret status. It publishes compilations of various kinds. Much of the scientific work is of interest to chemists and chemical industries. The Commission's most valuable single publication is *Nuclear Science Abstracts*, which includes the declassified documents of the Atomic Energy Commission. Copies of declassified documents are usually distributed by the Office of Technical Services (Department of Commerce). There are also a number of libraries in the United States, each of which has been designated as a depository library for a complete file of declassified and unclassified reports. These libraries are listed in the introduction to each number of *Nuclear Science Abstracts*.

Federal Reserve System. The publications of this agency are of business interest to the chemical industries. In addition to the *Federal Reserve Index of Production*, the Federal Reserve System publishes indexes relating to chemicals and chemical products.

National Science Foundation. The National Science Foundation, created by act of Congress, May 10, 1950, is an exceedingly important federal agency. All scientists, including chemists, should keep in touch with its work. It is the only agency concerned with an over-all policy for scientific research for the nation as a whole. One of its studies is a survey that gives statistical and fiscal information concerning the research and development programs of all federal agencies. This survey also includes research work being carried out by contract between government agencies and educational or other nonprofit institutions.

Information about publications and other information that has not been published can be obtained from the National Science Foundation, Office of Scientific Information, 1520 H Street, N.W., Washington 25, D. C. The first annual report of the Director appeared in 1952;

these reports should be read as they are issued. An excellent summary of the functions and organization of the National Science Foundation is given in a *Chem. Eng. News* Staff Report.[2]

National Academy of Sciences and National Research Council. See p. 212, Other Sources. These organizations are not government institutions in the usual sense of the word.

Smithsonian Institution. This Institution was created by act of Congress in 1846 under the terms of the will of James Smithson, who bequeathed his fortune to the U. S. government. It is partially supported by Congressional appropriations. Its publications include many valuable scientific and technical ones. A large proportion of the Smithsonian publications are not printed at public expense and are not cataloged or handled by the Government Printing Office.

Tariff Commission. It publishes valuable surveys and comprehensive studies of many chemicals, chemical products, and industries. It also provides much information on foreign industries and considerable statistical material. This commission, the Bureau of Foreign and Domestic Commerce (Department of Commerce), and the Bureau of Mines are the principal sources of information on the natural resources and industries of foreign countries. One particularly valuable publication is the annual report *U. S. Production and Sales of Synthetic Organic Chemicals,* which gives statistics and shows the manufacturer and the uses of each of thousands of products; it also gives discussions of the developments in each field. Another valuable point is the fact that this report has been published annually for many years.

Other Agencies. Many other government agencies occasionally issue a chemical publication or one of use to chemists. There are a number of agencies, other than those mentioned above, which issue business and statistical information of value to chemical industries; the Department of Labor is among these.

HOW TO LOCATE UNITED STATES PUBLICATIONS

A. The U. S. government provides a number of catalogs and indexes; these will be considered first.

(1) *Monthly Catalog of U. S. Government Publications.* 1895–   , Washington, D. C., The Government Printing Office, $3 per year. This catalog is compiled by the Library of the Division of Public Documents which, according to law, must receive one copy of each publication authored by any branch or bureau of the

United States government. It has an author and subject index for each number and for each volume. Since January 1936 it has included processed material (mimeographed, multigraphed, etc.). The titles are classified according to issuing bodies. The subject indexes depend on titles, which limits their value. There are few annotations so that a general idea of the work of the issuing body is a help in selecting those to be read. This catalog has a section called "Previews" which lists important titles for pre-publication orders. It also indicates where a copy can be obtained, its price (some are free), and whether a copy of the publication was sent to a deposit library. It is the best tool to use to watch for new government publications.

(2) *Supplements to the Monthly Catalog of Government Publications.* Three volumes cover the period 1941–1946. These publications were withheld as confidential during the war.

(3) *Monthly Catalog of Government Publications.* Collective Decennial Index, 1941–1950. Washington, D. C., Government Printing Office, 1953.

(4) *Catalog of the Public Documents of Congress and of all Departments of the Government of the United States for the Period March 4, 1893–December 31, 1940.* Washington, D. C., Government Printing Office, 1896–1945, 25 vols. This is commonly referred to as the *Document Catalog.* Each volume covers a two-year period. This is a dictionary catalog; the authors (personal or governmental) and subjects are arranged in alphabetical order. It gives considerable information about each title. This is much more valuable for locating publications issued before 1941 than the *Monthly List* (annual volumes), which has very unsatisfactory indexes for that period.

It is difficult to locate desired publications in either of the catalogs mentioned above, because the catalogs and the decennial index to the *Monthly Catalog* are based on the titles of the publications and frequently give little or no clue as to their contents.

(5) *U. S. Government Research Reports* (formerly the *Bibliography of Technical Reports*). 1946–   . See page 145. This covers **unpublished** government documents for which copies are available only as microfilm or photoprint for the most part. These documents are not included in the *Monthly Catalog* or the *Document Catalog.* This publication is issued by the Office of Technical Services, Department of Commerce. Many of the reports are those received by the government from organizations that did

work under contract for the government. There is material on chemical research among them. The titles are annotated to indicate the coverage of the reports.

(6) *Nuclear Science Abstracts*, 1948–   , is published by the Atomic Energy Commission and is particularly valuable for publications that it issues.

(7) Many of the government departments, bureaus, etc., issue their own catalogs and indexes to their publications and also send out announcements of new publications and services to those on their mailing lists. It is therefore well to get in touch with the particular departments, the documents of which may be of special interest, and to ask to be put on the mailing lists to receive announcements. Some of these publications are annotated; others are not. Many of the departments publish good indexes of their publications and aids for using their publications. Some examples of these are:

Bibliographic Review and Index of Publications Relating to Ground Water, 412 pp., prepared by the Geological Survey and cooperating agencies. (Water Supply Paper, no. 992, 1947.)

List of Publications of the Bureau of Mines, 1937–1943, with an author and subject index, 157 pp., 1943. Supplemented by annual and monthly lists. This includes cooperative publications issued by nongovernmental agencies, but prepared in cooperation with the Bureau.

Publications of the National Bureau of Standards, 1901 to July 30, 1947. (National Bureau of Standards Circular no. 460, issued August 1948, 375 pp.) This covers all of the printed publications of the Bureau since its founding with the exception of the annual reports of the Director and its periodicals. It gives abstracts and indexes of contents.

List of Available Publications of the Department of Commerce, January 1944, 202 pp. This includes descriptive notes that are very helpful.

A considerable number of new lists, aids, guides, and indexes or new editions of existing ones are issued by government departments and bureaus each year. The annual reports of the directors of bureaus and agencies usually summarize the current services, publications, programs, and functions of the agencies.

B. Other methods of locating government publications of chemical interest:

(1) The abstract journals and indexing serials. Abstracts of many government documents can be found in *Chemical Abstracts*. The Engineering Index and Industrial Arts Index both include quite a large number of them. The Bibliography of Agriculture in-

cludes all the United States agricultural publications (federal and state) as well as those of many foreign countries. See Chapter 8, Indexes, for more information on the last three sources just mentioned.

(2) A number of scientific periodicals give lists of government publications.

(3) *Scientific, Medical and Technical Books Published in the United States of America*, 1930–1944, and its supplements include the most important publications of the federal government departments, bureaus, and agencies that are of scientific interest. The content of each publication is summarized and notes indicate its value. This is edited by R. R. Hawkins and published by the National Research Council.

SOURCES OF INFORMATION ABOUT GOVERNMENT PUBLICATIONS

The field of government publications is so large that those who wish to make effective use of them need more information than can be given in this book. The following sources are particularly useful:

Boyd, A. M., and Rips, R. E., *United States Government Publications*, New York, Wilson Co., 1949, 627 pp., 3rd ed. This is a very comprehensive work written from the librarian's point of view. It is the most up to date of the comprehensive works. This book outlines the history and function of each government department, bureau, etc., and covers its publications. It also includes numerous bibliographies of books and papers in periodicals and much other useful information.

Brown, E. S., *Manual of Government Publications; United States and Foreign*, New York, Appleton-Century-Crofts, 1950, 121 pp. This is written from the point of view of the social sciences, political science specifically, but it contains much generally useful information.

Childs, J. B., *Government Document Bibliography in the United States and Elsewhere*, Washington, D. C., Government Printing Office, 1942, 78 pp., 3rd ed. This is the most comprehensive list that exists of the guides, indexes, catalogs, etc., that are published by the countries of the world to provide keys to their government publications.

Cohen, S. S., *The Businessman's Guide to Government Information and Advice*. Washington, D. C. The American Assoc. for Public Information, 1955, 97 pp.

Harden, Florence, "The Use of Government Publications in Chemical Research," *J. Chem. Educ.*, **21**, 326–332 (1944). Parts of this paper are out of date but it is still useful.

Hauser, P. M., and Leonard, W. P., *Government Statistics for Business Use*, New York, Wiley, 1946, 432 pp.

Hirshberg, H. S., and Melinat, C. H., *Subject Guide to United States Publications*, Chicago, American Library Assoc., 1947, 228 pp. This gives the indexes, catalogs, etc., that deal with specific subjects.

Lawrence, R. C. (ed.), *Sources of Information for Industrial Market Research*, New York, Chemical Industries, 1948, 98 pp. A considerable part of this is devoted to government publications that are useful to chemical industries.

Merritt, L. C., *The United States Government as a Publisher*, Chicago, Univ. of Chicago Press, 1943, 179 pp. This is not a guide to government publications, but it is a good survey.

Schmeckebier, L. F., *Government Publications and Their Uses*, Washington, D. C., The Brookings Institution, 1939. This is still useful, although out of date in some respects. It emphasizes materials of use to political scientists.

Wilcox, J. K., "New Guides and Aides to Public Documents Use," *Special Libraries* **40**, 371–377 and 406–412 (1949); **45**, 29–36 (1954). These two annotated lists cover the period 1945–1952 and include, for the most part, guides and aids published by the United States government for its own publications. There are some that cover publications of foreign governments.

LIBRARIES AND GOVERNMENT PUBLICATIONS

If one wishes to read, or refer to, a government publication, libraries usually have the most important ones, but these collections are frequently devoted to political science and certain phases of business. They may not contain many items of interest to chemists. There are over 500 libraries, widely distributed in the United States, that are "depository libraries." Of these only 125 libraries were receiving all of the U. S. government publications in 1947.[3] The balance are "selected depository libraries," which means that they choose the material to be received. These depository libraries receive the publications free of charge from the Superintendent of Documents, Government Printing Office, Washington, D. C. A list of depository libraries is published annually in the *Monthly Catalog of U. S. Government Publications*, usually the August number.

PURCHASE OF FEDERAL DOCUMENTS

All publications that are handled by the Government Printing Office can be purchased there. The others must be purchased from the issuing agency. The *Monthly Catalog of U. S. Government Publications* shows where a copy can be obtained. The Superintendent of Documents will send a number of price lists free of charge; among these is the *Price List of Government Periodicals*. Each of these price lists contains a catalog of all of the others available. The periodical list is mentioned particularly because it covers only those periodicals sold by subscription through the Government Printing Office; many other valuable ones are sold by the issuing agencies.

(*Monthly Catalog* gives a complete listing of periodicals only twice a year.)   Orders are sent to The Superintendent of Documents, Government Printing Office, Washington 25, D. C., accompanied by a check, money order, or postal note payable to The Superintendent of Documents.   All sales must be paid for in advance.   The Superintendent sells books of 20 coupons for $1, which are useful for small purchases, and also accepts deposits of $10 or more against which orders may be placed.   Remittances from foreign countries should be made by international money order or draft on an American bank, payable to The Superintendent of Documents.   Purchasers in foreign countries must pay the postage on the order (about one third of the cost of it).

State Publications

The state governments of the United States also publish much material of interest to chemists and chemical industries.   These include the work done at state universities, schools of mines, boards of health, agricultural experiment stations, etc.   The best way to obtain them is directly from the issuing body.   Some are free to residents of the issuing state.

The *Monthly Checklist of State Publications,* which is compiled by the Library of Congress, is sold by subscription (Superintendent of Documents, Government Printing Office, Washington, D. C., $1.50 per year, domestic) and is the key to these publications.

The *Book of the States* is issued frequently by the Council of State Governments, Chicago, Ill.   Vol. VII was issued in 1950.   It gives information on state publications.

W. S. Jenkins has compiled *Collected Public Documents of the States,* Boston, National Assoc. State Libraries, 1947.

R. R. Hawkins, *Scientific, Medical and Technical Books Published in United States,* has an appendix that lists state agencies that publish material on geology, engineering, agriculture, and similar subjects.

J. K. Wilcox, *Manual on the Use of State Publications,* is the most comprehensive work available (Chicago, American Library Assoc., 1940, 355 pp.). It covers the publications and methods of distribution.

FOREIGN GOVERNMENTS

A number of foreign governments maintain laboratories that carry out scientific work and publish the results.   Most foreign governments do not engage in such widespread scientific work as that of the United States if one excepts the Soviet Union, where the state controls all laboratories and scientific organizations.   But much valuable chemical information is published by foreign governments.   Many of these laboratories publish much of their work in periodicals abstracted by *Chemical Abstracts*. The tendency to issue separate bulletins and reports is less, on the whole, than in the United States, with the exception of countries within the British Commonwealth of Nations. *Chemical Abstracts* includes abstracts of many of these separate reports and bulletins. A discussion of all of the foreign governments and their scientific research is beyond the scope of this book. Some notes are included on those that issue a number of publications and on sources of information on the publications of foreign governments. Few governments publish more than an annual catalog of their publications.

The governments of Australia, Canada, and Great Britain publish a rather large number of reports, papers, and bulletins as separate publications that are of value to chemists.

Canada. The Department of Public Printing and Stationery, Ottawa, issues the *Monthly Catalogue of Canadian Government Publications* and the *Annual Catalogue of Canadian Government Publications*. The National Research Council, the Department of Mines, the Fisheries Research Board, the Department of Agriculture, and the Dominion Bureau of Standards are among those that frequently publish material of chemical interest.

Australia. The Commonwealth National Library, Canberra, issues the *Annual Catalogue of Australian Publications*. Since 1937 this has included all of the government publications.

Great Britain. Her Majesty's Stationery Office (H.M.S.O.), London, issues the *Daily List of Government Publications*, the *Monthly List of Government Publications*, and the *Annual Consolidated List of Government Publications*, which has an index. The British government laboratories have an extensive research program and publish much material of value to chemists. The Department of Scientific and Industrial Research includes a number of agencies. Among them are the Chemistry Research Board, the Food Investigation, Fuel Research, Forest Products Research, and Water Pollution Research Boards, and the National Physical Laboratory.

Two of the most useful recent publications on British Government publications have been published by the Library Association, London: (1) *The State as a Publisher; A Librarian's Guide to H.M.S.O. Publications*, Library Association Pamphlet no. 10 (1952) and (2) Ronald Stavely (ed.), *Government Information and the Research Worker*, 228 pp. (1952). The appendix of Stavely's book gives some information on India, Pakistan, and other countries within the British Commonwealth of Nations.

Sources of Information

The embassies of the foreign countries in Washington will answer inquiries about publications of their governments or in some cases refer inquirers to their information centers in this country that maintain libraries. The Library of Congress, Washington, D. C., has a very large collection of the publications of foreign governments and many of the government agencies in Washington have specialized collections in their libraries. Among the most useful of the published sources of information are:

Brown, E. S., *Manual of Government Publications; United States and Foreign*, New York, Appleton-Century-Crofts, 1950, 121 pp. This gives many sources of information on publications of foreign governments and lists many of their catalogs and indexes to them.

Cabeen, V. A., "Foreign Government Publications," *College and Research Libraries* **12**, 163–166, 1951). This has an excellent list of the catalogs and other publications that list and index the publications.

Childs, J. B., *Government Document Bibliography in United States and Elsewhere*, Washington, D. C. Government Printing Office, 1942, 78 pp., 3rd ed. Very little of this is devoted to the United States. The countries of the world are arranged alphabetically and the principal publications, catalogs, and indexes are listed under each one. Dr. Childs of the Library of Congress is an authority in this field.

Childs, J. B., *U. S. Library of Congress (Guide to the Official Publications of Other American Republics—Latin American Series)*, Washington, D. C., Government Printing Office, 1945–1949, 19 vols. These include most of the countries with the exception of Mexico. This series is being continued to cover all of the Latin American countries.

Gregory, Winifred, *List of the Serial Publications of Foreign Governments* (1815–1931), New York, Wilson Co., 1932, 720 pp. This lists about 30,000 titles that are found in about 75 American libraries. The list includes the patent office publications that are excluded from the *Union List of Serials in the Libraries of U. S. and Canada;* it is arranged by countries, and gives the departments, bureaus, etc., which issue the publications. The introductory material to these two publications of the Wilson Co. should be inspected carefully; certain classes of government publications are included in the *Union List of Serials in U. S. Libraries*, which has supplements covering publications through 1949.

Harden, Florence, "Foreign Technical Publications," *J. Chem. Educ.* **23**, 489–494 (1946). This deals with government publications of chemical value.

Index Bibliographicus, edited by Theodore Besterman, 2 vols., Paris, UNESCO, 1952 (sold in United States by the Columbia Univ. Press). Volume II contains a list of countries that publish bibliographies of their government publications. This volume also contains a list of national bibliographies that include all books, periodicals, etc., published in each of the listed countries; these bibliographies vary in how many government publications they include. The British National Bibliography includes the more important government publications.

Library of Congress, Quarterly Journal of Current Acquisitions. This publishes a great deal of information about the government publications of foreign governments.

UNESCO Bulletin for Libraries, Paris, (UNESCO), 1947–   , monthly. This frequently gives information on government publications. There is both a French and an English edition of this periodical. Subscriptions ($2 per year) are sold by the Columbia Univ. Press, New York.

LITERATURE CITED

(1) McBain, Evelyn, *Chem. Eng. News* **32,** 604–609 (1954).

(2) Staff Report, *Chem. Eng. News* **31,** 228–233 (1953).

(3) *Annual Report of the Public Printer,* Washington, D. C., Government Printing Office, 1947.

CHAPTER 6

TRADE LITERATURE

Trade literature is a useful part of the chemical literature; it provides much valuable information that is not available elsewhere. It is the primary source of information about commercially available chemicals, materials, processes, appliances, equipment, and apparatus; in the case of new ones, it is the only source for a considerable period of time. These publications, also, frequently contain technical information that appears much more tardily, if at all, in books and professional journals.

One type of trade literature, the trade journal that is issued by a publisher for profit, is not discussed in detail here. This type of publication was considered in Chapter 3 on Periodicals. Only a few comments are in order now. These journals serve as advertising media and provide business and commercial information in addition to some technical information. They are valuable publications for the chemical industries. The chemical abstract journals cover these trade publications for new chemical information; they do not abstract the business and commercial information. A part of the latter is covered by the indexing serials, *Industrial Arts Index* and the *Engineering Index*, but much of it is not. Business methods, export and import practice, insurance risks, industrial accidents, market conditions, freight rates, and similar factors all may have important bearing on the work of an industrial chemist or the operation of a chemical business; these are very incompletely covered by the indexing serials.

This chapter is concerned with the publications that are not usually covered by either the abstract journals or the indexing serials.

These are the technical bulletins, "house organs" and catalogs of manufacturers, the union catalogs, buyers' guides and directories that are compiled by publishers, the catalogs of dealers in equipment and chemicals, the publications of trade associations, and advertisements.

Advertisements are a valuable source of information. They often give the first clue that a chemical compound, a material, or a piece of equipment is being manufactured. The fact that a patent has been obtained does not always mean that the product will soon be on the market. Many patents are never used; there are a number of reasons for this. Then, too, the manufacture of many chemical compounds is not covered by patents. A compound may be known for years but be prepared only in small amounts in research laboratories. Industrial uses are found for many such compounds and production on a large scale results. Also manufacturers of chemicals are continually finding new uses for chemicals that they have been producing for years. As for equipment and apparatus, improvements in existing pieces are usually advertised; the manufacturer may not issue a new catalog of all of his products more than once a year. It is best to examine "ads" as they appear in the chemical journals because the advertising pages are discarded when most periodicals are bound. Most periodicals that carry a number of "ads" have a list of advertisers in each issue. This is a help in locating the products of a specific manufacturer. Some interesting comments on the way in which advertisements answer industrial problems will be found in Thomas's paper [1] and comments on the use of industrial advertisements as a source of information for chemistry teachers in one by Kessel.[2]

The **manufacturers' technical bulletins** on new products and those which they have been producing for some time are valuable sources of information. In the case of chemicals, these bulletins frequently summarize the chemistry of the compounds, give extensive information on physical properties, tell how to use them in various ways, and give references to the literature. For equipment and apparatus, the bulletins frequently summarize the theory involved in construction and operation in addition to giving directions on how to use and maintain it. Technical bulletins vary in size from a few pages up to publications of 100 pages or more. They frequently are original sources of information and contain material that never finds its way into books and professional journals. The technical data sheets give less detail but are useful. For those who are not familiar with these publications the following examples will give some idea of them, but it is best to obtain some and look through them. They are distributed free upon request. Of course they are a part of the advertising and consumer service program of the manufacturer.

The American Cyanamid Co. published a 95-page booklet on the chemistry of acrylonitrile in 1951.

H. Reeve Angel & Co. published a 145-page book, *A Guide to Filter Paper and Cellulose Powder Chromatography,* in 1952.

The Carbide and Carbon Chemicals Co. published a booklet on *Organic Acids* in 1954. It not only gives a detailed discussion of the eight organic acids that are available in commercial quantities but it also includes a section on the testing of these acids. Some of the methods are those of the American Society for Testing Materials, but others have been developed in the company laboratories.

The Rodney Hunt Machine Co. published a brochure on the *Turba-Film Evaporator* in 1954. This new type of evaporator, the theory involved in its construction, and its uses are discussed.

The Carborundum Metal Co. issued *Facts About Zirconium* in 1954. This publication discusses the physical and chemical properties of zirconium, methods of fabrication, and zirconium chemicals.

The Phillips Petroleum Co. has just issued a technical bulletin on its infrared analyzer. This piece of equipment can monitor as many as five process streams. The bulletin gives very complete information on the construction and use of the analyzer.

A very large amount of this technical literature is published by the manufacturers. A further discussion of it and many additional examples of it are found in a paper by Kessel [3] and in one by Cheyney.[4]

The **manufacturers' catalogs** of their products are also sources of technical information. These catalogs give information about chemicals, materials, and equipment that cannot be found elsewhere. Sometimes they contain compilations of information that can be found only by looking in many sources. So these catalogs are frequently useful for other purposes than information on prospective purchases. Old catalogs are occasionally of great value in patent litigation and they should also be retained to use in "state of the art" literature searches which are also a part of patent work. A few examples may be helpful.

The J. T. Baker Chemical Co.'s specification catalog of *Baker Analyzed Reagents and Laboratory Chemicals* is a very convenient source of information on ACS standards for many reagents, on specifications for reagent grade chemicals, on new reagents, on new primary standards, and on pH ranges of many compounds.

The Coleman Instruments Inc. Catalog for 1954, in addition to information on all of its instruments, has a section that discusses the theory and practice of pH measurement, colorimetry, nephelometry, fluorimetry, flame photometry, and absorption spectrochemistry.

The dealers in chemicals and/or equipment also issue catalogs that are useful in many ways in addition to providing information on their stock in trade.

There are several ways of **locating the manufacturers' technical literature and catalogs.** One is to read advertisements. Another is to look through the lists that a number of chemical journals print; among these are *Chemical Engineering, Chemical Week, Industrial and Engineering Chemistry,* and *Chemical and Engineering News. Chemical and Engineering News* has three sections devoted to these publications (Chemicals, Equipment, and Industrial Literature) in which the entries are annotated to indicate the contents. The *Journal of Chemical Education* contains a section, "Out of the Editor's Basket," which is largely an annotated list of trade literature. A third method is to look in one of the union catalogs, buyers' guides, or business directories (discussed below) to find out who makes the chemical or piece of equipment and then write for literature and/or a catalog. Of course, if it is known that a manufacturer makes certain chemicals or equipment or a dealer specializes in certain kinds of things, all that is necessary is to request a catalog or a bulletin.

The most comprehensive of these **union or consolidated catalogs** are:

The *Chemical Engineering Catalog* and the *Chemical Materials Catalog* (both published by Reinhold, New York) give information on equipment, laboratory equipment, machinery, chemicals, materials, and raw materials for chemical processing. They give the manufacturer, the dealer, and companies that offer engineering services to the chemical industries. These catalogs provide only brief entries and are issued annually. They also contain a number of useful lists.

Sweets' Catalog Files (Sweets' Catalog Service, New York) contains various manufacturers' catalogs bound together.

There are a number of **buyers' guides** and **business directories** that are useful for finding out who manufactures a product; three of the most useful are: Thomas's *Register of American Manufacturers,* which is the most nearly complete source of information on the names of the manufacturers of various products, their addresses, their trade names, and the names of their trade journals (house organs).

The *Chemical Week Buyer's Guide* is a special issue of the periodical *Chemical Week*, formerly called *Chemical Industries* (now published by McGraw-Hill, New York). It is a book of over 800 pages; it is usually issued in September. There are four sections: a directory of manufacturers, distributors, and dealers, a very extensive list of chemicals and raw materials together with their properties and their manufacturers, a directory of equipment for both plant and laboratory use, and a trade-name directory.

The *World Chemical Directory of Importers, Exporters, and Manufacturers of Chemicals, Drugs, Plastics, and Oils*, issued by the Atlas Pub. Co., New York, is frequently useful.

Many manufacturers publish periodicals known as **house organs**; these are primarily a form of advertising. Some house organs contain valuable technical information; a few are abstracted by *Chemical Abstracts* for new chemical information. They are useful for keeping up with products that the company manufacturers and for obtaining information on their uses. They also announce manufacturers' technical bulletins and catalogs. Some house organs include abstracts and/or review articles. A very large number of them are current: many are of chemical interest. For an excellent discussion of house organs of chemical interest and quite an extensive list of titles, see Lederman's paper.[5] A list of titles was also published in the *Journal of Chemical Education*.[6] Some of the most useful chemical house organs have been issued for many years. A number of the more useful house organs are listed in *Ulrich's Periodicals Directory* (New York, Bowker), which is classified. The most complete list of them is *Printers' Ink Directory of House Organs*, 3rd ed., 1951 (Printers' Ink Pub. Co., New York). It lists 5,532, but it is not classified according to subject matter. But, knowledge of the products manufactured can be obtained from the directories and buyers' guides that were mentioned in the preceding paragraph.

A recent development in the publication of trade literature is that some manufacturers are releasing some of their technical books for publication by book publishers. One example of this is the *Esso Series*, published and sold by Van Nostrand, New York. These books are designed for use within the company; they do not reveal truly secret "know-how," but they contain valuable scientific and technical information. A comment on this new policy entitled "To Receive, We Must Give," is to be found on the editorial page of *Chemical Engineering News* **28**, 2503 (1950).

The **trade associations** issue a considerable number of **technical publications;** many of these are of chemical interest. Some of these are distributed only to members of the issuing association; others are given or sold to all who are interested in them. These include abstract journals, technical bulletins, surveys, reports, and books. Most of this material that is available for public distribution is announced in the same sections of the chemical journals as the manufacturers' bulletins and catalogs. Some of these trade associations also maintain research laboratories. For information on trade associations, their activities and publications, see *National Associations of the United States* by Jay Judkins; this is a publication of the U. S. Department of Commerce (Office of Domestic Commerce), Washington, D. C., Government Printing Office, 1949, 634 pp.

Libraries seldom have extensive collections of trade literature. It requires a great deal of space, special indexing and cataloging, and the time of several librarians to maintain a large collection and keep it up to date. So it is necessary to obtain the material that one wishes to see directly from those who publish it in most cases. Nearly all of it is free.

The Carnegie Library of Pittsburgh (Technology Department), Pittsburgh 13, Pa., has maintained a very extensive collection of all types of trade literature for many years; it will answer requests for information.

The Library of the Cooper Union for the Advancement of Science and Art, 4th Avenue and 7th Street, New York, has quite a large collection of chemical trade literature; it will also answer requests for information.

To sum it all up, industrial chemists and chemical engineers cannot afford to neglect the trade literature. Other chemists will find it useful in many ways. In the case of new industrial problems and special problems which are not so new, it frequently happens that the best information available in print is in the trade literature.

LITERATURE CITED

(1) Thomas, V. P., *Printers' Ink* **217**, 37–39 (1946).
(2) Kessel, W. G., *J. Chem. Educ.* **21**, 437–438 (1944).
(3) Kessel, W. G., *J. Chem. Educ.* **25**, 222–223 (1948); **28**, 383 (1951); **31**, 255 (1954).

(4) Cheyney, LaV. E., a paper in *Searching the Chemical Literature*, no. 4 in the *Advances in Chemistry Series*, Washington, D. C., American Chemical Society, 1951.

(5) Lederman, L. F., a paper in *Searching the Chemical Literature*, no. 4 in the *Advances in Chemistry Series*, Washington, D. C., American Chemical Society, 1951.

(6) *J. Chem. Educ.*, section entitled "Here and There in the Trade Literature" **21**, 94 (1945); **22**, 38–39 (1946).

CHAPTER 7

OTHER SOURCES

IIIIIIIIIIIIIIIIIIIIIIIIIIIIIIIIIIIIIIIIIIIIIIIIIIIIIIIIIIIIIIIIIIIIIIIIIIIIIIIIIIIIIIIIIIIIIIIII

Besides journals, books, patents, and the additional publications already discussed there are a number of other sources that provide chemical information. Each of these will be considered briefly.

Annual Reviews

There are a large number of reviews of progress in the various branches of chemistry. This discussion is concerned with the kind of annual review that appears as a separate publication. These publications give a condensed account or survey of the work in a field and note any special advances that have been made within the year. They provide numerous references to the literature. The need for critical reviews was felt early in the development of chemistry. The first one to appear was *Berlinisches Jahrbuch für Pharmacie* (1795–1840); it was followed by many others. From 1795 to approximately 1890, these publications played a very important role as sources of information, but as the abstract journals developed they lost their outstanding position.

Nevertheless the reviews serve several decidedly useful purposes. The reviewer can select the more important pieces of work, examine their relations to one another and criticize them as the abstract journal editor cannot do. The current development of chemistry is so rapid and the quantity of the literature is so great that even the most competent chemist can keep up with a relatively small part of it. The annual reviews are a great help in keeping up with work outside of one's special field. In making literature searches, annual reviews are useful to find general trends, to locate outstanding developments, and to get oriented in a field that is new to the searcher. Two lists of these annual reviews are given here. The first is a classified list of current reviews, some of which have been appearing for many years, and the second is a list of discontinued reviews that are still useful for searches of older literature published before the abstract journals gave such good coverage. Neither list includes all of these publications, past or present, but an effort has been made to give the most useful ones. A few of those listed are issued every two years.

Current Annual Reviews

CHEMISTRY AS A WHOLE

Annual Reports on the Progress of Chemistry. 1904–   . These are published by the Chemical Society, London. The reports are well written by competent specialists and there are many references to the original articles. There is little emphasis on applied chemistry after 1916. These reports are especially useful for keeping in touch with the advancement of chemistry as a whole.

Chemical Age Yearbook, Diary and Directory. London, Benn.

Chymia. 1948–   . Philadelphia, Univ. of Pennsylvania Press. These are studies of the history of chemistry.

Fortschritte der chemischen Forschung. 1950–   . Berlin, Springer. These are good reviews with extensive bibliographies. This publication is not always an annual; at the present time four numbers per year are being issued.

INDUSTRIAL CHEMISTRY

Advances in Chemical Engineering. 1956–   . New York, Academic Press.

Jahresbericht über die Leistungen der chemischen Technology. 1855–   . Leipzig, Barth. This publication was founded by R. von Wagner. Numerous references to the literature.

Reports on the Progress of Applied Chemistry. 1916–   . Published by the Society of Chemical Industry (London), it was called *Annual Reports of the Society of Chemical Industry on the Progress of Applied Chemistry* until 1949. These are especially useful for keeping in touch with the advancement of industrial chemistry as a whole and compare favorably with the *Annual Reports of the Chemical Society.*

Almost every chemical industry or industry that uses chemistry is covered by one or more yearbooks, annual directories, or similar compilations. They vary greatly in the amount of review material that they contain. No attempt has been made to include all of these. Only those that are primarily review publications are given here.

AGRICULTURAL CHEMISTRY

Advances in Agronomy. 1950– . New York, Academic Press. These are published for the American Society of Agronomy.

Annual Report of the Agricultural and Hormone Research Station, Long Aston, Bristol, England.

Yearbook of Agriculture, The United States Department of Agriculture.

BIOCHEMISTRY

Advances in Biological and Medical Physics. 1948– . New York, Academic Press.

Advances in Cancer Research. 1953– . New York, Academic Press.

Advances in Enzymology and Related Subjects in Biochemistry. 1944– . New York, Interscience.

Advances in Genetics. 1947– . New York, Academic Press.

Advances in Virus Research. 1953– . New York, Academic Press.

Annual Review of Biochemical and Allied Research in India. 1930– . Bangalore, Society of Biological Chemists.

Annual Review of Biochemistry. 1932– . Stanford, Cal., Annual Rev. Inc., Collective index, Vols. 1–10 (1932–1942).

Annual Review of Microbiology. 1947– . Stanford, Cal., Annual Rev. Inc.

Annual Review of Plant Physiology. 1939– . Stanford, Cal., Annual Rev. Inc.

Annual Review of Physiology. 1939– . Stanford, Cal., Annual Rev. Inc.

Ergebnisse der Enzymforschung. 1932– . Leipzig, Geest and Portig.

Ergebnisse der Hygiene, Bakteriologie, Immunitätsforschung und Experimentellen Therapie. This is a continuation of *Jahresbericht über Ergebnisse der Immunitätsforschung* and continues its volume numbers. Berlin, Springer. It has been published for many years.

Ergebnisse der Physiologie, biologischen Chemie, und Experimentellen Pharmakologie. 1898– . Berlin, Springer.

Exposés annuels de biochimie médicale. 1945– . Paris, Masson.

Immitätforschung, Die. 1947– . Berlin, Springer.

International Review of Cytology. 1952– . New York, Academic Press.

Progress in Biophysics and Biophysical Chemistry. 1950– . London, Pergamon.

Soviet Annual Review of Biochemistry. 1951– . Moscow, Academy of Medical Sciences.

Vitamins and Hormones, Advances in Research and Applications. 1943– . New York, Academic Press.

FOODS

Advances in Food Research. 1948– . New York, Academic Press.

Survey of Food and Nutrition Research. This is prepared by the Food and Nutrition Research Board of the National Research Council. Washington, D. C. Government Printing Office. The volume for 1952–1953 was issued in 1954.

Fuels and Carbonization Products

Progress in Coal Science. 1950– . London, Butterworth. This includes the carbonization of coal and the chemical utilization of coal.

Review of Coal Tar Technology. 1950– . This is published semi-annually by the Coal Tar Research Association, Oxford Rd., Gomersal, Leeds, England. It includes an international review of patents.

Fats, Waxes, Detergents

Blue Book of Soap and Sanitary Chemicals. A supplement to the periodical *Soap and Sanitary Chemicals,* New York. 27th year (1954).

Metals and Metallurgy

American Society of Metals Review of Metal Literature. 1944– . This is an annual collection of sections of the periodical *Metals Review* (monthly). Cleveland, The American Society for Metals.

Mineral Resources of United States. 1883–1931. This was published by the Geological Survey up to 1924 and then by the Bureau of Mines.

Minerals Yearbook. 1932– . This is a continuation of *Mineral Resources of U. S.* (see preceding entry), but its coverage is broader. In 1944 a section called "Foreign Metals Review" was added and coverage is international from 1944 on. Issued by the United States Bureau of Mines, Washington, D. C., Government Printing Office.

Progress in Metal Physics. 1949– . London, Pergamon.

Yearbook of the American Iron and Steel Institute, New York.

Mineralogical and Geological Chemistry

Advances in Geophysics. 1952– . New York, Academic Press.

Fortschritte der Minerologie, Stuttgart, Schweizerbart.

Minerals Yearbook (see above under Metals).

Organic Chemistry

Advances in Carbohydrate Chemistry. 1945– . New York, Academic Press.

Advances in Protein Chemistry. 1944– . New York, Academic Press.

Fortschritte der Chemie organischer Naturstoffe. 1938– . Vienna, Springer. This review on the progress in the chemistry of organic natural products is an international one, and the authoritative papers are written in several languages (English, French, German). The bibliographies are very comprehensive.

Progress in the Chemistry of Fats and Other Lipids. 1953– . London, Pergamon Press.

Progress in Organic Chemistry. 1951– . London, Butterworth.

Synthetic Methods of Organic Chemistry. 1948– . New York, Interscience. An annual survey.

Synthetic Organic Chemicals, U. S. Production and Sales. This was formerly called *Census of Dyes.* It is actually a record of the United States organic chemical industry from about 1916 to date. Most of the material is of a statistical nature, but there are discussions of developments in each field of organic chemistry. Issued by the United States Tariff Commission. Washington, D. C., Government Printing Office.

PAPER AND CELLULOSE CHEMISTRY

Yearbook of the American Pulp and Paper Mill Superintendents Association. Chicago.

Zellstoff, Papier- und Kunstseidenerzeugung. Verein der Zellstoff- und Papierchemiker und -Ingenieure. Berlin, Otto Elsner.

PETROLEUM

Petroleum Data Book. 1947–   . Dallas, Texas, Petroleum Engineer Pub. Co. This is not an annual review but a source book of information that covers the entire world.

Reviews of Petroleum Technology. 1950–   . London, The Institute of Petroleum.

PHARMACEUTICAL CHEMISTRY

Annual Report on Essential Oils, Aromatic Chemicals and Related Materials. New York, Schimmel and Co.

Jahresbericht über Neuerungen auf den Gebieten der Pharmakotherapie und Pharmazie. 1887–   . Darmstadt, E. Merck.

PHYSICAL CHEMISTRY AND NUCLEAR SCIENCE

Advances in Catalysis and Related Subjects. 1948–   . New York, Academic Press.

Advances in Electronics. 1948–   . New York, Academic Press.

Annual Review of Nuclear Science. 1952–   . Stanford, Cal., Annual Rev. Inc. This is prepared in cooperation with the National Research Council.

Annual Review of Physical Chemistry. 1950–   . Stanford, Cal., Annual Rev. Inc.

Digest of Literature on Dielectrics. 1937–   . Washington, D. C., The National Research Council.

Progress in Nuclear Energy. 1956–   . New York, McGraw-Hill.

Progress in Nuclear Physics. 1951–   . London, Pergamon Press.

Reports on Progress in Physics. 1934–   . London, The Physical Society.

Structure Reports (annual review of crystallography, and X-ray and electron diffraction). Published by Oostoek (Utrecht, Holland) for the International Union of Crystallography.

PLASTICS

British Plastics Yearbook. 1931–   .

RUBBER

Annual Survey of American Rubber Chemistry. Pittsburgh, Pa., The Carnegie Institute of Technology.

Annual Report on the Progress of Rubber Technology. 1937–   . London, Institute of the Rubber Industry.

TEXTILES AND DYES

Review of Textile Progress. 1949–   . London, The Textile Institute. This is a joint publication with the Society of Dyers and Colourists, Manchester, England.
Technical Manual and Yearbook of the American Association of Textile Chemists and Colorists. Lowell, Mass.

WATER

Vom Wasser, Ein Jahrbuch für Wasserchemie und Wassererreinigungstechnik. 1927–   . Weinheim/Bergstrasse, Verlag Chemie.

DISCONTINUED ANNUAL REVIEWS

Berzelius' Jahresberichte über die Fortschritte der physischen Wissenschaften (last volumes der Chemie). 1821–1847.
Jahrbuch der Chemie. 1891–1918. Vieweg. R. Meyer, editor.
Jahrbuch der Electrochemie und angewandten physikalischen Chemie. 1894–1909. Knapp.
Jahrbuch der Erfindungen und Fortschritte auf den Gebieten der Physik und Chemie, der Technologie und Mechanik, der Astronomie und Meteorologie. Leipzig, 1865–1892.
Jahrbuch für ökonomische Chemie und verwandte Fächer. 1847–1849. Leipzig.
Jahrbuch der organischen Chemie. 1907–1932. Stuttgart, Wissenschaftliche Verlagsgesellschaft.
Jahrbuch der Spinnerei, Weberei und Textilchemie. 1911–   . Altenburg, F. L. Muller.
Jahresbericht für Agricultur-Chemie. 1858–1933. Berlin, Parey.
Jahresbericht über die Fortschritte der Agriculturchemie. 1860–1892. Berlin.
Jahresbericht über die Fortschritte der Chemie und verwandter Theile anderer Wissenschaften. 1847–1915. Founded by Liebig and Kopp.
Jahresbericht über die Fortschritte auf dem Gebiete der reinen Chemie. 1874–1883. Tübingen.
Jahresbericht über die Fortschritte der Tierchemie, oder der physiologischen und pathologischen Chemie. 1871–1919. Wiesbaden. Collective indexes decennially.
Jahresbericht über die Fortschritte in der Untersuchung der Nahrungs- und Genussmittel.
Jahresbericht der Pharmazie. 1866–   . Göttingen.
Neues Jahrbuch für Mineralogie, Geologie und Paläontologie. 1807–1950. In two Abteilungen (mineralogy-petrography and geology-paleontology). Stuttgart, Schweizerbart.
A Survey of American Chemistry. 1926–1935.
Technisch-chemisches Jahrbuch. 1878–1905. Biedermann (ed.). Vols. 1–3 were issued as supplements to the *Chemiker-Kalender.*

Other Reviews

There are also a number of periodicals that appear monthly or quarterly that are devoted entirely to reviews. Usually the articles in these periodicals have extensive bibliographies. These periodicals have been discussed in Chapter 3 and will be found in appropriate places in the classified list given there. Only a few will be mentioned here because they are particularly useful for their wide coverage.

Science Progress (England)	*Chemical Reviews*
Research (England)	(United States)
Scientia, Milan (Italy)	*Quarterly Reviews*
Experientia (Switzerland)	(Chemical Society, London)

A number of other journals make a practice of reviewing work within their field at intervals, usually once a year. These review articles vary considerably in their bibliographies; some of them list many references, others few. The list is too long to give here; it would be a repetition of a large number of the titles of periodicals listed in Chapter 3. *Chemical Abstracts* usually gives the title, states that the paper is a review, and gives the number of references in its bibliography; it seldom abstracts reviews. They are indexed in the author and subject indexes.

Organizations

Many foundations, research institutes, and scientific and technical societies publish scientific journals; those of chemical interest have been included in Chapter 3, Periodicals. Some of these organizations also issue bulletins and other types of separate publications on chemistry or of value to chemists. The trade associations, such as the National Canners Association, are not considered here; their publications were discussed in Chapter 6, Trade Literature. There are a large number of these organizations in the United States and in other countries. Sources of information on the work and publications of these organizations will be found in Appendix 5.

The National Research Council of the National Academy of Sciences, an important organization in the United States, cooperates with many scientific and technical organizations both in the United States and abroad. Most of its publications are bibliographic in nature and many are of interest to chemists. The National Research Council was organized in 1916 through an executive order of the President of the United States. It is not a government agency, but it works in close cooperation with the government.

The Carnegie Institution of Washington has published a large number of scientific books and bulletins, some of which are on chemistry. It also issues bibliographic materials. The results of part of its scientific investigations are published in various periodicals.

Theses

Universities ordinarily require theses (also called dissertations) of their candidates for higher degrees. These record original work. Most of them are doctoral dissertations, for most foreign universities do not grant a master's degree and many American universities do not require theses for the master's degree in chemistry. Some universities require them to be printed; others do not. In many cases the valuable part of the thesis is published in a chemical journal, but the journals do not have space for as much detail as is given in the theses. Some of them are never published, even in part. Universities that do not require printed theses preserve written or typewritten copies that may be consulted; in some cases there are several copies and a thesis can be borrowed by a library. Microfilm and photoprint copies can be obtained in most cases. Those institutions that require printed theses usually exchange copies with other universities; hence, some university libraries have valuable collections of domestic and foreign theses.

Because some dissertations are not published, or are published only in part, it is important to be able to learn the titles of theses, where they originate, and how copies can be obtained.

Theses that are published in part are not difficult to locate in most cases. In a literature search one does not depend upon the abstract which appears in an abstract journal but nearly always consults the original paper. If a paper in a journal represents a part of a dissertation, there is a footnote to that effect. It is unusual for the professor who directed the work to publish it under his name only. Abstract journals rarely state that a paper represents part of a dissertation.

The unpublished theses can often be located by various methods; the principal ones are use of union lists for various countries, use of university publications, and correspondence with university libraries. Only a part of these will be discussed here. A very comprehensive list of sources for the various countries of the world is given in a paper on theses and dissertations by Marr.[1] For the older dissertations accepted by U. S. universities and more information on other countries, see that paper.

There are two sources that cover the older dissertations from a large number of countries:

Bolton, H. C., *Select Bibliography of Chemistry*, Washington, D. C. Smithsonian Institution, 1901–1904. Section 8, "Academic Dissertations." This work covers theses for the period 1492–1902.

Catalogue des dissertations et écrits provenant des échanges avec les universités étrangères et reçus par la Bibliothèque Nationale, 1882–1925. Paris, Bibliothèque Nationale. The library has a very large collection of dissertations from all over the world because the Ministry of Education of France operates an exchange system, but this is its only printed catalog.

In a number of countries a union list is issued annually that covers all the universities in that country.

UNITED STATES

American Chemical Society Directory of Graduate Research. Washington, D. C., American Chemical Society. 1953– .
Doctoral Dissertations Accepted by American Universities. 1933– . Annual. New York, Wilson Co.
Dissertation Abstracts. 1938– . Ann Arbor, Michigan, University Microfilms. This is a guide to doctoral dissertations that are not printed but are available in full on microfilm. It is issued 6 times a year. It was called *Microfilm Abstracts* up to 1952. It is now abstracted by *Chemical Abstracts* when the theses are of chemical interest. *Dissertation Abstracts* is growing in value because a number of American universities have dropped the printing requirement for dissertations and many are available from *University Microfilms*.

CANADA

Chemistry in Canada publishes a list annually, beginning in 1949, of dissertations and theses accepted by Canadian universities.

GREAT BRITAIN

Index to Theses Accepted for Higher Degrees in the Universities of Great Britain and Ireland. Vol. I (1950–1951). London, Aslib, 1953. This is issued annually.

FRANCE

Catalogue des thèses et éscrits académique. 1884– . Paris, Ministère de l'instruction publique. Published annually.

GERMANY

Jahresverzeichnis der deutschen Hochschulschriften. 1885– . Berlin and Leipzig. Publisher varies. Title changed in 1935 from *Jahresverzeichnis der an deutschen Universitäten erschienen Schriften.* Published annually.

Jahresverzeichnis der schweizischen Universität. 1897– . Basel, Verlag der Universität Bibliotek. Published annually.

Bibliographies

Strictly speaking, a bibliography is a list of books; but in science, since most new information is published in journals, it is usually a list of articles. It may be either or both. A bibliography may also contain references to trade literature, patents, government publications, and dissertations. The typical bibliography is a list of references to writings on a particular subject or by a particular author. Some are arranged chronologically, others by authors, still others by subjects, and a large bibliography may be accompanied by one or more indexes. A bibliography may be found in an article, in a chapter in a book, at the end of a book, or it may be published separately.

Bibliographies are valuable sources of information and it is well to see how many have been prepared on a subject under investigation before a literature search goes very far. It sometimes happens that enough are available to cover most of a problem under investigation and only need to be brought up to date. Even if one is not so fortunate, any that are found save time and work.

The number of bibliographies on chemistry, or specific fields of chemistry, that exist as separate publications is relatively small. One usually needs to look for them in articles that appear in periodicals and in books. Many valuable bibliographies also exist only in manuscript form.

Bibliographies that are published as separate items are located through the same methods as books. See Chapter 2 for these.

Unpublished bibliographies are sometimes available. The Science-Technology Group of the Special Libraries Association maintains a pool of them at Battelle Memorial Institute, Columbus, Ohio; copies can be borrowed.

Usually the only way to locate a bibliography that is part of a paper is through the abstracting journals. Look for papers that deal with the subject of search. Occasionally the abstract mentions that a paper has a bibliography of a given number of references, but usually it is necessary to consult the original paper. *Chemical Abstracts* has asked abstractors in recent years to indicate bibliographies that are extensive enough to be of value.

The Bibliographic Index. 1937– . New York, Wilson Co. This is a collective bibliography of bibliographies. It is a subject index with good cross references and includes bibliographies that were published separately and also those published as a part of a book, an article in a periodical, or a pamphlet. A considerable amount of scientific material is covered.

There are a few compilations available, but they are useful only for the older material. No recent ones have appeared.

Berolzheimer, D. D., and West, C. J., *Bibliography of Bibliographies on Chemistry and Chemical Technology.* 1900–1924. Washington, D. C. The National Research Council, Bull. no. 50 (1925). First supplement, 1924–1928 (Bull. no. 71, 1929). Second supplement, 1929–1931 (Bull. no. 86, 1932).

Sohn, J. A., and Schaaf, W. L., *Reference Lists of Bibliographies. Chemistry, Chemical Technology and Engineering Since 1900.* New York, Wilson Co. 1924.

Bolton, H. C., *A Select Bibliography of Chemistry.* Washington, D. C., The Smithsonian Institution, 1893–1904. This covers publications of the period 1492–1902.

These three works include thousands of bibliographies on many subjects so it is well to check them when working with the period which they cover.

A few are found in general works like Besterman, Theodore, *A World Bibliography of Bibliographies*, 2nd ed., London, Oxford Univ. Press, 1947–1949.

Addresses and Lectures

The address is a freer form of expression than is the stated review. The speaker can sum up in half an hour a point of view developed through years of experience. When delivered by one who knows his subject well and at the same time has a gift for expression, the result is a delight and often a great stimulus. The addresses of presidents of scientific and technical societies, of medal recipients, and of speakers on other special occasions are frequently most profitable to hearers or readers. *Science* and *Nature* print many of these addresses; many on chemical topics appear in the chemical journals. Sometimes a bibliography is added when addresses are printed.

A lecture is usually a somewhat more didactic production. Singly it may amount merely to a review, but often it forms one of a series on the same topic, given on invitation by a person of some note. The series may be published later as a book. The "lecture" style is more familiar than that of a book. Sometimes lectures are printed in periodicals; they usually have a bibliography.

Preprints and Reprints

It is the custom of scientific journals to furnish the author of an article with reprints of the same. Reprinted articles take the form of a leaflet or phamphlet. Occasionally the article is printed in this manner before its appearance in the journal, when it is called a preprint or advanced print.

Reprints should always indicate exactly the reference to the place where the original article will be found, and they should retain the original page numbers of the journal (whether or not they also have a pagination of their own). An author can usually obtain any desired number of reprints by ordering them when he returns the proof of his article.

Some scientists make a practice of collecting and filing reprints of subjects of interest to them. Authors will usually honor requests for reprints from those who have legitimate use for them, if not too long delayed after the appearance of the article. Occasionally a periodical sells reprints of papers.

Personal Correspondence

The possibility of obtaining or exchanging information by correspondence seems so obvious as scarcely to need mention. It is worth while to note that in the earlier days of science personal letters held a very important place in announcing discoveries and in criticism. Such correspondence has not been entirely displaced by scientific publications and meetings. Those interested in the same special topics will continue to exchange notes and some material.

As a rule, scientists are very ready to respond to personal inquiries when the information wanted cannot be obtained through the regular channels.

Unpublished Material

The reader may wonder why unpublished material is mentioned in this book, which is devoted to the enormous body of published scientific information that is available. There are a number of cases, nevertheless, when it is worth while to seek unpublished information.

One instance has just been discussed, the thesis or dissertation, and it was pointed out that the unpublished ones contain a good deal of useful information.

Another case is the need for detailed information that does not appear in the published literature. The constantly expanding volume of scientific literature is causing the editors to condense it more and more strictly. The reason is not only that funds for publishing have a limit, but, also, that the reader may have new information as promptly as possible without being compelled to wade through details useful to only a portion of scientists. Some periodicals now use an auxiliary method of publication to cover this material; a footnote states that the full manuscript, or the unpublished portion of it, has been deposited with an organization that can provide photoprints or microfilm copies. But frequently the only way to obtain information on analytical procedure, methods of purification, quantitative and statistical records, and minutiae of methods is to write to the author. If too much time has gone by to get the information from the author, and if a considerable amount of work would be required to duplicate details, it is often wise to consult those who are currently working in the field to see if they have unpublished information available.

Another reason for seeking as yet unpublished information is delay in publication. The large volume of scientific work is slowing up the process of publication. Nearly all valuable scientific work is published eventually, unless withheld for commercial or national security reasons. One may attend a scientific meeting, read the program or abstracts of papers presented at a meeting, or in some other way learn of research that is valuable to him. He may need the information before it is published months later. Some scientists are slow in getting their papers into form for publication and some journals have backlogs of manuscripts or other reasons for delay.

Alexander [2] has pointed out other reasons for searching for unpublished information. Hers is an excellent paper. Alexander points out that there is a considerable amount of unpublished information for limited circulation that may be available under certain circumstances. Permission to use some of this information may save a great deal of time for a research worker.

Museum Collections

The collection of museum material and the use of it as a source of information have not attained the same importance in chemistry as in such sciences as botany or mineralogy. Chemists frequently do, however, make use of a substance already prepared by some other worker and even send long distances for it. Shelves of research laboratories serve as repositories to a certain extent, but such material is scattered and only local workers know about it. The Smith-

sonian Institution, Washington, D. C., has the Loeb Collection of
Chemical Types, valuable for reference and comparison.
The few collections of chemical apparatus are mostly of historical
interest. The Science Museum, London, has a very large collection
of scientific instruments and equipment dating back to the last half
of the eighteenth century.

Center for Rare Chemicals

A registry of rare chemicals is maintained at the Armour Research
Foundation. If the registry does not have a chemical sought, it will
furnish information on who makes it or help to locate it. Inquiries
should be addressed to the Registry of Rare Chemicals, Armour Research Foundation, 35 West 33rd St., Chicago 16, Ill.

Biographical Works

One might not think of a biography as a source of chemical information, but in the case of a scientist, a biography frequently contains a very complete list of his publications. This is true not only
of book-length biographies of chemists, but also of biographical material published in the scientific journals. For such writings the abstract journals usually list the title and state whether the paper is
biographical, an obituary, or a memorial lecture. Any one of these
may contain a very complete list of the scientist's writings and should
not be passed over in literature searches. Higgins [3] has published a
list of book-length biographies of chemists.

The Royal Society of London published obituary notices of fellows
of the society in its *Proceedings* until 1932; they are now published
separately. These notices include many chemists and usually give
complete bibliographies of their work. Volume 75 of the *Proceedings of the Royal Society* contains obituaries for the deceased members for the period 1898–1904 and an index for similar notices for
1860–1899. The Society has always had a considerable number of
foreign members.

The memorial lectures of the Chemical Society of London are
products of a long-standing custom. These have been delivered
before the Society for many years in commemoration of the lives
and works of eminent deceased chemists. Many of these chemists
were not members of the Society. Again these lectures are international in their coverage. Many of these have been printed in the
Journal of the Chemical Society (London). They have also been
collected and issued separately, *Memorial Lectures Delivered Before*

the Chemical Society, London, Gurney. Several volumes have been published since 1900. These lectures frequently contain a bibliography of the scientist's work. Vols. I–III cover the period 1893–1932.

Bugge, Günther, *Das Buch der grossen Chemiker*, 2 vols., Berlin, Verlag Chemie, 1929–1930. This also gives lists of the writings of great chemists.

The most comprehensive source is J. C. Poggendorff's *Biographisch-literarisches Handwörterbuch zur Geschichte der exacten Wissenschaften*. This was published by Barth, Leipzig, from 1863 to 1904. Verlag Chemie, Weinheim/Bergstrasse, resumed publication of the work in 1925 and published several volumes by 1941 (more may be issued). The six volumes issued thus far cover the lives and the writings of scientists from 1857 through 1931. It includes chemists of all countries and the detailed bibliographies include periodical articles.

The *Biography Index*, 1946–   . New York, Wilson Co. This is a cumulative index that is sometimes useful in locating biographical material on chemists. It has wide coverage of periodicals, books, and some newspapers.

The bibliography given in Smith's book, see below under "Portraits," is also very useful.

Portraits

In lieu of personal contact pictures make more vivid our memory of persons and stimulate the imagination. Portraits of well known chemists help to impart human interest in studying their work. Inquiries are made from time to time as to how such pictures can be obtained. Some appear in the scientific periodicals with biographical papers, obituaries, and memorial lectures. The photographs of many contemporary American chemists appeared on the cover of *Chemical and Engineering News*. The *Journal of Chemical Education* issued three portfolios of portraits of famous chemists in 1945 and may still have some available. Some libraries have clipped and mounted many portraits as they appeared in publications and have quite a large collection. The *Memorial Lectures of the Chemical Society* (London) and the *Obituaries of the Royal Society*, which were mentioned in the section above, contain a large number of portraits. The most extensive collection in a single publication is found in H. M. Smith's *Torchbearers of Chemistry*, New York, Academic Press, 1949. This book contains the portraits of 223 chemists active throughout the history of chemistry, including some contemporary chemists. Each portrait is accompanied by a very brief biographical sketch. An appendix to Smith's book, a bibliography of biographies, compiled by Ralph E. Oesper, gives references for each person and refers the reader to a wealth of material about them that has been published elsewhere.

Motion Pictures

Motion pictures are not searched as a source of chemical information for investigational use. However, they are useful sources of information for teaching and like purposes. Manufacturing companies have made a large number of them in recent years as one form of advertising; many of them are on topics of chemical interest. Many of these films are excellent and give a knowledge of industrial chemistry that is not conveyed by written material; they are the next best thing to plant inspection trips. There are also a number of films on various fields of chemistry that have been made specifically for teaching purposes. The American Chemical Society has compiled lists from time to time and has issued booklets on films available from industrial sources; it usually has a current list available. There are a number of guides for locating this material. The most useful current guides for educational films from all sources are: *The Bluebook of 16 mm. Films* (Chicago, Educational Screen); *The Educational Film Guide* and the *Filmstrip Guide* (New York, Wilson Co.); and *The Educators Guide to Free Films* (Randolph, Wis., Educators Progress Service).

Committee Work

The output of committees of scientific organizations constitute a special source of information. The reports and publications that they compile frequently contain information that is not available from other sources. Then, too, standing committees are sources of unpublished information on subjects within the fields of their work. There is a kind of work that can be done better by a committee of specialists than by individuals, or that requires the authority of a large body back of it to make it effective. Also, the work may be something that is very much needed, but it is not done until some committee is specifically asked to attend to it. Activities of this nature include the setting up of standards of all kinds, solving of questions of nomenclature, coordination of reseach, compilation of special data, etc.

Committees charged with the solution of a certain problem are usually glad to receive help from the outside and are in a special position to furnish information to others. It is advisable to be familiar with the committee work in progress under the International Union of Pure and Applied Chemistry, The National Research Council (United States), The American Chemical Society, and other organizations. Committee reports usually appear in the periodicals published by the sponsoring organization. Large reports are issued as bulletins or books.

Personal Contact

Any experienced chemist will testify to the value of frequent personal contacts with other scientific workers. Meetings with local scientists are valuable. But the occasions par excellence are the great annual or semi-annual gatherings of the members of a society from all over the country, or the periodic meetings of international scientific organizations. Here one may hear the latest advances explained or discussed, and may see or meet personally men with whose work he is already familiar. A single conversation at such a convention is often worth the whole trip. The discussion that occurs after the presentation of a paper may be just as valuable as the paper; in some cases it is more valuable. The papers will be published in the course of time but the conversations never are and the discussions in this day of scarce space in journals rarely are published.

If one is seeking information on a particular problem he may obtain more by talking with several persons at one of these meetings than by a great amount of work with the printed literature. What he needs may not even be in the literature.

Every scientist should belong to one or more scientific organizations and take an active part in their activities, not only because their meetings and publications are invaluable to him, but also to contribute his share to the organizations working for the good of his science. Union is necessary if science is to have its due influence in the world.

OTHER SCIENCES

Many chemical problems require the application of more than one science to solve them. A number of publications dealing with other sciences are included in Chapter 3, Periodicals, and in Chapter 8, Indexes, in this book because they frequently contain chemical in-

OTHER SCIENCES 223

formation or because they contain large quantities of it. When other publications are needed they may be located by the use of these guides.

GUIDES FOR SEVERAL SCIENCES

Jenkins, F. B., *Science Reference Sources*, Champaign, Ill., Univ. of Illinois Library School, 1954, 90 pp., mimeographed. (Distributed by the Illini Union Book Store, Champaign, Ill.) It is a classified list that covers the most important sources for general science, mathematics, chemistry, astronomy, geology, biological sciences, botany, zoology, psychology, engineering sciences, agricultural sciences, and medical sciences. Dictionaries, encyclopedias, bibliographies, indexes, abstract journals, reviews, surveys, directories, handbooks, tables of data, and some of the more comprehensive books or treatises are included. So are lists of articles that have appeared in periodicals that give valuable information. It is a very useful compilation.

Fleming, T. P., *Guide to the Literature of Science*, New York, School of Library Service of Columbia Univ., 1952, 56 pp., mimeographed. This is also a classified list of the same general type as Jenkins' *Science Reference Sources*. But it does not cover engineering, agriculture, or medicine.

GUIDES FOR SPECIFIC SCIENCES

The guides to the literature of chemistry are listed in Appendix I, page 329.

AGRICULTURAL SCIENCES

There is no guide to the literature of the agricultural sciences.

ASTRONOMY

There is no guide to the literature of astronomy.

BIOLOGICAL SCIENCES

Bouliere, F., *Eléments d'un guide bibliographique du naturaliste*. Macon, Protat Frères, 1940, Paris, Lechevalier, Supplements 1–2, 1941–1942.

Chamberlain, J. W., *Entomological Nomenclature and Literature*, 2nd ed., Ann Arbor, Mich., Edwards, 1946.

Smith, R. C., *Guide to the Literature of the Zoological Sciences*, rev. ed., Minneapolis, Burgess Pub. Co., 1952, 133 pp.

ENGINEERING

Dalton, B. H., *Sources of Engineering Information*, Berkeley, Univ of California Press, 1948, 109 pp.

Directory of Engineering Data Sources, A Guide to American Literature in Engineering and Related Sciences, Atlanta, Georgia, Southeastern Research Institute, 1948.

Holmstrom, J. E., *Records and Research in Engineering and Industrial Science*, 2nd ed., London, Chapman & Hall, 1947, 366 pp.

Parke, N. G., *Guide to the Literature of Mathematics and Physics Including Related Works on Engineering Science*, New York, McGraw-Hill, 1947.
Roberts, A. D., *Guide to Technical Literature; Introductory Chapters and Engineering*, London, Grafton, 1939, 279 pp.

GEOGRAPHY

Wright, J. K., *Aids to Geographical Research: Bibliographies, Periodicals, Atlases, Gazeteers, and Other Reference Books*, 2nd ed., New York, Columbia Univ. Press. 1947.

GEOLOGICAL SCIENCES

Pearl, R. M., *Guide to Geologic Literature*, New York, McGraw-Hill, 1951, 239 pp. This guide covers related fields.
Mason, Brian, *The Literature of Geology*, New York, the author, c/o Museum of Natural History, 1953, 155 pp.

HISTORY OF SCIENCE

Sarton, George, *A Guide to the History of Science*, Waltham, Mass., Chronica Botanica Co., 1952, 316 pp.

MATHEMATICS

See Physics, below.

MEDICAL SCIENCES

Jones, I. M., and Doe, J. (eds.), *Handbook of Medical Library Practice*, 2nd ed., Chicago, American Library Association, 1954.

PHYSICS

Parke, G. N., *Guide to the Literature of Mathematics and Physics*, New York, McGraw-Hill, 1947, 205 pp.
Whitford, Robert, *Physics Literature*, Washington, D. C., Scarecrow Press, 1954, 228 pp.

There is one useful abstract journal in the field of engineering that was not included in any of the guides given above, *Technische Zentralblatt* (Germany), 1951–   .

Attention is called to Sarton's *Guide to the History of Science*. It contains much information of use to a person making chemical literature searches or searches in other fields. The annotations on the older encyclopedias, on encyclopedias of more recent date for many countries, on biographical materials, on general scientific journals, and other materials are very valuable. There is also a list of publications on scientific instruments, a list of abstract journals and reviews that includes the date on which the periodical began and ceased publication, a list of museums, a list of international congresses, and, of course, many lists of books on science in general and on specific sciences.

The history of science and of specific sciences is a neglected field of study in most American colleges and universities. From the point of view of comprehensive literature searches in chemistry, it frequently happens that a history of chemistry or a history of science either for a specific country or a cultural group will yield suggestions and sources of information that would be missed without consulting it.

Information Service

The information bureau is a recognized institution—why not utilize it in science? However much this or other books or articles may seek to guide inquiries through the maze, definite questions arise that can be answered only by someone who knows; and this may raise the second problem—who and where is he?

Unfortunately, no definite answer can be given to the second problem. Apparently there is no compilation of the names and addresses of organizations that operate information bureaus or services for scientists. Some suggestions on sources of help are the best that can be offered.

The nearest library that has a good scientific collection may be able to answer the question. Librarians are usually happy to be of service. Libraries frequently have special files of material that they have built up over a period of time. Many of the present librarians in the science divisions of large libraries or in scientific libraries are both scientists and librarians. They deal with a great variety of questions and many types of literature searches so they may be able to suggest an approach that had not occurred to the inquirer even if they are not able to answer the question for him. Some librarians do not have a large enough staff to spend much time on a search. If the first library where inquiry is made cannot help, it will frequently get the information from another one or help to obtain it.

The larger chemical companies maintain extensive libraries and information services for their own use; some of them will gladly answer reasonable questions from outsiders.

A trade association may be able to answer questions for the inquirer. Trade associations often have information that is restricted to members of the association and is not published. When there is good reason, they sometimes give this information to outsiders.

Scientific and technical societies are helpful in locating persons or organizations to answer questions. The society of which you inquire may be able to answer the question for you.

The National Research Council (2101 Constitution Avenue, N.W., Washington, 25 D. C.) may be able to say where one can obtain the desired information or provide it. The Council has worked in cooperation with many scientific organizations, both in the United States and abroad, for many years.

The National Science Foundation (1520 H Street, N.W., Washington 25, D. C.) may be helpful. It is a comparatively new organization, but it is a federal agency and part of its work includes surveys of the work of scientific organizations, both public and private, and these surveys would be likely to cover information bureaus and similar services.

There are a few consulting chemists and consulting chemical firms that specialize in making literature searches and in supplying chemical information. The directory of consulting chemists and local sections of the American Chemical Society should be helpful in finding them.

Obtaining an answer to a question is partly a matter of presenting it to a suitable organization. It is obvious that those mentioned above are not equally suitable for all types of questions.

For directories of scientific and technical associations and trade associations see Appendix 5. For libraries see Appendix 3.

Means of obtaining leads and help have been outlined in many parts of this book. The individual, as a general rule, must expect to do his own searching. Success will depend on hard work combined with informed preparation for the work. Even employing another chemist to make a search will not succeed completely under some circumstances because of the difficulty in picturing needs to another.

LITERATURE CITED

(1) Marr, E. B., "Theses and Dissertations," a paper in *Searching the Chemical Literature,* no. 4 in the *Advances in Chemistry Series:* Washington, D. C. American Chemical Society, 1951.

(2) Alexander, Mary, "Searching for Unpublished Data," a paper in *Searching the Chemical Literature,* no. 4 in the *Advances in Chemistry Series,* American Chemical Society.

(3) Higgins, T. J., Book-length Biographies of Chemists, *School Sci. and Math.* **44,** 650–665 (1944).

CHAPTER 8

INDEXES

A reference work of any magnitude can usually be little better than its index. Dictionaries and encyclopedias are exceptions, but even the latter can be indexed to advantage. The value of a record is directly proportional to the availability of the information recorded; buried data and other information are lost to distribution and to use.

The need for full and complete indexing varies somewhat with the nature of the publication covered and the use to which it is put. It is much more important for an abstract journal to be thoroughly and properly indexed than for a journal only publishing full papers to be so indexed.

A reference publication should provide a sure means of locating every bit of information in it. Classification and logical arrangement often help and are worth while, but their applicability varies considerably. Except in special cases the main reliance must be placed on indexes.

It is not only desirable that the chemist should become familiar with the general nature and plan of the principal reference works in his field, whether they be books or journals, but also that he should become acquainted with the characteristics and limitations of their indexes. Existing indexes vary rather widely in quality as well as in kind. A chemist's knowledge of indexes and of how to use them effectively has much influence on his success as a literature searcher.

Kinds

Indexes may be independent of any specific publication, covering miscellaneous sources of information, as the *Industrial Arts Index* for example, or, as is much more common, they may be keys to specific books, journals, or other publications. They usually cover definite periods in the case of serials, as a volume or year. Collective indexes covering a number of years are published in some cases; these are particularly helpful in literature searches for they save much time. The indexes commonly in use in the literature of chemistry are of the following kinds:

(a) Author indexes.
(b) Subject indexes.
(c) Empirical-formula indexes of compounds.
(d) Ring-formula indexes of compounds.
(e) Patent-number indexes.

Each of these kinds will be treated separately in this chapter after a brief discussion of the general characteristics of all kinds and a few general hints for use.

In addition to the above well established kinds of indexes in use in chemistry, certain new kinds or variants of standard subject and formula indexes are being tried or contemplated. Cipher indexes, based on such new methods of designating chemical compounds as those worked out by G. Malcolm Dyson and William J. Wiswesser, have been suggested. Lawyers use citation indexes and some experimentation is going forward on the possibility of their being justifiably used by chemists. Indexing of compounds by groups is receiving consideration. Special types of subject index keys are variously known as desciptor indexes, coordinate indexes, and classified or systematic indexes. So-called coordinate indexing is sometimes called coincident indexing; Mortimer Taube calls his coordinate index a Uniterm index.

GENERAL CHARACTERISTICS

What constitutes a good index? It is one that will serve as a reliable means for the location, with a minimum of effort, of every bit of information in the source covered which, according to the indexing basis, that source contains. This test is broad enough in its applicability to be used in connection with any kind of index. To meet this test an index must be accurate, complete, sufficiently precise in the information supplied, and so planned and arranged as to be convenient to use. Existing indexes fall far short of this ideal in many cases and of course somewhat short of it in all cases.

It is not safe to assume that indexes are accurate, although usually they are reasonably so. It is easy for **errors,** particularly in references, to creep in during the compilation and printing, and only the most careful checking keeps them out. A common mistake of an indexer is to continue using a page number after he has turned to the next page; hence if the reference cannot be found on the page indicated it is well to look on the following page. The next most likely possibility is that two figures in the page number have been interchanged, as 2305 when 3205 is meant. It is sometimes possible to correct a wrong page number by referring to another kind of index in the same publication, as to the subject index if an author name and title have been located in an author index, or by referring to another subject obtained from the modifying phrase in case of a subject index entry with incorrect reference. In a reference work often in use it is advisable to make it a practice to write in corrections and additions as occasion demands.

Completeness is usually attained in author, formula, and patent-number indexes, but in subject indexes it can only be approximated and is frequently far from reached. More will be said about this in the section below on subject indexes. Consideration of precision and convenience in use will likewise be deferred till subject indexes are discussed, as their main importance is in connection with this kind of index.

The main purpose in indexing is sometimes partially lost sight of through an effort to bring some sort of **classification** into it. Classification in connection with indexing usually detracts from, rather than enhances, the efficiency and usefulness of an index and is beside the purpose. The Richter system of arrangement for entries in an empirical-formula index is an example of a mixture of classification and indexing to the detriment of the latter.

General Hints for Use

Conscious effort to become a good index user will well repay any scientist. Many a day has been spent in the laboratory seeking information by experiment that might have been obtained in a few minutes or hours at the most in the library had the literature search been efficient. Skill in literature searching involves skill in index using, and efficient index using is an art in itself—something to be acquired. This is particularly true with reference to subject indexes, as will be pointed out later. The first step in learning this art is to become familiar with the characteristics and peculiarities of the various kinds of indexes. An effort will be made to set these forth in this chapter.

The first general hint for use is found in the above statement that **index using is an art** in itself. This is not always realized, though it may seem to some to be too obvious to mention. It deserves emphasis. Of course, the ideal index would be one which anyone educated in the field covered can use effectively without special experience, but indexes vary much in quality, and even the best ones make it clear that the approach to the ideal is difficult. The index user must meet the indexer part way for really good results.

An index should be as little dependent upon separate explanatory matter as possible. An author index and to a large extent a subject index can be independent of such matter; the alphabetical arrangement of index headings (authors or subjects) is expected and assumed by the user. The arrangement in a patent-number index is likewise so simple as to be assumed. The arrangement in either an empirical-formula or a ring-formula index is less simple so that some sort of key or introduction in explanation of the system is a necessity. Though not really dependent thereon, important author and subject indexes sometimes are accompanied by **introductory matter** of an explanatory nature which is helpful. It is very much worth while to give careful attention to index introductions, no matter what the nature of the index, if one expects to make any considerable use of an index involved. One should be sure of the system.

It is important to avoid being too soon satisfied. Everyone has perhaps had the experience of looking for something, in an index or elsewhere, and after failing to find it has looked again, this time with success, and has wondered how he could have missed it before. It is worth while to look back and make absolutely sure in important cases. But much more important than this simple precaution is the advice to **be thorough.** There is no operation in which thoroughness is more important. It involves first a full knowledge of the system as advised in the preceding paragraph. Then one needs to be resourceful, exhausing all possibilities, if he is to avoid some futile searches or incomplete findings. This applies more particularly to subject indexes; these are the ones most used by far. One's fund of general knowledge can usually be brought into service to excellent advantage. This necessity for resourcefulness is less urgent in the use of the better-prepared indexes but it is always present. For example, in the best subject indexes well supplied with cross references it is less necessary to think up a variety of possible headings under which a subject might be entered, for in such indexes scattering will be largely eliminated and the cross references will lead the way to related subjects; but it is always well to remember that even the expert indexer has human limitations, and his range of knowledge of the subject in hand and of the subjects related to it may have been less than yours.

On account of the necessity of drawing on one's general knowledge in making a literature search in any field, it is in many instances greatly preferable that **one should make his own searches.** It is not always safe to let a librarian or some one else less well informed than oneself in a certain field make an index search when a complete survey is desired, even though his familiarity with indexes and the literature in general may be better than one's own. Just as some tasks in the laboratory can be turned over to another to advantage, but not the more important determinations and experiments, so some tasks in the library can safely be delegated to an assistant, but not all such tasks. Knowledge, skill, and power of observation are factors fruitful of important results in the library as well as in the laboratory.

The **kind of index best to use** in a given situation will usually be obvious. Sometimes in the use of one kind one will receive suggestions for the use of another kind. For example, if in looking up references on a subject in a subject index one finds that such and such an author has done considerable work on that subject, it may be advantageous to turn to that author's name, if an author index is provided, to see if some of his studies not located from the subject index may nevertheless have applicability, at least indirectly, to the subject. This is often worth while. If a compound is located in the formula index to *Chemical Abstracts*, it is not improbable that reference to the subject index at the place where the compound is entered by the name that follows the formula in the formula index will disclose derivatives or other related compounds of possible interest. A patent-number index will often serve as a lead to the name of a patentee, which name in an author index will lead to information regarding other patents of interest. The ring-formula index to *Chemical Abstracts* is a kind of key to the ring compounds entered in the subject index.

One should be prepared, persistent, and resourceful.

AUTHOR INDEXES

Although the use of indexes of author names is in general very simple, there are some special cases which at times lead to confusion and the missing of entries. Chief among these is the case of names from languages using different alphabet characters from our own. These must of course be transliterated before they can be entered in an index using Roman characters. The countries of most importance, as far as chemical literature is concerned, whose languages are printed in letters distinct from our own are Russia and Japan. These languages present somewhat different cases but the type of confusion resulting is the same.

The transliteration of **Russian names** is done according to comparative alphabets that have been worked out. If only one system were in use the trouble would not be great, but unfortunately such systems vary. They depend on pronunciation, and pronunciations vary in different parts of the world. This means that in the literature the same name may be and probably will be found spelled two or more ways if the author is a Russian. Sometimes such an author will be found entered in different places under different spellings in the same index. Some attempts have been made at standardization but no standard system has been universally recognized. A system worked out by a committee in England [1] has been adopted to a considerable extent; it is the predominant system in the English-speaking countries. It is used, with slight variations only, by *Chemical Abstracts*, by the Library of Congress, and in Webster's *New International Dictionary*. See Webster under "alphabet" for a table that shows this system or the annual author index to *Chemical Abstracts*. Some modifications in this English system of transliterating Russian names have recently been worked out by the Royal Society (London), and the International Abstracting Board is considering attempting to effect international standardization by its abstract journal members.

Some equivalents according to different spellings are noted below and should be kept in mind in looking up Russian names in the literature. Some of these, as "tsch," have come through German transliterations and are not necessarily desirable in English. Of course if a chemist settled in Germany, whose name was originally Russian, spells his name by German analogies his spelling should be respected. Of the equivalents listed below, the last in each instance is considered the preferable spelling.

"ce" is equivalent to "tze"

"tsch" is equivalent to "ch"

"j" is equivalent to "i," "y" or "ï"

"ks" is equivalent to "x"

"sch" is equivalent to "sh"

"ski," "sky" and "skago" (genitive form) are equivalent to "skii"

"w" and "ff" are equivalent to "v"

"i" is equivalent to "y"

"je" is equivalent to "e"

"sh" is equivalent to "zh"

"s" is equivalent to "z"

"ch" is equivalent to "kh"

"tz" is equivalent to "ts"

"schtsch" is equivalent to "shch"

Thus one will find in the literature both "Chugaev" (preferred) and "Tschugaeff" as spellings for the same name.

Japanese names can be written in our alphabet only on the basis of the pronunciation. Even though the exact pronunciation of a Japanese name is known there is usually more than one way in which that pronunciation can be expressed in English. For example, "chi" and "ti," "di" and "ji," "shi" and "si," "tu" and "tsu," and "zu" and "du" are used for the same respective pronunciations. Furthermore, Japanese authors at times adopt spellings for their names in our alphabet which may vary a little from the exact pronunciation. An example is the spelling Yebihara, where one would expect the spelling Ebihara. It is often difficult, even for a Japanese, to determine what the pronunciation of a given name is. Chinese letters are used for Japanese names. The pronunciation may be by proper Japanese derivation or according to old Chinese pronunciation. There is no way to tell which is the case. This means that two names spelled exactly alike in Japanese may properly be represented by very different spellings in our alphabet because of pronunciation differences. The confusion caused by this whole situation is not as bad, however, as one might expect. The more important Japanese chemical journals provide correct English spellings for the author names in connection with papers published. The Japanese government adopted a standard system of transliteration but this has not gained wide acceptance. *Chemical Abstracts* and some other publications now use the Hepburn system for transliterating Japanese names. *Chemical Abstracts,* urged to do so by Japanese individuals, adopted the Government system for the *Fourth Decennial Author In-*

dex, but went back to the use of the Hepburn system in 1947 when it became apparent that the proposed Government system was not taking hold in Japan as expected. When a Japanese has a name that is to be pronounced differently from what the ordinary educated Japanese might expect he usually puts Japanese letters under his name (first given in Chinese letters) to make the pronunciation clear.

Some differences in the transliteration of Japanese proper names by the Government system versus the Hepburn system are shown in the following table:

Government System	Hepburn System
si	shi
ti	chi
hu	fu
zi	ji
sya	sha
syu	shu
syo	sho
tu	tsu
tya	cha
tyu	chu
tyo	cho
zya	ja
zyo	jo
zyu	ju
nb	mb
nm	mm
np	mp
ō	o
zy	ji
e	ye

"Oh" in Japanese names denotes "o" with a long sound, which the Government system expresses as ō. Ohtake should be Ōtake, Itoh should be Itō, etc.

Dzu, é, du, j, and ye never exist in the Government system.

It is usually not difficult to recognize Japanese names. The names Aoyama, Hayashi, Ishikawa, Komatsu, Ogawa, Sugiura, Tasaki, Tashiro, for example, sound Japanese. There are certain characteristic end syllables, as -chi, -da, -do, -ji, -ki, -ma, -no, -ra, -ri, -shi, -su, -ta, -to, -wa, -ya, and -zu, which are very common in Japanese names. A Japanese name always ends in a vowel or "n" (a few Japanese in this country use "-oh" instead of "-o").

The **umlaut** is at times a source of confusion. It may be expressed by putting two dots over the vowel or an "e" after it. For example, one will see the name Röntgen also spelled Roentgen or Müller spelled Mueller. In some indexes a name involving an umlauted letter will be entered in the place where it comes alphabetically if the umlaut is disregarded (Plan A), whereas in others such a name will be alphabeted on a basis which considers the umlauted letter as being followed by "e" (Plan B). For example, in some indexes Müller will follow Mulhouse and in others it will precede it. If the confusion ended here it would not be bad, but there is another kind of mix-up that is likely to be involved that is more serious. Since umlauted letters are not used in English words, umlauts are rather frequently omitted when names involving such letters are reproduced in American and English publications. Typesetting keyboards and typewriters are not always so equipped as to make the reproduction of an umlauted letter as easy as the reproduction of the letter without an umlaut, and the umlaut is probably not considered of much importance by printers and typists. If this omission is not discovered the name is likely to get into an index minus its umlaut. The same name may also get in with its umlaut. Index entries for the same author in two different places because of an omitted umlaut are not common but they are to be found. In a large index such entries may be several pages apart if the name with the umlaut given is alphabeted by Plan B described above. Another common happening when names with umlauted letters are reproduced is the changing of an "ö," for example, to an "oe." If this is done part of the time, but not always, in the case of a given author name and an index in which this author name is entered is alphabeted according to Plan A above, it is obvious that the name would appear in two more or less widely separated places. Of course an alert indexer will be on the lookout for such situations and eliminate them. This is not always done, however, and the indexer is not always to blame. The safe plan is to look both places.

It is possible for the same name to get into an index in three different ways as a result of the above-discussed situations, the spellings Müller, Mueller, and Muller serving as an example.

The **Scandinavian letter "ø"** is sometimes like the umlauted letter "ö" as discussed in the preceding paragraphs. As a matter of fact, since printers outside of the Scandinavian countries do not as a rule have type for this letter, names involving it will be found with an "ö," an "o," or even an "oe" substituted for it. For example,

Sørensen's name will be found in the literature spelled Sörensen, Sorensen, and Soerensen, as well as the right way.

Another source of confusion at times is the **name with two or more parts** (the first part being frequently a preposition), as De Groot, Van Slyke, van der Meulen, Vom Baur, van Voorhout, van't Hoff, von Seelhorst, de Wisniewski, Pina de Rubies, etc. Other such name "prefixes" are D', Da, Dal, Del, Della, Des, Du, La, Le, Les, Mac, O'. It is always a question as to whether or not the alphabetic place in the index has been chosen on the basis of the first or last part. Different practices are followed in different indexes. Perhaps the most common way is to make the first part the basis for the alphabeting, if the beginning letter is a capital, and the second part if it is not; thus, De Groot, M.; and Seelhorst, T. S. von. Other indexes follow the practice of entering English and French surnames beginning with a preposition (except the French de and d') under the preposition, but making the entries under the word following with all other languages, irrespective of the use of capital or lower case for the first letter of the preposition; a name that has been anglicized is usually entered under the preposition, as Van Rensselaer. In a few indexes lower-case beginning letters and a secondary place are accorded the preposition or prefix, no matter what may be the practice of the author himself, and the name is entered under the second part. In the use of indexes in which the case of the first letter of the first part of names decides their place, the question of course arises as to which case is correct in any name. The indexer himself is often puzzled as to this as changes are often made in copied names. These usually occur either through carelessness or through lack of clearness as to whether a lower-case or capital letter is correct, because names are at times printed in capitals from beginning to end, thus: H. VAN DER MEULEN. Even if one knows the system followed in a given index and is certain as to the situation with reference to the letters in a name being sought, it is advisable, if the name is not found where expected, to try the other possible place since mistakes are not infrequent in this connection.

Some help is to be found in the following predominant national practices as to the above little problem.

In the British Commonwealth and in the United States "De" and "Van" in names start with capital letters and are considered in alphabetizing last names. In France "de" and "le" begin with lower-case letters. In Germany lower-case "v" begins "von." In Holland "van" is correct. In Italy "Di" is used. In South Africa "Du" is common. In South America "de" is commonly used.

The **custom in Spain** of using the mother's as well as the father's name at times is a source of bother to indexers and index users. Such a name will have the form A. Rius y Miro and will be found in indexes both as Rius y Miro, A. and as Miro, A. R. y. The former is preferable.

Related to the name with more than one part is the **compound name,** thus: Prinsen-Geerligs. This name will be found, in connection with papers, printed both as just given and without the hyphen, and it is not surprising therefore that indexes will have this and like names entered sometimes under the full compound name and sometimes under the last part.

In German-speaking Switzerland the wife's name is added with a hyphen to the husband's for social purposes. Thus Prof. Fr. Fichter's card reads Fichter-Bernoulli. Such compound names apparently rarely get into scientific literature.

Names starting with M' or Mc, as McMillan, are sometimes alphabeted as if spelled out Mac instead of in the strictly alphabetical place and sometimes under Mc. The former practice serves to bring together such names as MacLaurin and McLaurin. In an author index one may find such three different forms as M'leod, MacLeod, and McLeod. Occasionally an index will be found in which all the names starting with M' or Mc are separated entirely from the other M's as if the M' or Mc were a distinct part of the alphabet. **Names beginning with S., St., or Ste.** are usually alphabeted as though the prefix were written out (Sanctus, Saint, Sainte, respectively), but this rule is not applied to L' and O' since the prefixes for which these are contractions are not pronounced. In **Spanish CH** is a letter distinct from C and is given a separate place in certain foreign indexes. Again, because of the easy possibility of mistakes in spelling and because of the variation in practice, it is desirable to be a little wary in looking up such names.

Changes in names, which occur now and then, are usually taken care of in indexes by cross references. Sometimes they are merely slight changes in spelling and at other times they are radical changes. Aside from the case of the woman scientist who is married there is the case of the British scientist who has been raised to the nobility and uses a different name on that account.

Although in the United States only individuals can take out patents, in most foreign countries companies can do so. This means that in looking up the patent literature one will frequently find **company names** entered in indexes as author names. Occasionally one may have trouble finding a company name for such reasons as the following: At times only a part of a company name will be used, but an index will usually give the name in full. Such a case is that of Farbenfabriken vorm. F. Bayer & Co., which is commonly spoken of as just Bayer & Co. Another source of confusion is the translation of a company name from one language to another. As an example, attention may be called to a company in Switzerland (it is on the French border), where both the French and German languages are more or less commonly used, sometimes spoken of as Société anonyme pour l'industrie chimique à Bâle, at other times called Gesellschaft für chemische Industrie in Basel, and occasionally Society of Chemical Industry in Basel. This kind of situation is sometimes taken care of by the use in indexes of appropriate cross references.

Cross references are almost universally used for second, third, etc., authors except that it is not uncommon for such an expression as Smith, A. B., *et al.* to be used with no mention of other authors if the number of authors of a paper goes beyond two or three.

Instead of using author cross references an occasional journal repeats titles and all author names as shown by the following example:

Jones, A. B., and Smith, C. D., *Analysis of Steel*, 742.

Smith, C. D., and Jones, A. B., *Analysis of Steel*, 742.

An example of this is the collective index to the *Journal of the Optical Society of America* (Vols. 1–40, 1917–1950).

Mention has been made in the preceding paragraphs of the easy **chance for errors** to creep into author indexes in special cases. As a matter of fact, errors in spelling and in initials are comparatively common throughout author indexes. There are several reasons why this is so. The indexer is not to blame in many cases. Before a name gets printed in an index it usually has been copied several times. Errors are always likely when things are copied. Errors in copying ordinary words are almost always discovered and corrected because the correct spelling is generally known so that it is obvious that something is wrong; mistakes are frequently not obvious in the case of author names. And they seem easy to make, particularly if script is involved. The letters "n" and "u," not distinctly differentiated in the handwriting of so many, are often confused. The story of an author-name entry in the index to an abstract journal would show the possibilities of mistake. Between the submission of the original manuscript of an article and the printing of the abstract journal index entry there are at least eight separate chances for such an error to be made in an author name. Of course in well edited journals a good deal of care is exercised to check up the accuracy of the operations that come directly under the editor's supervision, but with many copyings by many different individuals—the author, the first editor possibly, the first printer, the abstractor, his typist, the abstract printer, the indexer, and the index printer—it is not surprising that author indexes in general contain a comparatively large number of errors as indexes go. The compiling and publishing of an extensive author index free from errors in spelling or in initials is a very exacting undertaking, and absolute accuracy is rarely attained. A realization of this situation may be of some little value to the index user under some circumstances. For example, one may feel sure that a given author has published a paper and yet failing to find it indexed, instead of giving up, may look around a little and find the name with a G instead of a C as an initial or with some other mistake made.

Instead of the spelling in an index being wrong, difficulty in finding an entry may be due to an **incorrect spelling in the mind of the searcher.** There are certain series of **names pronounced alike** or almost alike **but spelled differently** which rather frequently confuse the index user as well as the indexer. The series Hofman, Hofmann, Hoffman, Hoffmann and the series Myer, Myers, Meyer, Meyers serve as examples. A few other cases are: Ayres, Ayers; Findlay, Findley; Fisher, Fischer; Johnson, Johnston; Kaufman, Kauffman; Mathews, Matthews; Morrison, Morison; Neilson, Nielson; Newman, Neuman; Pierce, Pearse; Schmid, Schmidt; Schulz, Schultze; Seibert, Siebert; Stephenson, Stevenson; Thompson, Thomsen, Thomson; Zuntz, Zunz.

The custom more or less common among authors in France of signing their **last names only** to papers, omitting initials, is deplored by author indexes. The effect on indexing is obvious; either the initials have to be determined independently or omitted in the index involved. The latter procedure may throw several different authors together.

Mistaking the **French abbreviation M.** (Monsieur) for an author's initial has also given rise to errors.

Cases of **different authors with the same last names** and the **same initials** are not uncommon. In some indexes these get together, for example under Smith, J. F.; in others they are separated with different given names spelled out, as Smith, John Frank, and Smith, John Frederick; or, in others, where the given names are alike the address may be given to differentiate authors, as Smith, John Frank (Chicago) and Smith, John Frank (New York).

In using an author index one should be as sure as possible of his own spelling, not too sure of the correctness of the spelling in the index and ready to look around before being satisfied.

SUBJECT INDEXES

The subject index is the most important kind in chemistry, as in most other fields. It is the index most used. The subject part of an important chemical index is always the first to show signs of wear in libraries.

The object of a search often has a good deal to do with its nature. If a single bit of information is being sought, for example the density of some definite substance, the search may be soon terminated, but if one wants to learn all that he can from the literature about some more or less general subject the search may be a long and difficult one, requiring the greatest resourcefulness for even an approach to completeness.

The indefiniteness of subjects in general as index headings, as compared with author names and formulas of compounds for example, leads to many difficulties both in index making and in index using. This means that even the best subject indexes have limitations affecting their usefulness. Subject indexing is not a mechanical process; it involves the constant making of decisions of various sorts. It is perhaps not surprising, therefore, that existing subject indexes to books and periodicals of interest to chemists vary widely in quality.

Unfortunately the **indexing has not been well done** in a good many chemical publications. This constitutes the greatest weakness in the literature. The trouble seems to have been not so much a lack of appreciation on the part of authors and publishers of the importance of good subject indexes to scientific publications as a lack of realization that only a trained and experienced indexer can be expected to be able to make a good subject index. Subject indexing is all too often attempted by individuals unprepared for such special work, the belief seemingly being that the only requirement is a knowledge of the field to be covered. Subject indexing requires special skill and it is unreasonable to expect satisfactory results from untrained hands. Not even authors are qualified to index their own work unless they are equipped by training and experience with the qualifications of an indexer. Their intimate knowledge of the subject, a very desirable qualification though it is, will not make up for a lack of ability as an indexer. To measure up as a **satisfactory indexer** for a given publication one must have certain general qualifications for the work that can be acquired only by experience, these in addition to a considerable acquaintance with the whole branch of knowledge involved, the ability fully to comprehend the contents of the publication, and familiarity with the principles and practices of indexing. These **general qualifications** are good taste, good judgment, and a habit of conciseness and of liberal and comprehensive thought. Furthermore, and above all, one needs what may be called the "indexing sense"—"that is, the ability to feel instinctively, at the first glance, what and how subjects should be indexed in all their ramifications; the sense that is in touch with searchers, and appreciates just how subjects will be looked for and how to arrange them so that they can most readily be found." [2]

These qualifications of a good indexer are likewise good qualifications for the subject index user. **The use of subject indexes is more of an art than is usually realized.** It is very much worth while cultivating. **Effective searches require special knowledge, training, experience, and the exercise of judgment on the part of the searcher.** He must draw heavily on his general fund of knowledge, must know what to expect of subject indexes in general and of the more important particular ones, and he must go about the task with the same thoughtful and wide-awake attitude that is appropriate when one is making a search for information by conducting experiments in the laboratory. The differences between success and failure in finding a single bit of information or in making a reasonably complete general search may not lie so much in the indexes as in the index user.

An effort will be made here to set forth the general characteristics of subject indexes and to point out their faults. Then at the end of the chapter the more important individual indexes will be described. A part of the plan will be to indicate what is considered to be an **ideal subject index.** This should be helpful not only in guiding chemists to the best reference sources but also in helping them to realize what to expect, and therefore what may have to be done, in using indexes that are not up to standard.

Many so-called subject indexes are really **indexes of words** instead of subjects. There is a vast difference. Words are of course necessary in the make-up of a subject index, but it is important for an indexer to remember that the words used in the text of a publication are not necessarily the words suitable for index headings or even for modifications. In indexing parlance, *"modification"* is the term applied to the word or phrase that is usually supplied following an index heading to indicate the character of the information given in the source referred to, as "analysis of" under such a heading as "Aluminum alloys." Word indexing leads to omissions, scattering, and unnecessary entries. After the most suitable word or group of words from the indexing point of view has been chosen for a heading it should of course be used consistently no matter what the wording of the text may be. And yet one will find indexes with entries scattered under such different headings as "Accumulators," "Storage batteries," and "Cells, secondary," when the meanings of the indexed text are essentially the same and all entries should be grouped. Or, as an example of a type of unnecessary entry, one may find such a title as "Scheme for the qualitative analysis of the common metals in the absence of phosphates" word-indexed under the heading "Phosphates."

To illustrate a kind of **scattering of entries** that may result **from word indexing** let us consider such a series of article titles as follows: "An apparatus for the determination of carbon dioxide," "A new absorption apparatus," "Apparatus for use in the analysis of baking powder," "An improved potash bulb," and "Flue-gas analysis." Word indexes would no doubt contain an entry under the heading "Carbon dioxide" for the first title, one under "Absorption apparatus" for the second, under "Baking powder" for the third, under "Potash bulb" for the fourth and one under "Flue gas" for the fifth, and probably no others. These entries seem reasonable enough if the titles are considered separately without thought of the others. And yet the articles may all be descriptive of the same sort of apparatus. As a matter of fact all of these titles might conceivably be used for the same article; if the author happened to be working on baking powder or on flue-gas analysis when he conceived the idea for his novel piece of apparatus or had it in mind particularly for one purpose or the other he might choose one of the more specific titles for his article rather than one of the more general ones. In an index entirely based on subjects rather than words it would be the task of the indexer to see that all of these articles get indexed under one heading, or all under each of more than one heading, best with cross references pointing from the other possible headings to the one or more headings used. Or if there seems to be some justification for scattering owing to differences in point of view (word indexing cannot be gotten away from entirely) he will make sure that the necessary cross references are supplied to lead the index user about from heading to heading so that if any of the entries are missed it will be his own fault.

It is not hard to tell whether or not an index is a word index; when this is suspected or noted one should look around pretty thoroughly in its use instead of being satisfied that the entries found under the obvious headings are all that the index contains on the subject.

In an **index really based on subjects** rather than words, one of course will not always find the word or words used as the index heading or even in the modifying phrase when he turns to the page of text to which reference is made. It is important to bear this in mind for otherwise it is easy to miss a subject and conclude that the reference is wrong. For example, in the text the wording might be "test for suprarenine" and yet the index entry be made under the heading "Adrenaline" (this being a preferable and more used name and therefore more obvious and more suitable as an index heading), with the modification reading "detection of" rather than "test for" if some standardization of modifications for the sake of bringing like entries together has been attempted. As a matter of fact it is conceivable that the same subject might be word-indexed in the same index under such a variety of headings as Epinephrine, Adrenaline, Suprarenine, Adrenine, Adnephrine, Adrine, and Suprarenaline or under any one of these headings with such a variety of modifications as "detection of," "test for," "reaction for," "color reaction for," "qualitative analysis of," and "identification of," instead of all entries being grouped under one heading with one modification. Many examples of just this sort of thing can be found. Or such a wording in the text as "unstable nature of hydrogen peroxide" may have as its counterpart in the true subject index the heading "Hydrogen peroxide" with the modification reading "stability of," since "stability" really expresses the subject even if the negative of it is involved. "Stability" is the modifying word most likely to come to the mind of the index user who will of course not have the wording of the text in mind as does the indexer. In some indexes to abstract journals the location of subjects on the page is facilitated by giving author names along with subject index entries; this narrows the field for search down to one abstract in case there are more than one on the page. Another help in this direction is the practice of supplying the fraction of the page in ninths in which the subject is taken up.

Chemical Abstracts pioneered in narrowing down references to a fraction of a page, first by giving a small superior numeral after the page reference (only one column per page was then used and the reader was expected to estimate the fraction, which was not indicated on the page). Later *Chemical Abstracts,* having adopted a larger two-column page, went in for numbering the columns consecutively instead of the pages, with nine fractions marked between the columns. Then to avoid small superscript numbers, these fractions were designated by lower-case letters (*a–i*). This practice divides the page into eighteen parts for reference and is a great time-saver in literature searching, particularly since *Chemical Abstracts* indexes subjects, not words, and the words needed for this purpose may not appear at all on the page.

Accuracy is usually better **in subject indexes** than in author indexes, as far as little mistakes are concerned. The serious type of inaccuracy that is to be found occasionally in subject indexes is the misinterpretation of the meaning of the text. Although this sort of thing does not occur frequently, it is nevertheless a source of weakness in the literature. A subject index entry may be several times removed from the original in point of interpretation. For example, the entries in the subject index to an abstract journal represent the interpretation by the indexer of the subject as stated in the abstract, which statement is the interpretation by the abstractor of the meaning of the original author. The index user may of course misinterpret the meaning of the entry in the index, and therefore misjudge as to whether or not he is interested. The meaning of index entries, especially brief ones, is sometimes obscure.

There is perhaps no definite point at which a subject index may be said to have attained **completeness.** Some are much fuller than others. A great many subject indexes are not as full as they should be. Word indexes are usually cluttered up with entries that are of no value, and lacking in needed entries. An index may be reasonably complete from one point of view and not from another. For example, a chemist may have occasion to make use of a publication on bacteriology, the index to which is reasonably full from the point of view of bacteriology, but find it incomplete from the point of view of chemistry. That is the reasonable thing to expect; it should be kept in mind in making searches. Completeness may be considered both with reference to headings and modifications.

Some indexes to periodicals, particularly word indexes, are merely **indexes of the titles** of papers or abstracts as the case may be.

These are always incomplete. Titles do not always tell the whole story as to the contents of papers even in very general terms. They vary greatly in this qualification. Very frequently indeed papers will contain new data with reference to specific substances not mentioned in the titles (possibly referred to in a general way, for example as "salts"), which data should certainly be made available to those interested in the particular substances by means of specific index entries. And in a great many cases papers contain significant index information with reference to more or less abstract subjects (particularly in conclusions) which are not brought out in the titles at all. For example, a paper entitled "The determination of the atomic weight of silver" may contain a description of a novel method of preparing pure silver chloride, of a new analytical procedure, or of a new device to assist in making especially accurate weighings, any one of which might be of interest to some one not interested in atomic weight determinations. Or a paper entitled "Some dyes of the anthraquinone series" may contain some conclusions as to the relation between chemical constitution and color, and the paper is likely to contain new information on specific compounds, possibly new ones. It is obvious that if one finds an index to be based on titles only, that index is to be put down as being very far from complete. Ingenuity will be required in the use of such an index if even a small part of the "buried" subjects is to be ferreted out.

The unfortunate tendency in recent years for technical periodicals to make the **titles of articles** that they publish read like newspaper headlines makes the titles even less suitable as an indexing basis. The form of title so popular with many technical editors in recent years is exemplified by the following newspaper headline actually observed: "Combustion Causes Costly Conflagration."

Of course the **need for full indexing varies** somewhat with the nature of the publication covered. It is much more important for an abstract journal to be thoroughly and properly indexed than for a journal publishing full papers only, for abstract journals are used much more as a means of locating information. Abstracts are not always complete, however, so that information that would be useful if available is often practically lost to use because it never gets indexed any place. This is minimized nevertheless by the special efforts made by some of the abstract journals to have their abstracts prepared from the indexing point of view and by the thorough indexing that is attempted. As an indication of how the abstractor and indexer, cooperating, endeavor to make the record complete, the following rule is here reproduced from "Directions for Section Editors and Abstractors of *Chemical Abstracts*."

> Since *Chemical Abstracts* is intended to be a complete and permanent record of all chemical work it is very important that abstracts should contain or make specific reference to all of the information in articles that is suitable to be indexed. This would include every measurement, observation, method, apparatus, suggestion, and theory which is presented as new and of value in itself. All new compounds and all elements, compounds, and other substances for which new data are given should be entered in abstracts.

And in the Key and the Introduction to the Decennial Indexes to *Chemical Abstracts* as well as in those to recent annual indexes to this publication one will find the following pertinent statements:

> Subjects, not words, have been indexed.
> Abstracts, not merely their titles, have been considered in indexing.
> All new compounds and all elements, compounds, and other substances for which new data are given have been indexed.

The farther back one goes in point of years the less thorough one may expect to find the literature covered by abstract journals (1) in the percentage of suitable journals covered, (2) in the nature of the abstracts, and (3) in the character of the indexing. Indexing is receiving better attention than was once the case though the improvement is far from general.

Much of the indexing of *Chemical Abstracts* is done with original papers or patents as well as their abstracts before the indexer to ensure complete indexing of the literature. As a result the indexes contain some information not in the abstracts, usually with a modifying phrase or note added to make the situation clear.

Subject index modifications vary a good deal in several ways. A happy medium between desirable brevity and the supplying of details is the ideal. Adequate precision in phrases modifying subject index headings consists in supplying just as much information with reference to the contents of the text as is necessary to indicate its nature and scope and to prevent the searcher from being misled into thinking that he may find what he wants when it is not there, or vice versa. In many indexes, particularly word indexes, modifications are much too long. For example, such a title as "Study of a method for determining nitrites in water" will be indexed under the heading "Nitrites" with the modification reading "study of a method for determining, in water" when merely "determination in water" would be much better. Unnecessarily long modifications slow up the use of an index without anything being gained. On the other hand, merely "determination of" would not be a sufficiently precise modification in the above case. If on looking over the entries under a heading a modification is found that indicates that the entry involved refers to the phase of the subject in which one is interested, it is seldom safe to terminate one's search there even if the modifications have been arranged with some system. Suppose the modifications in an index were alphabeted and one were interested in learning what he could about the density of alcohol-water mixtures. Under the heading "Alcohol," or "Ethyl alcohol" as it is more likely to read, one may find a modification reading "density of mixtures with water" and then further on a modification "properties of mixtures with water," the latter more general entry being likewise of interest because one of the properties dealt with is density. In a word index there might also be an entry reading "specific gravity of mixtures with water." This illustrates the point.

Since the searching of the literature is a time-consuming task even under the best of conditions it is to be regretted that **convenience in use** has not received consideration in connection with many subject indexes. It is possible by efficient modification writing, systematic arrangement of entries, and judicious selection of printing form and style to facilitate the use of a subject index greatly. General quality of the indexing and the use of cross references, which will be discussed later, are also important factors. It is hardly worth while to discuss the various printing forms and styles here; these are obvious on turning to indexes and their description would require a good deal of space. The most convenient scheme perhaps is the use of the entry-a-line form with alphabetic arrangement of modifications, the significant word of which has been brought to the front.

The **alphabeting of headings** is done in accordance with two different plans. According to the more common plan (Plan A), when a heading consists of more than one word it takes its place among the other headings in strictly alphabetic order—the same as if the words were run together to make a single word. This is the plan usually followed in dictionaries. In the arrangement according to the other plan (Plan B), only the first word in such headings is considered first, the additional word or words being given consideration in a secondary alphabeting. For example, the heading "Heat of reaction" would follow the heading "Heaters" according to Plan A but precede it according to Plan B. Plan A has the advantage of greater simplicity. Headings with transposed words, as "Iron, metallurgy of," are usually alphabeted first on the basis of the part before the comma. In a few indexes headings and modifications are not considered separately in the alphabeting. When entries under a given heading are arranged alphabetically according to the modifications and there are entries with no modifications, these latter are customarily placed first because of the recognized rule that "nothing comes before something."

When the index modifications under headings are alphabeted, insignificant first words, usually prepositions, are not counted in some indexes (a good practice). For example, for the index entry "calcium, in blood" the word "blood," not "in," would control the alphabeting of the modification.

Cross references are an important help to an indexer as well as to the index user. Word indexing is really hard to avoid and cross references are the great preventive. It is a good sign if an index has a plentiful supply of cross references, both of the "see" kind and the "see also" kind. They make for uniformity and proper correlation, two very desirable qualities in indexes. "See also" cross references are of just as much importance as the "see" kind, though not as much used. The service which they render in directing the index user to related headings or to headings which, though dissimilar for the most part, have entries under them likely to be of interest to the investigator who refers to the original heading is often the chief means of making a search complete. It is not reasonable to expect an index user, or an indexer as a matter of fact, to think of all the headings representing related or significant subjects under which headings he may find valuable references that might otherwise be missed. Nevertheless, in the careful indexing year after year of a periodical devoted to a more or less definite field, an abstract journal for example, subjects are come upon in such a variety of connections and from so many angles that it is possible for a truly comprehensive list of cross references to be built up. The suitability of a given "see also" cross reference may not be clear, let alone suggest itself, until a specific case in which it is helpful is observed. It often pays to follow up such a cross reference even when it does not look as if it applies in a given case. The indexer in surveying the whole field year after year is in a position to make valuable suggestions in the form of cross references calculated to lead the index user from place to place in the index, so that the chances of his search being really exhaustive as far as that particular index is concerned are much better.

Suppose one were interested in temperature measurement or control in connection with a given process but did not happen to be familiar with the practice of using pyrometric cones in the ceramic industry. Suppose in addition that the pyrometric cone method, if not applicable in the case at hand, would at least be suggestive of the solution of the problem being investigated. In searching the literature such an individual would no doubt turn to the heading "Temperature" first in using available subject indexes. The advantage to him to find a cross reference to "Pyrometric cones" or "Seger cones" under the heading "Temperature" in such a case is obvious. There is always the chance that the "see also" cross reference under a heading may be suggestive of places to look that the index user might never have thought about and entries thus found may indeed be of more value to him than the entries under the heading originally used. This point is emphasized partly because the value of the "see also" cross reference is not always fully recognized by indexers (too many indexes are without them), but more particularly because of a suspicion that full advantage is not taken of them in the use of indexes in which they are to be found. It is surprising how often information of value in connection with a problem can be found under unexpected headings.

With a given problem at hand the **first step,** of course, is to think out the most likely places to look in the indexes to be used. This may be a simple matter or it may be a very difficult one, depending on the nature of the problem. Difficulty increases with indefiniteness. Experience is necessary. In fact the beginner is often completely at a loss to know what to do at this very first stage of his search. He tends to look for topics that are too general, failing to analyze the subject in which he is interested into its factors. If he fails to find any references to the problem as a whole as he has it in mind, he is likely to assume that there is nothing in the literature that will be of aid to him in his investigation. Were he to separate his subject into its essential parts and then to consult the literature on each, he would probably find considerable information. Even though some index headings, perhaps the more important ones, may be brought to mind without much ingenuity, the completeness of a search may be marred by a failure properly to analyze the problem. Indexes with cross references, particularly "see also" ones, help.

Too much dependence on cross references is not advisable. They may not be available at all, and they are never complete. With a given heading in mind it is well to cudgel one's brain for **synonymous words or phrases** to try, as well as for various **related subjects.** And it is advisable to try these even though entries are found as expected in the first place to which one has turned. Words or phrases with an *opposite meaning* to the one in mind may serve as subject headings under which desired entries may be found. For example, the searcher interested in viscosity may find significant entries under the heading "Fluidity" in addition to those under "Viscosity." Incidentally it is noted that the word "consistency" may serve as a heading for still other related entries. Or, some entries under "Electric resistance" may interest the searcher whose thought on turning to an index was of "Electric conductivity," or "Conductivity, electric," as the heading may read. If such related subjects are not suggested by cross references and have not been thought of in advance they may be suggested by the nature of some entry under the heading first turned to if one is on the lookout for them. Such an instance would be that of the searcher interested in refractory materials who might observe in an index an entry under the heading "Refractory materials" which reads "for furnace linings"; his cue would be to look to see if there is also a heading "Linings" under which different entries might be found concerning materials that are just as much refractory as those referred to under the heading "Refractory materials." In a word index, such materials would be referred to under "Refractory materials" only in case they happened to be called that in the text.

Other examples of words likely to be used to designate subject index headings under which like or closely related entries may be made in chemical indexes are: dehydration, drying, and desiccation; concentration, distillation, and evaporation; fusion and melting; carbonization, coking, distillation, and destructive distillation; adhesives, cement, glue, paste, and mucilage; sewage, refuse, and waste; radiations and rays; electrolytes, electrolytic ions and salts; grinding devices, mills, and pulverizers; disinfection and fumigation; drugs, medicines, and pharmaceutical preparations; etc. In the case of processes such as carbonization, entries may be found only under the substance to which the process has been applied in a study, as coal, or steel if the other meaning of the word is involved; or the entries may be limited to headings representing products of the process, as gas or tar. A patent, for example, may be entitled "Gas manufacture" and be indexed only under "Gas" and yet be as much a process of carbonization as other patents so called and so indexed.

The **resourcefulness which may be required in making a thorough search through subject indexes** can best be discussed by treating of an example. Suppose one were interested in looking up all possible references on vitamins. The first place to turn naturally would be the heading "Vitamins" in the indexes to the various reference sources to be used. This would rarely, if ever, be far enough to go. If only one of the indexes contained "see also" cross references these might be helpful in the use of the other indexes. This playing of one index against another, so to speak, is always a possible means of helping out. Cross references should be looked for. Since it is not always possible to find such cross references and it is not safe to depend too much on them to be complete, one might well follow out in such a case a line of thought like the following: Vitamins are constituents of foods. It may be worth while to look under "Foods." Entries may be found there with some such modifying phrase as "accessory constituents of." Vitamins are a factor in health, and the effect of foods on health involves the idea of diet or ration. These headings, or this heading if they are combined under "Diet," for example, as would seem best in a true subject index, would no doubt prove fruitful of significant references. Studies of proper diet or of adequate ration for an army would beyond doubt involve the vitamins. Experiments to determine the nutritional value of foods are frequently called feeding experiments, so a heading "Feeding experiments" may be looked for to advantage. Food is taken for the purpose of nutrition, and the vitamin problem is a nutrition problem. Therefore the general subject "Nutrition" needs to be examined in the indexes. There is of course such a thing as plant nutrition as well as animal nutrition. One might seek to determine, if he did not know, whether or not there is a theory of plant nutrition analogous to the vitamin theory in animal nutrition, so the heading "Plant nutrition" or the heading "Plants" would be suggested to try. If he did not know it he would likely learn that there are substances supposed to be factors in plant life, sometimes called auxins, which are analogous to the vitamins in animal nutrition. The heading "Auxins" would of course then be suggested for reference. The lack of vitamins in the diet is one of the causes of certain diseases (for example, beriberi, pellagra, polyneuritis, rickets, scurvy, and xerophthalmia). These ought to be referred to, therefore, as index headings. The general heading "Diseases" should be tried also, such a modification as "deficiency" being looked for. Perhaps the next thing for the index user to do would be to ask himself, or someone else, whether or not there is a definite name for this general type of disease; he would find that there is, and that the name is avitaminosis, which should then be turned to as a heading. The word "avitaminosis" suggests the possibility of its opposite, "hypervitaminosis," just as the

word "vitamins" should suggest the possibility of entries for influenc-
ing substances of possible interest, as "antivitamins" and "provita-
mins." Certain specific foods have been used and studied particularly with reference to the vitamins, as, for example, polished rice,
milk, butter, orange juice, yeast, tomatoes, etc. It seems unreasonable to be expected to think of all of these, and yet an article entitled,
say, "The effect on pigeons of eating polished rice" may be word indexed only in some index and therefore only get under the headings
"Rice" and perhaps "Pigeons." Vitamins have been differentiated
as "fat-soluble A," "water-soluble B," etc., and are sometimes spoken
of merely in these ways. It is conceivable that some indexes may
have these names as headings. In the earlier literature on the subject
vitamins may be found referred to under the name nutramines (a
name introduced by Abderhalden). The text referred to from any
one of the above mentioned headings may suggest still other headings
to try, as the names of specific foods supposed to be rich in vitamins.

The above discussion of resourcefulness with vitamins used as the
subject first in mind could be extended a good deal. For example,
chemists, in addition to discovering new so-called vitamins from time
to time, have learned the chemical structure of many of the vitamins
so that instead of using letters after the word "vitamin," a common
practice introduced at the indefinite early stages of studies, chemical
names have become possible and have been introduced. Examples
are ascorbic acid, nicotinic acid, carotene, and even such structure-
showing names as "3,7-dimethyl-9-(2,6,6-trimethyl-1-cyclohexen-1-
yl)-2,4,6,8-nonatetraen-1-ol." Instead of going forward with this example here, it is suggested that the interested reader turn to the headings "Vitamins" in the latest index to *Chemical Abstracts* where
dozens of cross references are to be found.

The principle of referring to the general as well as to the specific
subject, as exemplified in the preceding discussion by the subject
"avitaminosis" for the general, and by the individual deficiency diseases (beriberi, etc.) for the specific, is a good one to keep constantly
in mind in using subject indexes. If, to give a further example, one
is interested in the action of, say, diastases in any general way, it
would not be at all unlikely that he might find useful information by
referring to the heading "Enzymes" as well as the heading "Diastases"
in indexes used. The reverse of this may also be true.

The resourcefulness necessary in the location of information by
means of the great variety of subject indexes in existence may seem
to be little more than clever guessing at times. A paper on milk, so

called and indexed only under "Milk," may reveal information of general significance regarding emulsions. Authors often fail to see the full significance of their experimental results, and it is not often that the indexer will go further than the author in bringing out this significance for attention. The kind of **flexible ingenuity necessary for the location of information in this way** is perhaps only to be acquired by experience. It is really more than guessing that results in the location of information in this way, and yet it seems as if a little more than reasoning power, something like intuition, is necessary sometimes.

Confidence in the completeness of the array of headings to search can often be increased by noting the increasing frequency with which the same paper is picked up through different parts of the array. The array should expand with the literature search and also with the laboratory work. **This index-searching process is a developing, unfolding sort of thing;** it is really an educational process—the more one knows, the more varied is the information that becomes acceptable and useful. It is highly improbable that all the useful information will spring from the index at the first glance.

Once a desired heading has been located, the best method of searching among the modifications becomes the next concern. Many times a glance will reveal the desired information or its absence. Under the larger headings, it will take something more than a glance. Since experience has shown it difficult to predict the word starting a modification, it may be necessary to read every modification. This is not such a loss of time as it might at first seem, since it offers a good opportunity of discovery of substitute, related, and accidental information. The modifications can be arranged then into an order of probable importance to the index user, or a number of modifications can be selected and arranged likewise. The list can be looked up, starting with the most important, and the process continued until too little relevant information is discovered to justify continuance.

After the main entries have been looked up, read, and digested, it is sometimes desirable to read again the modifications under the more important headings, since the increased background of knowledge on the subject will make more information understandable and acceptable to the searcher. Now that a start into the literature has been made, the references found printed in most scientific papers will probably provide much further information. Author indexes are often of help, at this point, in locating more information, since authors tend to specialize in their research. In some respects, searching the literature may resemble a nuclear chain reaction; it may be difficult to start, but once started, it may be difficult to control, since the reference multiplication factor is usually much greater than one.

It is **desirable to read the entries under a heading slowly** because it takes time to add, from the imagination, the supplementary information that the indexer had to leave out of the index. One might think of an index user as a paleontologist. The entries he discovers are the bones of yesterday's information. As he looks at these entry bones he must judge, from their size, shape, quality, and location, the kind of subject animal to which they belonged. The paleontologist reconstructs the whole animal from the fragment of bone he holds in his hand; the index user reconstructs the source information, with similar imagination, from the entry he holds in his mind. An index entry, "Phenanthrene, purification of," suggests the possibility of finding the melting point of phenanthrene; it also implies a source of the compound and perhaps even a method of preparation. A melting-point apparatus is possibly described. The fact that an index entry seems, by its wording, to indicate nothing new should not mislead the user, for it is frequently impossible to indicate the novelty in a modification of reasonable length. One should expect every index entry to lead to novel or emphasized information.

Chemical Nomenclature and Indexes

GENERAL CONSIDERATIONS

Chemical publications present a special problem both to the subject indexer and to the index user in that many headings must consist of the names of chemical compounds. The difficulties encountered are to be attributed to the facts that (1) many compounds have, or may have, more than one name, (2) the names or at least the best names of the more complex compounds may be difficult to ascertain, and (3) new compounds are constantly being prepared that, if named at all, may receive more than one name that is justifiable from one point of view or another. The possibilities of incorrect names are great.

With the simple and more commonly known compounds there is not much trouble. There is usually a best name for each of these that is pretty well known among chemists; other names can readily be, and frequently are, taken care of by cross references. The use of a good dictionary will often help if one wishes to look up such a compound but is not sure that the name that he has in mind is the best one or at least the one most common or most likely to be used as a subject index heading. Often the index or indexes to be used do not solve this problem by cross references. Furthermore, if more than one index is to be used it may be well to have in mind more than one name, as indexes vary somewhat in the names chosen for index headings.

It is with the thousands of more or less complex compounds that the real difficulty comes in; but a few of these are so commonly met with as to be generally known by some simple name. Complex organic compounds, being so plentiful, have chiefly to be dealt with in indexes. It is not possible to index these compounds by name with entire satisfaction. They cannot be so named and entered that the average chemist will be sure to find every one given that he may seek to locate. It is on this account and because of language differences that some other basis than the names has been sought for the indexing of compounds; their empirical formulas have been chosen. Formula indexes will be discussed a little further on in this chapter. They are few in number. Those appearing in periodicals usually do not stand alone; they are often made supplementary to name indexes as a less convenient (in many cases at least) but more certain means of locating individual compounds.

For many years inorganic chemistry had to do almost exclusively with more or less simple compounds, except in the field of mineralogical chemistry, where trivial mineral names are used. The nomenclature problem for the chemist interested in inorganic compounds has passed from a comparatively simple one to one of great difficulties with the preparation and study of many complex inorganic compounds. The International Critical Tables, on account of the difficulties involved, discarded inorganic names altogether in its tables and indexed such compounds by formulas alone. Complex inorganic compounds may be indexed under headings like "Cobalt compounds" or "Platinum compounds," depending on the significant element in them. The formula indexing plan helps much with them.

Considerable attention has been given to the nomenclature of complex organic compounds, and many rules for systematic, descriptive naming have been worked out and standardized. Nevertheless it is frequently a problem to ascertain just what name may have been given a compound that one may wish to look up, partly because the proper naming of complex compounds is often difficult in itself and partly because different names correct from one point of view or another may be used. In addition, the number of poorly chosen and unsatisfactory names to be found in the literature is large.

The entering of compounds in subject indexes to publications is desirable even though formula indexes may be provided. A very useful grouping of related compounds is possible in indexing by names.

The first prerequisite in the proper indexing of chemical compounds by names is the adoption and consistent application of a definite system of nomenclature. This is far from being done always. The system should come as close to common usage as possible. It is a distinct advantage if it is described in connection with the index to which it is applied, so that the index user may become familiar with the general principles followed. This is justified in connection with the larger indexes at least.

Consistent nomenclature is hardly enough. Names satisfactory for general usage may not be wholly satisfactory for index entries until inverted so as to bring the so-called parent compound part of the name to the front. For example it is better to have the three chloroacetic acids entered as Acetic acid, chloro- (monochloro- is usually to be assumed when only chloro- is used), Acetic acid, dichloro-, and Acetic acid, trichloro-, thus bringing them all together, than to have them one under the C's, one under the D's, and one under the T's. The indexes to the *Bulletin de la société chimique de France* serve as an example of this plan of indexing. The systematic arrangement of radical names in the names of compounds is also advantageous. The value of the grouping of derivatives and otherwise related compounds under the name of the parent or index compound is obvious. This is a case in which the true purpose of indexing is not sacrificed, and is in fact helped, by a kind of classification. If a supplementary formula index is supplied, the indexing of compounds is thus made to approach the ideal as nearly as is possible.

Of course the necessity for so much care in the handling of compounds varies in urgency with the nature of the publication being covered. A smaller publication, such as a textbook, may within reason index the compounds described or discussed in it under several names in each case where several are known, but it is not reasonable to expect a more comprehensive publication, such as an abstract journal, to do this, as the expense would be prohibitive. There are chemical indexes in which different entries for the same compound are to be found scattered under different names (word indexing),

others in which different names are used as headings but each group
of entries is made complete (this type is rare), still others in which
one name is used consistently as the heading but no cross references
are supplied, and finally the type in which one name is used consistently with cross references given directing the user from other names
to the one used as the index heading (the best type). Once an index
is thus classified in one's mind it is possible for it to be used with
greater efficiency.

For a discussion of nomenclature with particular reference to names
for indexing see the introduction to the 1945 subject index to *Chemical Abstracts* and the paper by Patterson and Curran.[3] There is also
a brief discussion with each annual subject index to *Chemical Abstracts*.

GROUP VERSUS SPECIFIC NAMES FOR COMPOUNDS

The principle discussed previously in this chapter, of referring to
general as well as to specific subjects, applies aptly in searches for
information regarding compounds. Group names for compounds may
serve as headings under which entries of interest to the searcher concerned with an individual compound may be found. An example will
serve to illustrate. Suppose one were interested in finding all the
information he could with reference to the electrolysis of sodium
chloride. In addition to looking up the references under the heading
"Sodium chloride" in the indexes to be used, it would be desirable to
look also for entries of interest under such headings as the following:
"Alkali chlorides" or "Alkali metal chlorides," "Sodium halides,"
"Alkali metal halides," "Chlorides," and "Halides." A process described for the electrolysis of alkali metal halides in general may be
of just as much interest and value to the search in hand as one specified to be particularly for sodium chloride, and yet the indexes are
not likely to carry entries under each of the members of a group of
compounds if a definite group is under discussion. Cross references
may be supplied in some cases, but it is hardly reasonable to expect
an index to go further. A process for electrolyzing chlorides, for instance, could not within reason be entered under headings representing each of the numerous known chlorides. The index user must
expect to think of such possibilities and make his search complete
accordingly. Another different kind of lead to follow to ensure a complete search, particularly when word indexes are involved, is to think
of the products of the process being studied, in this case chlorine,
sodium hydroxide, and possibly sodium hypochlorite. And in addi-

tion to looking up the headings represented by the names of these compounds completeness is ensured only by trying the headings "Halogens," "Alkalies," or "Alkali metal hydroxides," and again possibly "Alkali metal hypohalites" and "Hypohalites." The product of some simple electrolytic process that does not involve the recovery of chlorine or alkali may be called merely "bleaching solution" or be given some like name. And further it may be worth while to look up such a heading as "Potassium chloride" as representative of a closely related compound that might be studied with a similar purpose. It would probably be a waste of time, however, to look up the heading "Sodium iodide," at least if commercial processes were the kind in which one were interested. Still other headings worthy to be tried are "Electrolytic cells" or rather "Cells, electrolytic," as it is more likely to be given, and possible "Electrolysis"; this last heading, however, is too general to be used as an index heading for every process involving electrolysis and is not likely to be used for studies or discussions of specific substances. This whole example serves to show again that resourcefulness and the use of one's general knowledge of chemistry must come prominently into play in the making of index searches.

In some studies involving compounds, only one constituent of the compounds in each case may be of significance, and the indexing may be influenced thereby. This is particularly likely to be true in biological chemistry. For example, someone may study the effect of calcium chloride and calcium sulfate on muscle contraction. Any one of the following titles might reasonably be used for a paper reporting such a study: (1) "The effect of calcium chloride and calcium sulfate on muscle contraction," (2) "The effect of calcium salts on muscle contraction," and (3) "The effect of calcium on muscle contraction." Calcium is the significant thing, and it would not be far out of the way if this study were indexed under "Calcium salts," "Calcium," "Calcium ion," or under the names of the specific salts. Of course metallic calcium was not used in the study, but "calcium" is really the subject. The point is that calcium the subject is not limited to calcium the substance, so that in making a search with reference to a specific compound it may be necessary to look not only under the name of the compound but also under the heading represented by the significant constituent of the compound.

Nomenclature in Other Fields

Related to the chemical nomenclature problem is the problem of nomenclature in other fields. Take botany for instance. The chemist interested in plants may want to look up a given plant in chemical indexes to see what chemical work has been done with reference to it. Plants usually have one or more common names as well as a scientific name (genus and species), as corn, maize, and *Zea mays*. It is of course the same with animals. One indexer may prefer to make entries under the commonest of the common names as being the one most likely to come first to the mind of the index user, and another indexer may prefer to use as a heading the genus and species name as being more scientific. Different authors may use different scientific names for the same plant. A word index may use more than one name without the realization that different names for the same thing are being used as headings, with resultant scattering of entries.

Importance of Learning Chemical Nomenclature

The only chemist competent to use the existing subject indexes to chemical publications with genuine efficiency, as far as the location of compounds other than the simple and more common ones is concerned, is the chemist who is reasonably well informed on chemical nomenclature. This is true with reference to the most carefully prepared indexes; no one can use some of the poorly prepared indexes with efficiency. A knowledge of chemical nomenclature is a prerequisite if one expects to be able to make effective searches of the literature of chemistry. This is particularly important for the organic chemist. Every chemist ought to give adequate attention to chemical nomenclature anyhow. It is important. It is a factor in exactness in scientific communication, and exactness in this connection is just as important as exactness in scientific work in the laboratory. Every chemist should consider it a duty to attempt to learn the best name for each compound that he has occasion to mention, particularly if he is a teacher or if he is writing for publication. Except that very commonly accepted names must be recognized, systematic names of compounds should as a rule be such as to bring out clearly the composition and constitution so that structural formulas can be ascertained from names alone. This is usually possible in organic chemistry.

Unfortunately there is no single authoritative standard of good nomenclature to be used as a guide. Nevertheless there have been efforts in the direction of standardization, and it is usually possible to learn what the preferred usage is for a known compound or what the best name or at least a good name would be for a new compound. The various national chemical societies have nomenclature committees and the International Union of Pure and Applied Chemistry has active commissions for inorganic, organic, and biochemical nomenclature.

Every chemist should read Nutting's paper [4] on the necessity for being well informed on chemical nomenclature, the relation between indexing and nomenclature, and the importance of improving nomenclature to cope with the flood of new compounds. The facts it presents will be a revelation to many chemists.

Information on Chemical Nomenclature

Before giving sources of information on nomenclature, one point should be emphasized. **Chemical nomenclature has been undergoing a process of evolution ever since 1787,** when Guyton de Morveau and his associates introduced the first system of nomenclature and published the book *Méthode de nomenclature chimique*. In using indexes and making literature searches that go back more than a few years, this must be kept in mind. It is necessary to revise the list of names and terms being used in a search at intervals as one works back or much valuable information will be missed. Some useful comments on this situation have been made by Huntress [5] in a paper entitled "Influence of Nomenclature Evolution upon Comprehensive Literature Searches." Space does not permit the enumeration of all the useful sources of nomenclature information, but many of those given here contain extensive bibliographies and these will be indicated. A general discussion of chemical nomenclature with a good bibliography is included in both Thorpe's *Dictionary of Applied Chemistry* (4th edition) and in the *Encyclopedia of Chemical Technology* edited by Kirk and Othmer.

The most comprehensive works on chemical nomenclature are these:

Chemical Nomenclature, no. 8 in *Advances in Chemistry Series*, Washington, D. C., American Chemical Society, 1953, 111 pp. This includes the papers of a symposium on chemical nomenclature presented at the 120th meeting of the American Chemical Society in September, 1951. These papers cover all phases of the problem and have extensive bibliographies. Most of them were written by those who were members of nomenclature committees of the chemical societies in various countries that cooperate with the commissions on chemical nomenclature of the International Union of Pure and Applied Chemistry, or by members of these commissions.

Gaade, W., *Beginselsen der Organish-Chemisch Nomenclatur*, Amsterdam, Elsevier, 1948, 224 pp. This is a rather elementary textbook that has good bibliographies.

Mitchell, A. D., *British Chemical Nomenclature*, London, Arnold, 1948, 156 pp. This is an excellent book. It includes a comparison of nomenclature in Britain and in the United States. There has been cooperation between the Chemical Society (London) and the American Chemical Society in much of the work on nomenclature for a great many years.

The Naming and Indexing of Chemical Compounds by Chemical Abstracts (Introduction to the 1945 Subject Index). Reprints of this 109-page discussion are available from the office of *Chemical Abstracts*, Ohio State University, Columbus 10, Ohio, at one dollar each. This is a comprehensive discussion of chemical nomenclature. It includes an extensive bibliography and useful appendixes on: (1) Miscellaneous chemical prefixes, (2) Inorganic groups and radicals, (3) Anions, (4) Organic groups and radicals, (5) Organic suffixes, and (6) 1945 ring index. The bibliography gives sources for names of individual substances, including trade names.

Reports of the nomenclature committees of the chemical societies of the various countries and the commissions on nomenclature of the International Union of Pure and Applied Chemistry provide much information. These appear in the journals and can be located through *Chemical Abstracts*—see the heading "Nomenclature" in the subject indexes. The office of *Chemical Abstracts* (Ohio State Univ., Columbus 10, Ohio) distributes copies of the reports of the *American Chemical Society's Committee on Nomenclature, Spelling and Pronunciation*, copies of reports of the nomenclature commissions of the International Union of Pure and Applied Chemistry (some in French, others in English translation), and copies of this journal's own nomenclature booklets. The list of nomenclature publications available from the *Chemical Abstracts* office appears frequently on the front or back cover of the issues of *Chemical Abstracts;* some are free, others are sold at nominal prices. Among the available reports are the important (1) *Rules for Naming Inorganic Compounds* (report of the Committee of the International Union of Pure and Applied Chemistry for the Reform of Inorganic Nomenclature, 1940) and (2) *Definitive Report of the Commission on the Reform of Nomenclature of Organic Chemistry*, 1930 (International Union of Pure and Applied Chemistry) ; both reports are being revised.

Chemical and Engineering News started a section on "Nomenclature" in 1951, written by Austin M. Patterson until 1956. It was called "Words about Words" until 1954. This is helpful in keeping up with current work.

For ascertaining the various names for individual compounds and substances these sources are useful: (1) the chemical dictionaries, handbooks, and encyclopedias (see Chapter 2 for these), (2) *Webster's New International Dictionary* (for the more common compounds), (3) the indexes to *Journal of the Chemical Society* (London), to *British Abstracts*, and to *Chemical Abstracts* (they contain many names as entries and as cross references, and a special effort has been made to use good nomenclature in these indexes), and (4) the indexes to standard reference books in many fields of chemistry.

Some of the nomenclature information most frequently needed in using indexes is given here: (1) general points on nomenclature, (2) name endings, and (3) foreign language equivalents of English names of compounds.

1. General Points on Nomenclature. A few more or less general points on the nomenclature of compounds or on indexing procedure with reference thereto to be borne in mind in index searches are noted below:

1. Inorganic compounds are preferably named in the simple form "potassium chloride" rather than "chloride of potassium" or "chloride of potash," and are so entered in indexes. Even the French, who do not say "potassium chlorure," but "chlorure de potassium," recognize in most instances that *Potassium, chlorure de* is the preferable index entry.

2. In looking up compounds of copper, gold, iron, and tin it is necessary to remember that index entries may be found under headings beginning "cupric(ous)," "auric(ous)," "ferric(ous)," and "stannic(ous)," respectively, rather than under headings beginning "copper," "gold," etc.

3. Acid salts may be named as shown by the following names for $NaHCO_3$: "sodium hydrogen carbonate," "sodium acid carbonate," "sodium bicarbonate," and "sodium hydrocarbonate." They may be indexed under any of these names or under such a heading as *Sodium carbonates*.

4. Organic salts and esters are often indexed under the names of the acids involved, as the acid is usually the significant part of the compound. For example, sodium naphthalenesulfonate or ethyl naphthalenesulfonate would be indexed under *Naphthalenesulfonic acid*, with a modification "sodium salt of" or "ethyl ester of" as the case may be. If the base is the more significant, as in geranyl acetate, the full name may be used for the index heading or the entry may be made under the name of the base, as *Geraniol*.

5. A principle used by some in the naming of organic compounds is that of expressing the chief function in the main part of the name wherever possible, and not as a substituent, thus: pyrrolecarboxylic acid, not carboxypyrrole; pentanone, not ketopentane. This is important for indexing by the so-called parent-compound or inverted-name system. In compounds of mixed function an order of precedence is to be followed. The parent compound is preferably made as large, and the substituents are made as small, as is practicable in conformity with the above principle; as, ethylbenzene, not phenylethane.

6. The arrangement of the names of substituent radicals in the names of compounds naturally affects their place in a subject index, particularly in one that does not use inverted names. This is very frequently not done systematically. Some prefer a so-called logical order, some an alphabetic order. An approximately complete list of preferred names of organic radicals, arranged by empirical formulas as well as by names, is to be found in the Introduction to the 1945 annual index to *Chemical Abstracts* and in that to the *Decennial Indexes*. The introductions to subsequent annual indexes contain supplementary lists of a few entries. Mono- is usually not used as a prefix to radical names in the names of compounds, the assumption being that mono will be understood where di, tri, etc., are not used.

7. The names and also the numberings of complex organic ring systems vary in many cases; thus, one author may call a certain hydrocarbon naphthofluorene which another calls benzofluorene, whereas for acridine two conflicting systems of numbering are in use. The searcher needs to know what particular system, if any, is used by the index he consults. To this end it is a great advantage to have synonyms, structural formulas, and numberings freely given, as is done for example in the subject indexes of *Chemical Abstracts*.

8. Trade names for compounds may come into sufficiently general use to be justified as index headings at times for entries referring to the compounds when not the products of particular firms, this practice being justified on the principle that entries in an index should be made where the most users can be expected to look first. Examples: Adrenaline and Aspirin.

2. Name Endings and General Points. *Nomenclature Rules Adopted by the Nomenclature Committee of the American Chemical Society and that of the London Chemical Society.*

1. In naming a compound so as to indicate that oxygen is replaced by sulfur the prefix *thio* and not *sulfo* should be used (sulfo denotes the group SO_3H); thus, HCNS, *thio*cyanic acid; H_3AsS_4 *thio*arsenic acid; $Na_2S_2O_3$,

sodium *thio*sulfate; $CS(NH_2)_2$, *thio*urea. The use of *thio* as a name for sulfur replacing hydrogen is only in cases in which the sulfur serves as a link in compounds not suitably named as mercapto derivatives; thus, $H_2NC_6H_4SC_6H_4NH_2$, *thio*bisaniline. *Hyposulfurous acid*, not hydrosulfurous acid, should be used to designate $H_2S_2O_4$.

2. The word *hydroxide* should be used for a compound with OH and *hydrate* for a compound with H_2O. Thus, barium hydroxide, $Ba(OH)_2$; chlorine hydrate, $Cl_2 \cdot 10H_2O$.

3. Salts of chloroplatinic acid are *chloroplatinates* (not platinichlorides). Similarly salts of chloroauric acid are to be called *chloroaurates*.

4. Hydroxyl derivatives of hydrocarbons are to be given names ending in *-ol*, as glycer*ol*, resorcin*ol*, pinac*ol* (not pinacone), mannit*ol* (not mannite), pyrocatech*ol* (not pyrocatechin).

5. The names of the groups NH_2, NHR, NR_2, NH, or NR should end in *-ido* only when they are substituents in an acid group, otherwise in *-ino;* thus, MeC(:NH)OEt, ethyl im*ido*acetate; $NH_2CH_2CH_2CO_2H$, β-am*ino*propionic acid (not am*ido*propionic acid); $NHPhCH_2CH_2CO_2H$, β-anil*ino*propionic acid; $CH_3C(:NH)CO_2H$, α-im*ino*propionic acid.

6. *Hydroxy-*, not oxy-, should be used in designating the hydroxyl group; as *hydroxy*acetic acid, $CH_2(OH)CO_2H$, not *oxy*acetic acid. *Keto-* is to be preferred to *oxy-* to designate oxygen in the group —CO—.

7. The term *ether* is to be used in the usual modern acceptation only and not as an equivalent of *ester.*

8. Salts of organic bases with hydrochloric acid should be called *hydrochlorides* (not hydrochlorates nor chlorohydrates). Similarly hydrobromide and hydroiodide should be used.

9. German names ending in *-it* should be translated *-ite* rather than *-it;* as permut*ite*. If it seems desirable to retain the original form of a trade name it should be placed in quotations, as "Permutit." Alcohols such as dulcitol (German Dulcit) are exceptions.

10. German names of acids should generally be translated by substituting *-ic acid* for "*-säure.*" Some well established names are exceptions, as Zuckersäure (saccharic acid), Milchsäure (lactic acid), Valeriansäure (valeric acid), etc. When the names end in "*-insäure*" the translator may substitute *-ic acid*, unless another acid already bears the resulting name; thus, Acridinsäure, acridic acid, but Mekoninsäure, meconinic acid, because meconic acid (Mekonsäure) is different. Names ending in "carbonsäure" are to be translated *-carboxylic acid* (not -carbonic acid).

3. Foreign Language Equivalents.

The fact that chemical literature searches frequently involve the use of publications printed in foreign languages complicates the problem of index examination considerably unless one happens to be especially well versed in the language involved. To the average individual it is much harder to recall the foreign language equivalent of a word or phrase in his native tongue than it is to translate the foreign word or phrase if it is before him. It is therefore a little hard to determine sometimes just where to look in a foreign-language index for a subject that one may have in mind, let alone select related and otherwise appropriate subjects to be looked for as index headings in order to ensure a complete search. The use of an English–foreign language dictionary is about the only help to be found. The following notes are intended to be of help in determining the **French and German equivalents of the English names of compounds.**

Endings corresponding to -*ide*, -*ate*, -*ite*, -*ic* and -*ous* in English are, respectively, in French -*ure*, -*ate*, -*ite*, -*ique* and -*eux* (feminine -*euse*). In German the forms corresponding to the first three of these endings are, respectively, -*id*, -*at*, and *it*. To indicate a lower compound in German the ending -*ür* is used where -*ous* or *sub*- would occur in English; thus, *Kupferchlorür* (cuprous chloride). *Silberchlorür* (silver subchloride). Another way in the German language of distinguishing between two compounds of the same element is to use Latin combining forms; as, *Cuprochlorid*, cuprous chloride; *Cuprichlorid*, cupric chloride; or to use *di*-, *tri*-, etc., as in English. Compounds are also named in German merely by compounding the names of the elements; as, *Jodkalium* (potassium iodide), *Siliziumfluorwasserstoff* (hydrogen silicofluoride, fluosilicic acid); this practice is restricted largely to compounds named with the -*ide* ending in English.

Higher and lower oxides are distinguished as -*oxyd* and -*oxydul* (German) or *oxyde* and *oxydule* (French), respectively, as *Eisenoxyd*, ferric oxide; *Eisenoxydul*, ferrous oxide. In German the Latin forms, such as *Ferrioxyd*, ferric oxide, and *Ferrooxyd*, ferrous oxide, are also used. "Hydroxydul" may be used to designate an -*ous* hydroxide in German.

In French acids are named very much the same as in English except that the names of hydracids differ in construction from the English names; as, *chlorhydrique*, hydrochloric. In German the names of acids are formed merely by attaching the word *Säure* to some other word; -*säure* is usually the equivalent of -*ic acid* in English. Hydracids are designated by the ending -*wasserstoffsäure;* as, *Bromwasserstoffsäure*, hydrobromic acid. The German equivalent of -*ous* in naming acids is -*ig;* as, *schweflige Säure*, or, less commonly, *Schwefligsäure*, sulfurous acid. Similarly, *unter*- corresponds to *hypo*- and *über*- to *per*- (*unterchlorige Säure*, hypochlorous acid; *Übermangansäure*, permanganic acid). The English -*carboxylic acid* is *acide -carbonique* in French and -*carbonsäure* in German. There are a few differences in the French and English equivalents of the German ending *-insäure*, the *in* being dropped sometimes in one language and not in the other and *vice versa*.

The hydroxyl group is not usually designated by *hydroxy-* in either French or German but by *oxy-*, though the latter usage is now recognized as less correct. *Oxy-* is also used sometimes in these languages to designate the ketonic group instead of *keto-* (careful writers use *keto-* or *oxo-*).

Amino- usually has *amido-* as its equivalent in French and German, but the use of *amino-* according to the rule given on page 264 seems to be on the increase.

The final *o* in such combining forms as *chloro-*, *cyano-*, etc., is not used in German and is frequently omitted in French.

In English the endings *-in* and *-ine* are usually differentiated systematically, the latter being used for basic substances and for them only, and the former for glycerides, glucosides, bitter principles, proteins, etc.; in French the ending *-ine* is used for both basic and neutral substances, and in German the ending *-in* for both kinds.

As between the endings *-ol* and *-ole* in the names of compounds, it is well to remember in making translations that the former ending is restricted to alcohols and phenols in good English practice, a distinction not made in French and German. Such rules as this cannot be applied with strictness to commercial names.

Hydrate in French is used to designate hydroxide as well as hydrate.

As between the endings *-an* and *-ane* in English, the latter is used for hydrocarbons (and parent compounds of the heterocyclic series) which are fully saturated; in French the ending *-ane* and in German *-an* are used without differentiation.

In French the use of adjectives in organic names instead of combining forms as in English and German is to be noted; thus the compound $C_6H_4Cl_2$ (dichlorobenzene) is often called *benzène* (or *benzine*) *dichloré*.

Another peculiarity of the French language is the use at times of the name of the alcohol radical prefixed to the name of the acid in the names of esters; as, *éther amylacétique* (amyl acetate). It is to be noted that "ester" is *éther* in French.

For a list of English–foreign language dictionaries, see page 322.

EMPIRICAL-FORMULA INDEXES

Owing to nomenclature and language differences and difficulties, another basis than that of names has been sought by a few publications for the indexing of chemical compounds. The object has been to find a basis that is more definite so that every entry can be found with certainty by any properly informed user. Since the kind and number of component atoms of a chemical compound are its most unvarying characteristics, empirical formulas serve as the best basis for obtaining the desired certainty. It is sufficiently easy to ascertain empirical formulas to make this basis satisfactory from the point of view of convenience. While for some compounds the names may be more easily determined or brought to mind than the formulas, the opposite is true in many other instances, and while it is always possible to ascertain empirical formulas it is sometimes impossible to find out names. There may be more than one name for a compound, but there can be but one empirical formula (excepting disputed cases and polymeric forms, the latter of which causes very little trouble).

An index of compounds by names, particularly if the parent or index compound plan, with inversion of names, has been followed, serves as the best help in literature searches for information regarding related compounds, which will be found grouped largely there; an index by formulas is the best kind to use for the certain location of individual compounds. A comprehensive formula index is particularly helpful if one has prepared and analyzed a compound and wants to determine whether or not a compound of the same empirical formula, if not an identical compound, has been previously prepared. New compounds that are of unknown structure and are not named are at times described in the literature; a formula index is the only kind that will index these satisfactorily. Some subject indexes enter such compounds under the heading "Compound," arranging the entries there systematically by empirical formulas.

The symbols for the atoms of the individual compounds and then the complete formulas themselves must of course be arranged systematically. There are **two systems of arrangement** that are in more or less prominent use. These may be called the Hill system [6] and the Richter system. [7] The former is simpler than the latter and easier to use.

In the **Hill system** the elements in formulas are arranged alphabetically except that in carbon compounds C always comes first, followed immediately by H if hydrogen also is present. In the **Richter system** the symbols in formulas are arranged in the order C, H, O, N, Cl, Br, I, F, S, P and the rest alphabetically. The arrangement of formulas in the Hill system is strictly alphabetical except that the number of atoms of any specific kind influences the order of compounds. For example, all compounds with 1 C come before those with C_2, thus: CCl_2O, CCl_4, $CHCl_3$, CHN, $CHNO$, CH_2Br_2, CH_2O, CH_3Cl, CO, C_2Ca, $C_2H_4C_2$. With the Richter system the arrangement of formulas is the same with one important exception, namely that according to this system the number of kinds of elements in each formula is first considered and formulas with the same number of kinds of elements are grouped together. This brings about a certain amount of classification, but it complicates things and classification in a formula index is of doubtful value. It slows up the finding of compounds in it just as the location of words in a dictionary would be slowed up if the words were grouped according to the number of kinds of letters before being alphabeted. Experimentation by one familiar with the Richter system but unused to the Hill system has shown that compounds can be located in a formula index by the Hill system with greater rapidity and with less chance of oversight than in such an index by the Richter system. In addition to the advantage of simplicity, the Hill system is better, for a general index at least, in that it is much more suitable for inorganic compounds than the Richter system. The latter system was worked out for organic compounds primarily; it is not suited to the indexing of inorganic compounds. Formula indexing is just as much needed and as helpful with complex inorganic compounds as with organic compounds although there are not nearly so many inorganic as organic compounds to be indexed. It is a distinct advantage for both kinds of compounds to be indexed together if the publication being indexed covers both kinds.

Other systems of arrangement here have been suggested, but no other system is in common use. One suggestion is that H be moved away from the front parts of formulas because hydrogen is difficult to determine exactly in the analysis of compounds. G. M. Dyson [8] has proposed a so-called Molform Index with an SNOCH order of symbols involved, which formula indexing plan is worthy of study. This method will not be described here as it is not in general use.

Compounds are not always formula indexed under their own formulas. It would seem that any departure from the indexing of compounds under their own formulas is a departure from the ideal. Nevertheless some departure from a policy of making separate formula entries for derivatives of all kinds is customary and seems reasonable. The interest in a salt of a complex organic acid, for example, is likely to be mainly in the acid, and it is more valuable to have the record of it under the formula of the acid for the use of searchers looking up that acid. Such departures are explained in connection with the existing formula indexes. The following statement from the key to each formula index to *Chemical Abstracts* will serve to show more fully the nature of the exceptions made.

> Entries under their own formulas are made for all strictly inorganic and strictly organic compounds and for the true organic derivatives of organic compounds, both addition compounds and true reaction derivatives (this includes esters, hydrazones, methohalides, oximes, picrates, semicarbazones, etc.). Inorganic salts of organic acids and inorganic addition compounds of organic compounds (hydrohalides, chloroplatinates, perchlorates, sulfates, etc.) are not given separate entries, but are indicated in modifying phrases under the formulas of the compounds from which they are derived (under the acid in the case of a salt). Salts of formic, acetic, and oxalic acids are exceptions; these are entered as such.

Water of hydration is usually not made a part of formulas indexed but is indicated following the formulas used as the headings.

Polymers are variously handled. The most common practice is to enter under their accepted formulas all polymers having different names and recognized as different substances, as acetaldehyde and paraldehyde, but to enter under the simplest formula only definite compounds for which different polymeric formulas are in use, as Cl_3Fe for ferric chloride. Cross references are frequently used for formulas not used as headings for entries.

The **most important compilations** of compounds **arranged according to the Richter system** are Richter's *Lexikon der Kohlenstoff-Verbindungen* (see p. 16 for a description) and Stelzner's *Literatur-Register* (see p. 16), which is virtually a continuation of the *Lexikon*. These are in a sense formula indexes to *Chemisches Zentralblatt*, to which reference is continually made. Beginning in 1925 **organic formula indexes** have been published by *Chemisches Zentralblatt*. The *Literatur-Register* was merged with the *Zentralblatt* as a collective formula index to the latter in 1925.

Organic compounds are indexed by formulas according to the Richter system in the following journals. All of these publish original papers only.

The Journal of the Chemical Society (London) published abstracts up to 1926 but the formula indexing has always been limited to the original papers.

Annalen (Liebigs) (since 1899). Collective indexes cover volumes 277–328 (years 1893–1903) and 329–380 (years 1903–1911).

Journal of the Chemical Society (London). Transactions only (since 1907).
Chemische Berichte (since 1898).
Journal für praktische Chemie (1899 to date).
Recueil des travaux chimiques des Pays-Bas (since 1899).

Beginning with the 1920 volume *Chemical Abstracts* has published annual formula indexes. Since this journal lays great stress on completeness and the policy as far as the formula index is concerned has been to enter all new compounds and all compounds for which new data are given, **this index is virtually a record by formulas of all compounds studied during the period covered.** The Hill system, slightly modified, is used and **inorganic compounds are entered as well as organic ones.** The simpler and more common compounds are simply entered as cross references to the subject index. This index is supplementary to the subject index to *Chemical Abstracts.* The names of compounds given following the formulas are made to correspond exactly with the names used as headings in the subject index so that one can refer to that index for derivatives or related compounds which may be grouped there. A collective formula index has been published for the period 1920–1946.

RING-FORMULA INDEXES OF COMPOUNDS

The number of parent ring complexes in organic chemistry has been so large, and is being added to so rapidly, that a key to them has become almost necessary as an adjunct to any comprehensive index of organic names. A convenient basis for such a key is found in the number of rings in the complex and the number and kind of atoms in each ring. A ring index of this kind is available in the decennial indexes to *Chemical Abstracts* and in the annual indexes commencing with 1916. In it the ring systems are arranged in order of complexity, commencing with single three-membered rings having formulas (ring atoms only) such as C_2O and C_3, following these with four-membered rings such as C_3N and C_4, then five-membered, six-membered, etc., and progressing to polynuclear systems such as C_5—C_6 and C_5N—C_6—C_6, the number of nuclei in the system extending even to twenty. By this means one can discover whether any particular ring system is represented in the index, and if so under what names it and its derivatives will be found.

PATENT-NUMBER INDEXES

Patents issued by the various countries are given numbers. A few publications that contain abstracts of patents furnish indexes thereto

PATENT-NUMBER INDEXES   271

by numbers. The numerical order is naturally the one followed. In most countries the practice is to number patents continuously as issued (not true of German patents). Until 1916 it was the practice in Great Britain to start a new series of patent numbers each year, so that the patent-number indexes for British patents previous to that year are arranged first by year and then numerically.

Japanese patents are no longer promptly given consecutive numbers irrespective of the year of issue. This was done up to 1950. Then it became the practice to give patents consecutive annual numbers, the numbers starting over for each year with the promise of providing consecutive numbers later. *Chemical Abstracts* has not awaited the provision of these consecutive numbers, but is publishing abstracts with the annual numbers for the sake of promptness.

The **usefulness** of these indexes is apparently pretty much limited. Occasionally, a chemist will have the number only of a patent which he wishes to look up, in which case these indexes are undoubtedly helpful.

Patent-number indexes are to be found in connection with the following journals for the years indicated in parentheses.

Journal of the Chemical Society (London) (1913–1925).
Journal of the Society of Chemical Industry (1901–1925).
Chemical Abstracts (1912–1914) and (1935–   ).
Chemisches Zentralblatt (1897–   ).
British Abstracts (1926–1953).

Two collective patent-number indexes have been issued for *Chemical Abstracts*, one covering the period 1907–1936 and the other covering 1937–1946. Further such collective indexes are to follow.

Card Indexes

Some business concerns and certain individuals find it expedient to maintain their own card indexes to the literature of subjects in which they have special interest. It is often the practice to copy or clip and paste on cards excerpts from papers or to make or take over abstracts. These cards must of course be arranged systematically, usually by subjects, with cross references added; they constitute a kind of index and more or less detailed information source combined. The greatest drawback to such an index is the fact that a number of subjects may be covered in a single abstract, so that for thorough indexing the card needs to be duplicated, in part at least, as many times (not often done fully). As such an index grows the classification problem increases.

The preparation of such an index and keeping it up to date present quite a task, more than most chemists feel that they have time to undertake. A good, well indexed abstract journal should go a long way toward making such indexes unnecessary in most instances. If business and other information outside the strictly chemical literature make up a part of personal or corporation card indexes, the situation is somewhat different. Such indexes are bulky and expensive.

There is no existing general strictly chemical card index service on the market so far as the authors know.

PUNCHED-CARD INDEXES

Machines have done much to reduce manual labor and improve the products of work. Machines are also helpful in various ways in reducing mental effort, as by the use of calculating devices. Since the early '40's there has been growing interest in the possibility of utilizing machines in the recording and searching of scientific information. The principal methods tried have involved punched cards. Some success has been attained but this sort of thing is still in its infancy.

Electronic devices have entered the investigational picture.

Of course, machines have long aided in the recording of information. Typewriters and printing presses are machines. *Chemical Abstracts* is indexed by the use of magnetic recorders, plus electrical typewriters. Well informed and highly trained indexers dictate entries and thus are spared any clerical operations in indexing.

The object of high enthusiasm in the field of literature mechanization has been the hope that literature searching could be so facilitated that it would be a matter of pressing buttons and the like to obtain needed references or even the information itself.

Various punched-card procedures have been proposed and some with certain limitations are in use. For the simpler purposes, edge-punched cards have been provided. For the more extensive or complicated purposes, punched cards sortable by complex machines (IBM machines, for example) are being tried.

No comprehensive mechanization system has been found yet for a field as broad as the whole of chemistry and the related sciences in which chemistry is often used. The most important successful American project of this sort is that of the Chemical-Biological Coordination Center sponsored by the National Research Council, National Academy of Sciences, in Washington, D. C. It is limited to chemical compounds (about 60,000 of them) for which certain recorded biological properties are correlated with coded structural elements. Dealing with chemical compounds by means of punched cards is more promising than is the mechanical handling of the less definite information (chemical phenomena, for example) recorded in scientific literature.

Successful punched-card files relate for the most part to limited subject matter with the operation of the system in the hands of the builder thereof.

The effort for scientific literature mechanization is worthy and it should be continued. The objective should be kept high, and the limitations should be recognized. Machines cannot think, but they can tirelessly do many things with great rapidity and accuracy. Machines cannot provide information that human beings have not, with forethought, put into them, but machines have real possibilities for the manipulation and helpful correlation of information. Machines cannot grow as can a human literature searcher in the course of a search, but there may be ways to introduce opportunities for the latter kind of growth. A possibility is machine searching by steps, with the human searcher entering the picture between strides. At least the manipulation, correlation, and organization of information by machines may under some circumstances put information in a form more amenable to growth by individuals in the course of searches. Really successful mechanization will not be obtained until machines can do at least as much as standard indexes can do and do this as well.

The recording, distribution, and use of information on cards is more expensive than is distribution in indexed journals. The latter method will continue in use when mechanization is completely successful because of the expense factor. Individuals will often not be in a position readily to acquire mechanized information.

There are many more or less specific purposes in the field of scientific information for which machines can provide effective help. Our purpose in emphasizing limitations is to suggest the wisdom of substituting an element of precautionary realism for some of the enthusiasm that is leading to higher claims for literature mechanization than present attainment has provided. The enthusiasm, however, should continue for the objective is most worthy.

The fundamental problem in all indexes or other keys to recorded information is to bring into coincidence the vocabulary of the maker of the key and that of the user.

For information on the use of punched cards see: H. F. McGaw, *Marginal Punched Cards in College and Research Libraries,* Washington, D. C., Scarecrow Press, 1952, 218 pp., and R. S. Casey, J. W. Perry, M. M. Berry (editors), *Punched Cards: Their Application in Science and Industry,* 2nd ed., New York, Reinhold, 1957, about 500 pp. Both of these books have extensive bibliographies.

The National Bureau of Standards, Washington, D. C., started a catalog of organic and inorganic compounds on punched cards in 1952. These cards give physical constants and a bibliography for each compound. The cards may be sorted by either a simple machine or an International Business Machine. The Bureau intends to sell these cards. See *Chemical and Engineering News* **33,** 3444 (1952), for further information. To the best of the authors' knowledge this is the only chemical punched card index on the market.

OPTICAL CARD INDEXES

These cards use microfilm on which the coded material has been photographed and are sorted by a photo-electric machine. This is really a variation on the punched-card idea and involves the same coding problems. The method of sorting is different. This method of indexing has not been investigated as extensively as the punched-card one. The United States Department of Agriculture Library has equipment of this kind and is experimenting with its development and use; a brief description of it appears in *Chemical Industries* **62,** 189 (1949) and *The Library Journal* **78,** 310 (1953). Ralph Shaw, former librarian there, has patented his Rapid Selector, U. S. Patent 2,594,358 (1952).

Making Indexes

The making of indexes is not within the scope of this book, but information on methods of doing it is often valuable for those who use indexes.

The standard manual for indexing in general is M. T. Thorne's *Indexing: Principles, Rules and Examples,* Albany, Univ. of State of New York Press, 4th ed., 1942, 76 pp. (Univ. of State of N. Y. Bulletin no. 1230, February 16, 1942).

Indexing with Special Emphasis on Its Technique: An Annotated Bibliography 1939–1954, compiled by J. M. Wayne (New York, The Special Libraries Association, 1955, 16 pp.) includes many references to material of use to scientists.

Indexing Your Book by S. Spiker, Madison, Univ. of Wisconsin Press, 2nd ed., 1955, 28 pp., gives a detailed outline of indexing principles and procedures.

The general aspects of indexing are discussed in the periodical, *Special Libraries* (July–August, 1940).

The question of systematic subject indexing is discussed by R. C. Vickery, *Journal of Documentation* **9**, 48–59 (1953).

Indexing abstracts is discussed by C. L. Bernier and E. J. Crane, *Ind. Eng. Chem.* **40**, 725–730 (1948). This paper also contains useful information on how to use an index, particularly a subject index.

Developments in subject indexing, including alphabetical indexing and the use of machines in indexing, is discussed by B. C. Vickery, *Journal of Documentation* **11**, 1–11 (1955).

Trends in indexing practice (German, British, and American Chemical Societies) are discussed by R. Brightman, *Nature* **160**, 615–617 (1947).

The relationship between abstracting and indexing is discussed by E. J. Crane, *Journal of Chemical Education* **20**, 537–539 (1943).

Two UNESCO conferences on abstracting and indexing are discussed by E. J. Crane, *Chemical and Engineering News* **27**, 2327, 2400–2401 (1949). General conclusions and specific recommendations are outlined. These conferences were concerned mostly with a service such as that of the *Engineering Index,* but the other element of indexing was considered to some degree in its international aspects.

Coding and indexing knowledge is considered by J. E. Holmstrom, *Chemistry and Industry* **27**, 826–831, 908–909 (1949).

Chemical and Engineering News **31**, 4910 (1953) reports briefly on the annual meeting of the American Documentation Institute at which mechanical devices to aid in making indexes were considered. More information may be obtained from the Institute, c/o the Library of Congress, Washington 25, D. C.

EXISTING INDEXES

The indexes most used by chemists are the subject indexes to the chemical abstract journals. These indexes are briefly discussed as a part of the descriptions of the various abstract journals in Chapter 2, the index equipment of each being mentioned there. One should look at the beginning of a subject index before use, because indexing practices change and the explanation is usually given there. Subject indexes to most abstract journals have improved greatly during the last thirty years. It is particularly **important to watch for changes in nomenclature and methods of indexing when a literature search goes back many years.** Many of the older subject indexes are based on words, not subjects; some of them are little more than lists of titles of the papers that were abstracted and consequently are very inadequate. Experience in the use of subject indexes to abstract journals is revealing as to adequacy and suggests the degree of resourcefulness required for success in searches. The more important abstract journal indexes will be described more fully here. The author indexes to abstract journals do not vary enough to require comment; the only formula indexes existing have already been discussed. For patent indexes see Chapter 4.

Chemical Abstracts. The most extensive of the abstract journal subject indexes is that to *Chemical Abstracts.* This index contains many more entries each year than do any of the other similar indexes. This is a true subject index for the most part (not a word index) and abstracts, not merely their titles, have been considered in the indexing. Even the full papers or patents abstracted are frequently examined for needed index entries and the entries made. The entries are comparatively brief, only "essential" words being used, with frequent word abbreviations. The wording in the indexes often differs from that in the abstracts or their titles. Since 1916 it has been the practice of this journal to publish a so-called Key and an Introduction to its subject indexes (placed at the beginning). It is recommended to the student of chemical indexes that these be examined because they serve to point out, with examples at hand, the various considerations that enter into chemical subject index building. The Introduction contains rules for the systematic naming of compounds for indexing purposes, a list of names of organic radicals, and the index of ring systems. From 1916 on the *Chemical Abstracts* subject indexes furnish a typical example of the entry-a-line form with alphabetic arrangement of modifications. Organic compounds, after being systematically named, are entered by the so-called parent compound or, more accurately, index compound method in the subject index and by formulas in the formula index. For example, aminodeoxyinositol is entered "Inositol, aminodeoxy-." The subjects are arranged alphabetically. Cross references are numerous and notes explaining the indexing practice with reference to certain subjects are to be found here and there in the index. Column references are given to the fraction of a column (in ninths), columns being numbered instead of pages. The collective indexes, published at ten-year intervals, save much time.

Journal of the Chemical Society (London). While this journal was publishing abstracts (1871–1925), its subject indexes gradually improved and word indexing became less. The general features of its subject index were carried over into that for *British Abstracts* (see below).

Journal of the Society of Chemical Industry (London). While this journal was publishing abstracts (1882–1925), its subject indexes were based very largely on titles of papers and the wording of these adhered to very closely. This caused many scattered entries and this must be kept in mind when one is using this index. There are a considerable number of cross references.

British Abstracts. The subject indexes to this journal do not have the subjects arranged entirely in alphabetical order; there is some classification. For example, one will find hypobromites and bromides under bromine. If the subject does not appear as a main heading, it is well to look under a class to which it might belong. Organic compounds (the nomenclature is good) are, for the most part, entered without inversion of names to bring the so-called parent compound of each group to the front. This means that there are many entries under such radical names as "Methyl-," "Phenyl-," etc. when these are not the significant parts of the compounds. These indexes do not always consider the contents of abstracts, but depend more on their titles than the subject index of *Chemical Abstracts* does. It is best, therefore, when using the subject index to *British Abstracts*, to look at all abstracts that might be useful.

Chemisches Zentralblatt. This index is good. It has shown distinct improvement from time to time. For example, a tendency to index words instead of subjects too much has largely disappeared. Word indexing is especially bad in German, in which language there are so many compound words. For example, in certain of the earlier indexes instead of finding all of the entries relating to spectra under Spektren one is likely to find these scattered under Absorptionspektrum, Bandenspektrum, Elementarspektrum, Emissionsspektrum, Flammenspektrum, Linienspektrum, etc. Cross referring in such cases, as well as general cross-reference entering, has been pretty thorough, which helps considerably. Another improvement is the change in 1925 to the use of inverted names for organic compounds entered in the index, so the method of entry is now the same as in

Chemical Abstracts. Up to 1924 author names were given in the subject index; this is no longer done. Abbreviations are common, but not hard to comprehend. There is frequent departure from the alphabetical arrangement of subjects, particularly after 1925. Many subjects are classified in this index, which is helpful when general aspects of a topic are needed. But when a specific piece of information is wanted, it is necessary to look under several headings to be sure that all references are found. The fact that in this index the entries under each heading are set "running" instead of "entry-a-line" makes continued use a little tedious.

Chemiker-Zeitung. The subject indexes are divided into separate alphabetical arrangements of entries for each of the sections of the abstracts (over 30), which makes them inconvenient to use. They are fairly adequate.

Bulletin de la société chimique de France. Full "modifications" are used and author names are given in this subject index. The entries under each heading are "run in" (not started on separate lines), and the numerical order of page references is followed. Since the number of entries under some headings is large this is not a convenient form of index to use. Organic compounds are entered under a modified inverted-name, parent-compound system; this journal was the first of the abstract journals to adopt such a form. Salts are entered under headings designated by the names of the significant elements involved, as Ferric chloride under Fer. Cross references are somewhat limited in number. In using a French index it is necessary to bear in mind that the order of words in phrases is likely to be just the opposite of that in English, as Terre rares, Points d'ébullition, and Bleu de Prusse. Much of this index is based on words and titles of papers, not on subjects.

Chimie & industrie. The subject index to this journal appears twice a year. With its roomy, entry-a-line form and its fairly numerous cross references it is easy to use in so far as it goes, but it seems to be rather far from complete. Apparently only titles are indexed and in them only outstanding subjects. Specific salts and oxides are not indexed under names with the significant element first but under such headings as Chlorure de magnesium and Oxyde de fer. This practice in French of using an order of words opposite to that of English practice also has resulted in such headings as Indice d'iode. It seems unfortunate that the more significant word is not so placed that it becomes the one alphabeted.

Bulletin signalétique. This abstract journal does not have an annual subject index in the true sense of the word. It is just a comprehensive table of contents.

Zeitschrift für angewandte Chemie. The subject indexes like the earlier ones of *Chemisches Zentralblatt* involve considerable word, not true subject, indexing.

INDEXES INDEPENDENT OF ANY SINGLE PUBLICATION

There are a number of compilations of more or less interest to the chemist that consist of indexes only or indexed lists of titles. Some cover journal articles only, some books only, and some both. Indexes that refer wholly or partly to journal articles are listed below alphabetically by titles, with descriptions of those of most importance to the chemist.

Agricultural Index, (1916–   ). A subject index to a selected list of agricultural journals and bulletins. Monthly. New York, Wilson Co.

Alphabetisches Verzeichnis von Trivialnamen der organischen Verbindungen. This is an index of about 8,000 names of organic compounds. It was compiled from Stelzner's *Literatur-Register* and the *Chemisches Zentralblatt* index from 1922 to February, 1926. It covers the literature from January, 1910, to February, 1926. There is a list of 242 common radical names at the beginning. It was compiled by the editorial staff of the *Chemisches Zentralblatt* and published by the *Deutsche Chemische Gesellschaft* in 1926.

Australian Science Index (1952–   ). This is a monthly publication of the Commonwealth Scientific and Industrial Research Organization, Melbourne, Australia.

Bibliographia medica. Recueil mensuel. Classement méthodique de la bibliographie internationale des sciences médicales, 3 vols., 1900–1902, Paris, Institut de Bibliographie. See *Index Medicus,* below.

Bibliographia scientiae naturalis helvetica (1925–   ). This is published annually by the Schweizerische Landesbibliothek, Bern, Switzerland. It includes book titles as well as papers in periodicals.

Bibliographie der deutschen Zeitschriften-Literatur (1897–   ). A classified list of articles arranged by subjects taken from over 3,000 journals. The printing is close. Published by Felix Dietrich, Gautzsch bei Leipzig, Germany. Semi-annual.

Bibliographie der fremdsprachigen Zeitschriftenliteratur (1911–   ). An international index to periodicals. Published by Felix

Dietrich, Osnabrück, Germany. This covers periodicals from more than thirty countries. It is much more comprehensive than the *International Index to Periodicals* (see below).

Bibliographie scientifique française. Paris, Gauthier-Villars, 1902–. A bimonthly publication.

Bibliography of Agriculture (1942–   ). This is prepared by the Library of the United States Department of Agriculture. It is classified and lists all current publications, both foreign and domestic, in the field of agriculture. Papers in more than 12,000 periodicals, many serials and thousands of books, pamphlets, and documents are included. This bibliography covers much of interest to chemists: nutrition, food processing, soils, fertilizers, and insecticides—to mention a few topics. Washington, D. C., United States Government Printing Office. Monthly.

Bibliography of Scientific Publications of South Asia (1949–   ). This is prepared by the Science Cooperation Office of South Asia (which is an agency of the United Nations Educational, Scientific and Cultural Organization). It covers periodicals, books, pamphlets, and reports for India, Burma, and Ceylon. Delhi, India, UNESCO Science Cooperation Office for South Asia. Semi-annual.

Boletin del Centro de Documentación científica y tecnica de Mexico (1952–   ). A classified list of titles of papers that appear in the scientific periodicals of the world. Titles are given in both the original language and in Spanish. Papers from Latin American countries are annotated in English or French.

Bulletin signalétique. See page 137.

Catalogue of Scientific Papers (1867–1925). This work of the Royal Society of London is the most comprehensive index to general science ever attempted. It is still incomplete. It consists of a catalog of papers arranged alphabetically by authors covering the century 1800–1900. During the period 1867–1923, 19 volumes in four series were published. First series (Vols. 1–5), 1800–1863; second series (Vols. 6–8), 1864–1873; third series (Vols. 9–11), 1874–1883; fourth series (incomplete), 1884–1900. The subject indexes were issued separately; but only three volumes were published that do not include chemistry. This is a very valuable guide to nineteenth century scientific literature. Cambridge Univ. Press, London, 1914–1925, and London, Clay (1867–1902).

Current Chemical Papers (1954–   ). This is a classified world list of new papers in pure chemistry which is prepared by the Chemical Society (London). It gives titles only, but it appears very promptly and is a help in rapidly developing fields of chemistry because it takes the abstract journals much longer to produce abstracts. It is a partial replacement for *British Abstracts*, which ceased publication in 1953. London, The Chemical Society. Monthly.

Current List of Medical Literature (1941–). This is a monthly listing by titles of the papers in current medical journals. It is classified. There are collective annual indexes. It covers more than 12,000 medical journals of all countries. It is useful for many phases of biochemistry. Washington, D. C., The United States Army Medical Library.

Engineering Index (1884–). This is something more than a subject index, international in scope, for periodicals and publications of technical and scientific societies, government bureaus, and various research organizations. It gives a brief digest for each entry. It has been issued in two forms for many years: an annual collective volume and a daily or weekly card service. Subscribers to the card service may obtain just the classes in which they are interested. This index was started by J. B. Johnson and was published in the *Journal of the Association Engineering Societies* (1884–1892). The Engineering Magazine Co. (New York) became the publisher in 1892 and issued four volumes in book form that cover the period 1884–1905; then they continued it as *The Engineering Index Annual* (1906–1919). In 1920 the American Society of Mechanical Engineers became the publishers and issued it annually under the title *Engineering Index* until 1934, when Engineering Index, Inc. was formed to publish it. The current publisher is Engineering Index, Inc., New York. It contains much of interest to chemists and chemical engineers.

Engineering Index Annual (1906–1919). See under *Engineering Index*, above.

Guide to Russian Scientific Periodical Literature (1948–). This gives the translated titles of papers and translations of some abstracts for Russian periodicals that are received at the Brookhaven National Laboratory. It also lists translations of entire papers that are available. This is distributed by the Office of Technical Services, Department of Commerce, Washington, D. C. Monthly.

Index Catalogue of the Library of the Surgeon General's Office, U. S. Army Medical Library (1880–1950). A very extensive author and subject index. The first series consists of 16 vols. and covers the period 1880–1895; the second series has in it 21 vols. and covers

1896–1916. The third series in 10 vols. covers the period 1918–1932; and the fourth series covers 1933–1948, but the fourth series is incomplete (A–Mz, in 10 vols.). Publication was discontinued in 1950. Much information of biochemical interest can be obtained by the use of this index. Washington, D. C., Government Printing Office.

Index Medicus (1879–1927). This is a classified record (titles) of the medical periodical literature of the world. It was founded by John S. Billings and Robert Fletcher. The first series of 21 vols. covers the period 1879–1899. The index appeared as *Bibliographia medica* (see above) during 1900–1902. The Carnegie Institution of Washington assumed responsibility for publication in 1903, and the second series (18 vols.) covers 1903–1920, the third series (1921–1926). Such subjects of chemical interest are included as deficiency diseases, immunology, metabolism, pharmacology, physiology, therapeutics, and toxicology. In 1927 *Index Medicus* was merged with the *Quarterly Cumulative Index to Medical Literature* to form the *Quarterly Cumulative Index Medicus.*

Index to the Literature of Explosives, by Charles E. Munroe. Part I was published in 1886, Part II in 1893. Since then no volumes have been published, but a new manuscript which includes the two earlier parts is on file with the Committee on Explosives Investigations, National Research Council, Washington, D. C. The aim has been "to get as complete a bibliography of articles published in periodical literature as possible." The list of periodicals covered is somewhat limited, but it includes the more important ones. The periodicals covered have been examined back to their beginnings, the *Transactions of the Royal Society of London* back to 1665, for example. Dependence on titles of papers has not been a limitation. "The titles of articles cited are accompanied not only by full bibliographic references but also, not infrequently, by critical, or explanatory, notes."

Index of Mining Engineering Literature, by Walter M. Crane. Two volumes were published, one in 1909 and the other in 1912. A classified list of titles only, taken from 18 periodicals and published without an author index. New York, Wiley, 1257 pp.

Index of Periodical Publications in the British Patent Office Library, 1906. A large number of references are arranged alphabetically by titles.

Industrial Arts Index (1913–   ). This is a cumulative index to more than 200 engineering, trade, and business periodicals (mostly American), including metallurgical and chemical journals. The entries are arranged alphabetically by subjects with repetition of entries when desirable and with cross references. This index is of particular value to one whose interest in the current periodical literature includes business and nonchemical technical subjects in addition to chemical advances. Since 1932 it has been published monthly with annual cumulations. There is a rather wide variation in the values of articles listed. New York, Wilson Co.

Indice di periodici scientifici e tecnici (1948–). This index covers the scientific literature of the world. There are brief annotations. It is published in fifteen separate parts, of which Part IV is on chemistry. Rome, Consiglio nazionale delle ricerche. Monthly. This is a comprehensive and useful publication.

International Catalogue of Scientific Literature (1901–1921). A continuation of the *Catalogue of Scientific Papers* (see above). Publication was authorized by an international conference held in London, credit established by the Royal Society of London having made it possible for the central bureau to proceed. Regional bureaus in the various cooperating countries furnished the material; that of the United States was under the direction of the Smithsonian Institution. This catalog was published annually for the period 1901–1914 (completed in 1921). A practically complete list is given of all purely scientific books and papers published each year in the 25 countries of most importance scientifically. Individual catalogs have been issued for each of the following 17 branches of science:

a. Mathematics
b. Mechanics
c. Physics
d. Chemistry
e. Astronomy
f. Meteorology
g. Mineralogy (including Petrology and Crystallography)
h. Geology
j. Geography
k. Palaeontology
l. General Biology
m. Botany
n. Zoology
o. Human Anatomy
p. Physical Anthropology
q. Physiology (including Pharmacology and Experimental Pathology)
r. Bacteriology

The annual volume of each part contains an author index and a subject index. The subject indexing is thoroughly done. Pure science is given greater attention than is applied science. There are 4,673 journals on the list of those covered that was published in 1903.

The *International Catalogue* is a very valuable index. London, Harrison.

International Index to Periodicals (1913–). A cumulative author and subject index devoted chiefly to the humanities. New York, Wilson Co.

List of Scientific Papers Published in Latin America (1951–). This is published annually by the UNESCO Field Science Cooperation Office, Montevideo, Uruguay.

List of Scientific Papers Published in the Middle East (1950–). Published by UNESCO Science Cooperation Office, Cairo, Egypt. Semi-annual, beginning in 1950.

Monthly List of Russian Accessions (1948–). This covers the titles of papers in Russian periodicals and titles of books that are received by the Library of Congress and cooperating libraries. Washington, D. C., Government Printing Office.

Poole's Index to Periodical Literature (1802–1907). *Poole's Index*, a subject index of titles, is of general, more or less popular, interest and is little used by chemists. The first volume, in two parts, covers the period 1802–1881; five other volumes bring the index down to 1907. Boston, Houghton.

Quarterly Cumulative Index to Current Medical Literature (1916– 1927). This was a publication of the American Medical Association (Chicago). Subjects and authors are given in one index.

Quarterly Cumulative Index Medicus (1927–). This periodical resulted from the merging of the *Quarterly Cumulative Index to Current Medical Literature* and *Index Medicus*. This is a subject and author index to over 1,200 periodicals. It gives almost complete international coverage for medical journals and includes lists of new books. This publication is useful for many subjects in biochemistry, particularly for the period 1933–1948, before the abstract journal *Excerpta Medica* was started. Chicago, the American Medical Association.

Reader's Guide to Periodical Literature (1896–). This subject index of titles resembles *Poole's Index* in being of general, more or less popular, interest. New York City, Wilson Co.

Repertorium Commentatorium a societatibus litterariis editarum (1801–1821). This work by I. D. Reuss (Göttingen, Germany, H. Dietrich) is in 16 volumes of which fourteen are devoted to natural and medical science. Volume 3 covers chemistry and metallurgy. It is a valuable index to papers written before 1800.

Repertorium der technischen Journal-Literatur (1823–1911). The first volume, which covers the years 1823–1853, was published by F. Schubarth, Berlin, 1409 pp. The next six volumes published by Bruno Karl cover the periods 1854–1868, 1869–1873, 1874, 1875, 1876, and 1877, respectively, and the annual volumes covering 1878 to 1909 were published by the Kaiserliches Patentamt. Two volumes, for 1910 and 1911, were published as *Fortschritte der Technik*. It is a subject index to more than 400 periodicals (not limited to German journals), arranged alphabetically by the German word, followed, in volumes from 1892 on, by the French and English equivalents. Each volume has a detailed subject index to this subject list and from 1897 on there are author indexes also. Prior to 1879 this index was called *Repertorium der technischen Literatur*. It is a very nearly complete list of available technical literature for the period 1823–1909. It includes many chemical papers that were not covered by the chemical abstract journals of this period.

Repertorium der technischen Literatur. See *Repertorium der technischen Journal-Literatur* (above).

Subject Index to Periodicals (1925–   ). This is a publication of the Library Association, London. It is an annual publication that is now limited to British periodicals for the most part. It is the British equivalent of the *Reader's Guide to Periodical Literature* and covers periodicals of general interest.

Translated Contents Lists of Russian Periodicals. This is published monthly by the Department of Scientific and Industrial Research (British Government), London.

U. S. Government Research Reports. See page 145.

LITERATURE CITED

(1) *Nature* (February 27, 1890).
(2) Nichols, J. B., *Library J.* **17**, 406 (1892).
(3) Patterson and Curran, *J. Am. Chem. Soc.* **39**, 1623–1638 (1917).
(4) Nutting, H. S., "Why Have a Nomenclature," *Chem. Eng. News* **31**, 939–940 (1953).
(5) Huntress, E. H., a paper in *Searching the Chemical Literature*, Vol. 4 of *Advances in Chemistry Series*, Washington, D. C., American Chemical Society, 1951.
(6) Hill, E. A., *J. Am. Chem. Soc.* **22**, 478–495 (1900); **29**, 936–941 (1907); **34**, 416–418 (1912).
(7) See Introduction to *Richter's Lexikon der Kohlenstoffe-Verbindungen*.
(8) Dyson, G. M., *Chemistry and Industry* **1952**, 676–684.

CHAPTER 9

LIBRARIES

|||||||||||||||||||||||||||||||||||||||||||||||||||||||||||||||||||||||||

The literature discussed in the preceding chapters must exist in ordered collections, that is libraries, if it is to be of practical use. The average chemist's collection is far too small for his needs; he must therefore look to the larger library of his university, company, technical society, community or local, state, or national government.

It is not necessary for a library patron to understand much of the technique of library work, as the librarian or an assistant can always be found to serve as a guide. Nevertheless, it will save the time of the reader and of the librarian if the patron familiarizes himself with some common library practices and services. The resources of a library can be utilized to the fullest extent only if the patron takes the time to become acquainted with the librarian and his staff, and with the resources of the specific library. The notes in this chapter apply to libraries in the United States. But many library practices are universal. A few chemical libraries in other countries will be commented upon at the end of the chapter.

The librarian, or librarians, of scientific libraries or of the science divisions of large general libraries are usually both scientists and librarians. They stand ready to help the user in every feasible way and to make the information in the library accessible. The modern librarian is equipped to give valuable assistance in literature searches; he is far more than a person who orders books and periodicals and attends to keeping the collection in order and to all of the innumerable details. The amount of time, thought, and patience given to library work is almost incredible, but not out of proportion to the

286

need. It is an altruistic service of immense value, usually taken for granted, sometimes abused, but rarely used to its fullest extent.

A great deal of useful information on libraries, their practices and services is given in *Technical Libraries,* edited by Lucille Jackson, published by the Special Libraries Association, New York, 1951. This was intended primarily for librarians, but it is equally valuable for their patrons.

AMERICAN LIBRARIES

Only a few general comments on scientific collections in the libraries of the United States appear here. See Appendix 3 for a list of libraries of interest to chemists and of sources of information about libraries.

Public Libraries. These include libraries that are maintained by the city, state or federal governments. If a city has a population of less than 100,000, it is unusual to find a large enough collection of chemical publications in its public library to be of much value to chemists. This is not entirely a matter of population; it depends on the nature of the economy in the locality. If the city is the center of an industrial area, the library needs a larger scientific collection. These libraries specialize to a certain degree. The Tulsa Public Library, Tulsa, Oklahoma, has specialized in petroleum and petroleum technology. Other examples could be cited. Considered as a group, there are few outstanding collections of chemical publications in the public libraries of the cities.

State Libraries. The state libraries very rarely have enough chemical publications in their collections to be of adequate use to chemists. These libraries specialize in legislative and legal material for the most part. A notable exception is the New York State Library, Albany, New York, which maintains a good collection of scientific periodicals.

Federal Libraries. The federal government libraries of the greatest value to the chemist are in Washington, D. C. A number of them are listed in Appendix 3. Only one of them, the Library of Congress, will be commented upon here. The Library of Congress has always contained much scientific material although it does not make a specialty of it. In recent years it has become the official depository for a large quantity of scientific material collected by other government agencies from many sources, both foreign and domestic. A science division was established within the Library of Congress in 1950. It now receives a number of scientific periodicals from foreign countries that are received by very few of the other libraries in the United States; and it makes a particular effort to make scientific material originating in the Soviet Union more accessible to American scientists.

Educational Institutions. A large proportion of the important libraries for chemical research workers are found in the colleges, universities, and technical schools. The best ones are at the larger institutions that maintain graduate schools and have been granting the Ph.D. or Sc.D. in chemistry or chemical engineering for some time. An educational institution is usually glad to have chemists who are not on its faculty or staff use its library for publications that are not available elsewhere in the community, but it is usually necessary to make arrangements to do so.

Special Libraries. There are a very large number of these in the United States to meet the needs of manufacturers, scientists, business men, and others. They make no attempt to cover the whole field of knowledge but concentrate on specialties. Most of these libraries are members of the Special Libraries Association, founded in 1909, which has a Science–Technology Division. The address of the Association is 31 East 10th Street, New York 3, N. Y. Most of the libraries maintained by manufacturers and trade associations are members of the Special Libraries Association. The librarians cooperate not only with each other but also with outsiders, so that the library resources of corporations having chemical interests are of value to chemists in general. There are over 200 libraries in the Science–Technology Division of the Special Libraries Association; some of these are primarily chemical and others give emphasis to chemistry in their collections. A few of the scientific libraries maintained by industry are well-rounded collections, but most of them are highly specialized, and some cover very limited fields of industrial chemistry; these libraries are not open to the public, but arrangements can be made to consult their collections in most cases.

Classification Systems

Libraries have devised various classification systems to enable them to keep their collections in order and to locate items when needed. Sometimes a library has its own system; the New York Public Library, New York City, is one of this kind. The most commonly used system in the United States is the Dewey Decimal System. The Library of Congress system has been adopted by a number of other libraries in the United States. The third system which it is useful to become acquainted with is the Universal Decimal Classification (based on the Dewey System). This is used by a few libraries in the United States, the Engineering Societies Library (New York) being one of them; and it has other uses besides book classification.

There are a number of reasons that make it worth while to know the fundamentals of these classification systems and the one used by the library which a person uses most frequently if it is not one of these three. Such knowledge saves a lot of time in locating material in a library that has open shelves or allows patrons to use the stacks. It is also an aid in locating books and other material in the subject catalog of the library; the subject heading under which a book will be entered in the card catalog is related to its classification plan. Some libraries have files and indexes that depend entirely on these classification systems for the location of material in them. Some publications use them to classify their contents.

DEWEY DECIMAL CLASSIFICATION

This system is named for its originator, Melvil Dewey. It can be consulted in any library or purchased (Melvil Dewey, *Decimal Classification*, Standard 15th ed., Forest Press, Lake Placid Club, N. Y., 1951). Only a brief outline is given here. See the full work for further information; many libraries have abridgments available for the use of patrons. The system uses Arabic numerals. Knowledge is divided into ten classes.

000	General Works	500	Natural Science
100	Philosophy	600	Useful Arts
200	Religion	700	Fine Arts
300	Social Sciences	800	Literature
400	Philology	900	History

Each of these classes is subdivided into ten divisions and these in turn are subdivided. Two classes (the five hundreds and the six hundreds) cover most of the material of interest to chemists. Some of the subdivisions of the five hundreds are shown below:

500	Pure Science	550	Geology
510	Mathematics	560	Paleontology
520	Astronomy	570	Biology
530	Physics	580	Botany
540	Chemistry	590	Zoology

The six hundreds are divided in a similar way:

600	Useful Arts	650	Commerce
610	Medicine	660	Chemical Technology
620	Engineering	670	Manufactures
630	Agriculture	680	Manufactures
640	Domestic Economy	690	Building

Then each of these is again divided:

540	General Chemistry	545	Quantitative Analysis
541	Physical Chemistry	546	Inorganic Chemistry
542	Experimental Chemistry	547	Organic Chemistry
543	Analytical Chemistry	548	Crystallography
544	Qualitative Analysis	549	Mineralogy

These illustrations are sufficient to show how three main figures are used to assign a book to one of 999 sections. These in turn can be subdivided almost indefinitely by the use of decimals. One example illustrates this. A book that covers all of inorganic chemistry is designated 546; a part of inorganic chemistry 546.1; subdivisions of this part 546.11, 546.12, 546.13, and so on. The Dewey classification is used in a number of publications; among them is *New Serial Titles*, a monthly publication of the Library of Congress and the British National Bibliography.

LIBRARY OF CONGRESS CLASSIFICATION

This system uses the letters of the alphabet to divide knowledge into 21 groups; there are five unused letters to allow for expansion. A second letter shows subdivision of the group, and further subdivision is designated by Arabic numbers. Decimals are not used. A few illustrations follow. The four groups of most interest to chemists are:

Q	Science	S	Agriculture
R	Medicine	T	Technology

Some of the subdivisions are:

Q C	Physics	T A	Engineering
Q D	Chemistry	T P	Chemical Technology

Further subdivision is designated by numbers:

Q D 71	Analytical Chemistry	T P 785	Glass
Q D 248	Organic Chemistry	T P 890	Dyeing

For further information see *Outline of the Library of Congress Classification*, Washington, D. C., Superintendent of Documents, Government Printing Office. The system may be purchased in parts.

Most libraries have a copy for reference even if they do not use the system.

UNIVERSAL DECIMAL CLASSIFICATION (U.D.C.)

This system, based on the Dewey system, follows the same general method but provides for much greater detail. The International Federation for Documentation (successor to the International Institute of Bibliography) has committees at work in countries all over the world. The U.D.C. numbers are internationally standardized. This system was not worked out as a book classification method but as a method of arranging extremely large bibliographies that include all kinds of materials: books, articles in periodicals, trade literature, patents, theses, abstracts, etc. A few examples will show how closely it is related to the Dewey system.

Dewey		U.D.C.	
500	Science	5	Science
540	Chemistry	54	Chemistry
543	Analytical Chemistry	543	Analytical Chemistry
547	Organic Chemistry	547.63.07	Synthesis of Aromatic Ketones

Some chemical journals give index numbers to their articles in accordance with the U.D.C. system and some publications use it to classify the contents. The third edition of *Classification Décimale Universelle* was issued 1927–1933; publication of an English translation was started in 1943 by the British Standards Institution, London. Most of it has appeared and the classes are sold separately. This is entitled *Universal Decimal Classification: Complete English Edition and 4th International Edition.*

AUTHOR NUMBERS AND CALL NUMBERS

The object of the classifications just described is to bring together on the shelves all of the books on the same subject. Another number is needed to designate those on the same subject that are written by different authors; this is the author number. The most commonly used author numbers are "Cutter numbers" which arrange the books alphabetically by author. The author's name is abbreviated to one or two letters and is followed by a number.

The call number for a book is made up of its class number, its author number, and any additional marks that may be needed (volume or edition number).

CATALOGS

Most libraries use card catalogs to show their contents. The most frequent form is the dictionary catalog in which all of the cards for author, subject, title, and other entries are placed in drawers in one alphabetical arrangement. This catalog is really an index to the contents of the library and requires the same skill in its use as do other indexes. See Chapter 8 for suggestions on the effective use of indexes.

Some libraries have one card catalog for subjects and place all other entries in a second one.

The practice with respect to periodicals varies greatly. Some include periodicals in the dictionary catalog; others have a separate catalog where periodicals are listed alphabetically by title.

Some libraries have a classified catalog, based on the Dewey or other system, and an index to this classified catalog—arranged alphabetically. This type of catalog is useful to see what all the holdings of the library may be in a given class and it avoids looking under many subject headings. It is particularly useful for research work in a large library, which can enter a great variety of information in it —pamphlets, trade literature, and other items. The library that uses a classified catalog also has an author and subject catalog arranged alphabetically.

Cataloging practices for materials other than books or periodicals vary considerably. The government publications and reports, trade literature, theses, dissertations, and patents that vary from a single page to pamphlets or bulletins of about 65 pages all present somewhat different problems. How libraries deal with them depends mostly on their relative numbers in the collection. If there are few of them, they are frequently included in the dictionary catalog together with the books. Most libraries have one or more special catalogs, files, or indexes for these materials. It is best to inquire in each library where one works as to how it treats these materials.

Microfilm and microcard copies of books and periodicals are usually entered in the dictionary catalog for the library. Some libraries have large collections of photoprints. Again, it is best to inquire about how much of this material a library has and how it catalogs or indexes it. Some libraries have a considerable amount of material in these forms.

Since punched cards and other kinds of automation have been introduced into library work, cataloging and filing practices are changing. Some libraries are building up punched-card files that can be sorted mechanically to locate a publication or certain kinds of information. This is a comparatively new development and some libraries are using it for a number of things. A considerable quantity of experimental work is in progress to find methods for using punched cards that are better than a subject catalog or index for some purposes. It is well to inquire what is being done in a library used frequently and to find out whether or not any of these aids are available. For more detailed information on automation in libraries, see McGaw's book [1] and the bibliography compiled by Loftus and Kent.[2]

Consulting Service

Libraries vary greatly in the degree of freedom allowed readers, but are usually willing to go just as far in this direction as is consistent with the general good. The smaller and more select the clientele, the greater are the privileges; a great public library must obviously enforce more restrictions than a special library consulted by those trained in sciences. Nowhere else does conduct better proclaim breeding; quietness, orderliness, and considerate care for books, periodicals, microcards, and microfilm are among the cardinal virtues of a library patron.

The Reference Department. Works of general reference, such as dictionaries, encyclopedias, and handbooks are nearly always immediately accessible to the reader. They may be in a special room by themselves or in the general reading room.

Current periodicals may be free of access, or it may be necessary to call for them. There may be a separate reading room.

Using the Stacks. If the reader is allowed to consult books, periodicals, pamphlets, etc., in the stacks, a little study of the library system and of the card catalog will avoid his troubling the library employees needlessly. Most librarians prefer to have the reader leave books and other materials down after using them as the risk that he may put them back on the wrong shelves is too great. However, one should use common sense; if he is consulting a whole series of annual indexes one after the other it will be to everyone's advantage if he put them back correctly. The fact that the stacks are not open to the public may not prevent the chemist from using them; in most cases proper identification or a letter of reference will open them. Most libraries are glad to cooperate in every reasonable way with research workers who must consult many periodical sets and a large number of other publications.

Peculiarities of Arrangement. Some libraries separate books of various sizes and shelve them separately; accordingly, there may be more than one set of shelves for the same subject. Periodical files are frequently shelved in one place and books in another. Pamphlets, patents, theses, and other materials may be shelved separately. It is easy to learn the system used by each library.

Calling for Books and Other Materials. In libraries where it is necessary to keep nearly everything in locked cases and closed stacks, it saves a great deal of time if care is used in making out call slips which the library provides for that purpose. If more than one item is ordered at one time, it also saves time and disappointment.

If **microcards** and microcard readers are being used, care should be used to keep the cards in order in the drawers and in handling the equipment. **Microfilm** readers provided for library patrons also require care in use and in handling.

Lending Service

Each library has its own rules as to borrowing books, and these must be ascertained. As a rule reference books including bound periodicals are not lent. Most library lending is now free, but the borrower's responsibility must be established in some way.

Interlibrary Loans. Libraries do not like to make loans to individuals living at a distance. Instead, they have worked out a system of interlibrary loans, by which the individual applies to his local library. The local library does the borrowing from the distant library and assumes the responsibility. The willingness of libraries in this manner to lend books of great value, or even in some cases a volume from a journal file, is remarkable. The individual usually bears all of the transportation costs.

Special Services

Photographic Copying. Most libraries are able to provide photoprint copies of a portion of a book, of a journal article, or an extract of it. It is an indispensable method of obtaining copies of materials that are not available in local libraries and is better than interlibrary loans in most cases. It is also a cheap and accurate method of copying materials that are available locally. Many libraries have equipment for making microfilm copies and these are better for long papers or long passages from books. There are several relatively inexpensive microfilm readers on the market, and most libraries provide them for patrons. Libraries usually do such work at approximately cost. For details of the microfilm services of the large libraries in the United States, see Muller's paper.[3]

Abstracting and Translating. There is considerable variation in how much of such services libraries can provide. Some libraries have a large enough staff to help patrons with translations, others do it for a fee, and still others refer patrons to those who do it on a commercial basis. If a translation or a different type of abstract is needed than is found in abstract journals, it is well to inquire in a library that specializes in chemistry or a scientific library where much of the work is done in chemistry, because general translators and abstractors are seldom familiar with technical terminology. The Special Libraries Association is operating a pool of translations and so is the Library of Congress; these both apply to scientific papers. Libraries are helpful in obtaining copies from these sources. See Chapter 3, page 153, for more information on these translation pools.

Bibliographies and Literature Searches. Few scientific libraries or science divisions of general libraries have a large enough staff to make an extensive literature search and prepare a bibliography for a patron. They are glad to assist patrons and to locate information that does not require too much time. Again, the library will often refer a patron to a person who makes a business of this type of consulting work. There are a few scientific libraries that make literature searches and prepare bibliographies for a fee.

Information Services. Most scientific libraries or the science divisions of large general libraries provide information services on an informal basis. Libraries are glad to be of assistance to patrons and answer reasonable questions or help the patron locate a source of information. This work overlaps to a certain degree with literature searches. Few libraries can provide an extensive information service; there are a few that do so for a fee.

For information on American libraries of interest to chemists and their special services, see Appendix 3.

FOREIGN CHEMICAL LIBRARIES

There are a number of these, but only two will be mentioned here. Some sources of information on foreign libraries will be found in Appendix 3.

The library of the Chemical Society of London is one of the most complete chemical libraries in existence. Fortunately, it has escaped damage in two world wars. It not only has a very large collection of periodical files and current books on chemistry; it also possesses a fine collection of old and rare chemical and alchemical books. It is housed in Burlington House, London W1, England, the headquarters of the Society. Throughout its long history this library has been in contact with the other European chemical libraries and has considerable knowledge of their resources.

The International House of Chemistry, "La Maison de la Chimie," was opened in Paris in 1934. This was established with the aid of 65 nations and its library is now one of the most important and complete chemical libraries in the world and is being kept up to date. For further information on this library and its many services, see M. V. P. Deschien's, "Documentation and Bibliography in La Maison de la Chimie," *J. Chem. Educ.* **31**, 97–99 (1954).

LITERATURE CITED

(1) McGaw, H. F., *Marginal Punched Cards in College and Research Libraries,* Washington, D. C., Scarecrow Press, 1952, 218 pp.
(2) Loftus, H. E., and Kent, Allen, "Automation in the Library—An Annotated Bibliography," *American Documentation* **7**, 110–127 (1956).
(3) Muller, R. H., *College and Research Libraries* **16**, 261–266 (1955).

CHAPTER 10

PROCEDURE
IN LITERATURE SEARCHES

Literature searching is an art. Efficiency in it can be gained only by experience, and no hard and fast rules of procedure can be laid down. The reasons for this lie in the great diversity of problems to be solved, in the heterogeneous nature of the chemical literature, and in variations in the scope of the searches. The method of search is also modified by the quantity of knowledge that a worker has gained by previous work in the field of search. Information that is found during the search may change the procedure. In some cases the library facilities available to the worker affect the method of searching the literature. Patent searches offer a special problem. Many searches in industrial chemistry involve a number of factors that are not chemical ones. Nevertheless, some generally helpful principles for searching the literature can be outlined.

Literature searches, like other arts, can be practiced at several levels of competence. The best searches are creative. The chemist who uses all of his scientific training, his experience, and his imagination while making a literature search will be richly rewarded. He will be thinking and evaluating the information that he finds as he works through the literature. When he finishes a search, he has far more than a bibliography and notes on existing information; he sees areas that have not been explored and those that have been imperfectly investigated. He comes away from a literature search with a lot of new ideas for experimental work. He may see how to combine existing pieces of information into a new and useful whole that requires little or no experimental work. He may see an explanation for a body of experimental fact that has eluded previous workers.

297

Nearly all of the growth in scientific knowledge has occurred because certain scientists could evaluate previous work and use their creative ability to build upon it.

Much emphasis has been put on the importance of searching the literature to avoid repeating work and to obtain information. These purposes are important, but little significance has been attached to the creative aspect of literature searches. A comprehensive and exhaustive search may prove very costly, because of the amount of time required, unless it is carried out by a gifted and experienced chemist who sees far beyond the printed page and obtains all of the "plus values."

After procedure has been treated, a number of matters closely related to literature searches will be considered. These include record keeping during the search, mechanical aids to literature searching, the preparation of bibliographies and reports, and a list of scientific and chemical dictionaries for various languages. This chapter will close with a chronological table of abstracts and annual reports.

BRIEF SEARCHES

These include many questions that do not require any particular procedure. They are answered by having a thorough knowledge of the kind of information to be found in each of the sources of chemical and other scientific information that are considered in this book and by selecting the proper one or a combination of them to find the answer. As one grows more familiar with his tools, he gains efficiency by knowing which authority or type of source to choose and how to consult it readily. Many of these questions can be answered quickly, even in a small library, and satisfactorily enough for the purpose. Some of the methods used in systematic searches are applicable in brief ones.

SYSTEMATIC SEARCHES

There are many other problems that cannot be disposed of so easily; they either involve an extensive subject or require an exhaustive search. In these cases a systematic search is essential to locate existing information, to show that a certain piece or type of information is nonexistent, and to conserve time. In these searches one starts with organized sources of information (encyclopedias, dictionaries, treatises, bibliographies, annual reviews, and books) to see how much information has been collected by other workers. He then turns to the unorganized sources (periodicals, patents, government publications, trade literature, dissertations, and others) and uses the abstract journals and indexing publications to locate information in them. Unfortunately some unorganized sources are not covered by abstracts as thoroughly as are the chemical periodicals. Abstracts and indexes are guides to only a part of the information recorded in other sources. It is usually best to start with the most recent information and to work back to a given date or until the desired information has been found; this locates all bibliographies, books, and reviews in which previous workers have collected information. A systematic search should have two parts: the preliminary search and the search proper.

The Preliminary Search

The preliminary search is the foundation for the work and determines to a large degree whether or not it will be successful. The amount of preliminary work varies greatly with the nature of the problem to be solved and with the degree of familiarity which the searcher has with the field in question.

First of all the purpose, subject, nature, and scope of the search should be defined as clearly as possible in writing. The purpose of the search determines its nature and scope. If a literature search is concerned with the validity of an important chemical patent, it should be both comprehensive and exhaustive, and every possible source of information should be examined with particular attention paid to publication dates. If a research worker wishes to investigate a problem that requires much expensive equipment and will probably take a considerable period of time to solve, a comprehensive search is needed, but usually it does not need to be as exhaustive as in the case of the validity of a patent. If a general summary of existing knowledge on a subject is wanted, the search is even less comprehensive and exhaustive.

The care with which the subject of the search is defined, including an analysis of this subject to break it down into its component parts, determines to a large degree how successful the search will be. Inexperienced workers tend to define a subject in too general terms, do not recognize its essential parts, and do not consult the literature for each part.

The next considerations are: How much is the information actually worth? How thorough and extensive should the search be? How much time should be spent on it?

How far back in the literature should the search go? This depends entirely on the subject. All of the information may be in the literature that has been published within the last ten years, or this information may be distributed over a long period of time. It is perhaps true that most of the old work of value has been incorporated in current treatises, monographs, compilations, and bibliographies, or incorporated in publications of more recent date. It is very difficult to say at what point chemical information is obsolete; this depends upon the kind of information and upon the point of view. The importance of a piece of work is not always realized at the time of discovery, the results do not always find their way into compilations and are not carried over into the later literature; the information drops out of sight. A knowledge of the history of chemistry, of the history of technology, and of the history of science is often an invaluable asset in deciding how far back to go in a literature search. A background of historical knowledge of a subject under investigation, or of the industry into which it fits, is not only useful in determining how far back to go in a literature search, but such knowledge is also valuable in selecting countries whose patents and/or other forms of chemical literature are most important to examine. Some countries have developed certain fields of chemistry and certain industries more extensively than others. As time passed these centers of specialized activity sometimes shifted from one country to another; in other cases the field of chemistry and chemical industry became much more widespread.

The term "extensive" applies not only to the period to be covered, but also to the width of territory covered. How many of the possible sources of chemical information should be searched, how many branches of chemistry should be considered, and should the search be extended to an entirely different science? There is no rule. These considerations depend on the problem and the judgment of the worker, but the fact should be kept in mind that an apparently remote source has often furnished the answer to a perplexing problem. This question of how extensive a search should be is worth considerable thought because the store of chemical knowledge is so great and time must be used to the best advantage.

A survey and summary of existing knowledge is then prepared by consulting the organized forms of reference material: encyclopedias, dictionaries, bibliographies, treatises, annual reviews, and books on the subject. For methods of locating books see Chapter 2. A number of the reference works in each field of chemistry will also be found in that chapter. Beginning textbooks are useful sometimes.

If a subject is in a field that has been studied for many years, it is often worth while to examine the older books and reference works. This gives an idea of how the field has developed. Also, useful information or the reference to the original work upon which a statement is based is sometimes dropped as time goes on in an effort to keep down the size of books and to include only material, which in the opinion of the editor or author, is not obsolete and is currently useful.

The annual reviews for perhaps three years should be read. These reviews give one an idea of the present trend, help to locate places where research is being done currently, identify the most prolific workers in the field, and usually point out the most significant portion of the recent work. A classified list of these reviews is given in Chapter 7.

The amount of time that should be spent looking for existing bibliographies during this preliminary survey should not be too great; it has been pointed out, in the case of chemistry, that most bibliographies are found attached to papers in periodicals, to chapters of books, and to sections in treatises and other reference books. These will be found as the search progresses. However, the files of the libraries in one's locality should be checked for bibliographies because one or more may have been prepared but not published for various reasons. The Special Libraries Association's pool of unpublished bibliographies should be checked. Sometimes an inquiry should be made at centers where much work is in progress to find out if copies of unpublished bibliographies can be obtained. It is also worth while to check the *Bibliographic Index* for a few years and, if the older work is to be considered, the bibliographies of bibliographies compiled by West and Berolzheimer, Sohn and Schaaf, and Bolton (see Chapter 7). Of course all of the pertinent bibliographies that are found in books, treatises, annual reviews, and encyclopedias during the preliminary survey should be noted. These are valuable starting points for further work.

At this point in the preliminary survey, a little work with the latest annual indexes of *Chemical Abstracts* is valuable to locate books, reviews in periodicals, and some of the recent papers on the subject. If a problem in industrial chemistry is under consideration which involves considerable business information, it is also worth while to refer to the latest annual volumes of the *Industrial Arts Index*.

This preliminary survey and summary should contain a record of all of the sources consulted and a note of the information found in each one, both positive and negative. Particular attention should be paid to bibliographies, all names for substances (including synonyms and trade names), variations in terminology and theories, names of reactions and of pieces of equipment, names of prolific workers in the field, countries and centers where there is greatest activity in this field of research, and all patents pertaining to the subject.

One should also ascertain the existence of specialized journals in the field of search and check to see if they publish abstracts. The existence of specialized abstract services that are not a part of a periodical should also be determined. Chapter 3, Periodicals, will be found to be particularly helpful. These special publications will be valuable later in the search. The abstracts sometimes locate papers in obscure journals, frequently include nonchemical material of value, sometimes abstract important nonchemical papers for business information in industrial searches, and, sometimes, are longer than those in the general abstract journals and may be adequate in case of the unavailability of the original paper. The specialized journals are particularly valuable for information that is not abstracted.

The last step in the preliminary search is to plan the search proper. This is necessary to make the search systematic, to prevent omission and duplication, and to obtain the best results in the least time. If necessary the definition of the subject of the search should be revised after the preliminary survey is made.

The plan for the search proper should contain a list of the indexes, indexing serials, and special abstract journals that are to be consulted in addition to the general chemical abstract journals. It should also be decided whether only *Chemical Abstracts* or all of the general abstract journals that have been in existence in recent years should be used. If possible a decision should be made on whether to consult the literature of other sciences.

The plan for the search proper should contain a written list of all of the items that the preliminary search indicates will be fruitful in using the indexes of the abstract journals and the indexing serials to locate information. These are: (1) the subject, (2) all topics that are subdivisions of the subject or related to it, (3) key words, terms, and phrases, (4) names of reactions, as Grignard reaction, (5) names of operations, as filtration, (6) names and formulas of chemical compounds, (7) synonyms and trade names, (8) names of theories, principles, or laws, (9) names of pieces of equipment and apparatus, (10) names of individuals and manufacturers, (11) names of countries and centers where much work has been done, (12) names of government laboratories or departments that are active in the field of research, and (13) a list of nonchemical information in the case of some industrial searches. Obviously, few searches will include all of these elements.

The Search Proper

The following outline of procedure for the search proper is a guide only for inexperienced literature searchers. Many variations in the suggested outline are possible and parts of this general outline do not apply to every case.

(1) It is usually best to start with the most recent annual indexes of *Chemical Abstracts* and to look up all the items in the list of the plan of search except the names of countries and research centers. If an industrial search that involves business information is being made, the *Industrial Arts Index* should be checked too. Three years should be covered and all references noted that might be fruitful.

Then look up the original papers, patents, books, reviews, and other forms of information. One should go to the full paper, patent, government publication, etc. Abstractors have their faults, and there is the additional chance in abstracts for printer's errors. Even if the abstract is perfectly composed and printed, it may not be prepared from the viewpoint in which the searcher is especially interested. Abstracts are useful as summaries which give a general impression of the nature of the article, the most essential data (in the case of the best ones), and enable the reader to decide whether it will be worth while to consult the originals. Occasionally an informative abstract is invaluable because the original is not available.

A book is usually announced only by title in abstract journals. If a book is not available in the local libraries, it is best to get some information about it before trying to borrow it from a library at a distance or to buy a copy. See Chapter 2 for sources of information about books. Most periodicals which review books index the reviews both by subjects (from book titles) and by authors' names.

In checking the original publications (located through *Chemical Abstracts* or the *Industrial Arts Index*) **note** should be made of

all pertinent bibliographies that are found. Sometimes the bibliography is the most important part of a publication.

In examining material, time must be husbanded; in an extended search one can hardly read everything in detail. The faculty of scanning quickly and knowing when to read more closely is very valuable. Nor should time be spent uselessly in note taking; photographic copies can be procured so easily that articles need not be copied by hand and often not even abstracted. The worker must learn when to copy citations, when to abstract, and when to obtain a photoprint.

(2) Then all of the information that has been located thus far should be consolidated with what was found in the preliminary search. All bibliographies that have been found should be examined and the references in them looked up. The information should be studied to see where it originated and how it is distributed in periodicals, books, theses, government publications, patents, etc. This will aid one in deciding which of the sources that are only partially covered by abstract journals and indexing serials should be searched (dissertations and theses, government publications, trade literature, and patents).

If an active research program exists currently at a university in a given field, enough of the results should have been published and located thus far in the search to indicate which universities may have **unpublished dissertations** or portions of them that should be examined. A footnote usually indicates whether or not a paper represents a portion of a dissertation. If a considerable amount of work originated in a university, it is well to check its dissertations anyway; custom varies as to whether the portion which is published is designated as a dissertation. See Chapter 7, page 213, for methods of locating dissertations and university publications which contain lists of them and/or abstracts of them.

If several references to **government publications** have been found, or if an especially valuable piece of work originated in a government laboratory, the catalogs and indexes of government publications should be examined to see if others exist. See Chapter 5 for methods of locating government publications. Some problems or phases of them are in areas in which certain government laboratories work continually. In these cases the government publications should be checked anyway.

Very little **trade literature** is covered by the abstracting and indexing serials, so the decision to search this source must be based on the nature of the subject under investigation. Usually only the trade literature that is current or of recent date is worth looking for. See Chapter 6 for methods of locating trade literature.

If a considerable part of the information was found in **patents,** a thorough patent search should be made in cases where the industrial aspects of the problem are paramount. Patent searches present special problems and will be considered later in this chapter in a separate section.

(3) The next step is to search, for a period of about three years, those sources that are only partially covered by the abstract journals and indexing serials. Then the indexes of abstracts in specialized chemical journals and specialized abstracts are searched, use being made of the same list of items as was used for *Chemical Abstracts* for three years. The indexing serials, such as the *Engineering Index,* *The Bibliography of Agriculture,* and others, which are mentioned in Chapter 9, Indexes, should be examined for a three-year period if the search involves fields that they cover. All of the new references located in these ways should be examined in the original, and again all bibliographies should be checked.

(4) All of the information obtained so far should be evaluated. If the needed information has not been found and the search must continue, necessary changes in the plan of search should be made at this point. It frequently happens that some aspects of a problem do not occur to one while the plan for the search is being made, but become clear after he has worked with it. Ideas may result from reading that suggest a different line of attack for a problem. It does not take long to see whether or not the new items added to the plan of search are fruitful, if only a few years must be rechecked.

(5) After the work outlined above has been done, the most recent work should be looked for in the numbers of *Chemical Abstracts* that have not yet been indexed and in the periodicals not yet abstracted. This can be done more effectively at this point than in the very beginning of the search because the searcher will know by this time which individuals, manufacturers, or government laboratories are currently working on the problem and which journals publish most of the work in the field.

(6) The search should be continued by working backward, by checking the original sources at frequent intervals, and by evaluating the material that has been found at intervals until the goal of the search is attained. One should turn to collective indexes as soon as possible. If a search covers quite a long period of time, it is necessary

to watch for changes in nomenclature, terminology, and theories, because these affect the subject index headings. Then, too, it must be remembered that indexing practices change with the years. Working backward in the literature saves much time because previous workers compiled bibliographies. The time comes in a well ordered search, if the subject is not hopelessly wide, when leads cross and very little important new material is found. Then the worker can properly feel that the ground has been fairly well covered.

Of course anyone who has a search that goes back into the work that was done before 1907 will need to use a combination of abstract journals, annual reports, and indexes as the starting point in the search. For so-called "pure chemistry" it is necessary to consult the abstracts in the *Journal of the Chemical Society* (London), *Bulletin de la société chimique de France,* and *Chemisches Zentralblatt* to get fairly good coverage for the period 1871–1907; no one of these three journals was a complete and comprehensive abstract journal during that period. If so-called "applied chemistry" (industrial chemistry and technology) is to be covered in the search, fairly good coverage can be obtained for the period 1882–1907 by adding three other journals to the list: *Chemiker-Zeitung, Zeitschrift für angewandte Chemie,* and *Journal of the Society of Chemical Industry* (London). This means a minimum of six abstract journals that must be examined to get fairly good coverage of the pure and applied aspects of any phase of chemistry for the period 1882–1907. In a comprehensive search that includes work before 1907, it is necessary to examine all of the specialized abstract journals that existed at the time to get good coverage and, even then, the percentage of existing information located will not be as high as it is with *Chemical Abstracts* alone in a search of recent literature. A comprehensive search before 1907 is very time-consuming. For more detailed information on the abstract journals and their coverage see Chapter 3.

The **annual reviews** are useful tools to use to supplement the abstract journals before 1907 and the most valuable ones are included in the chronological list of abstracts, annual reports, and indexes that is given at the end of this chapter.

The indexes vary considerably in their usefulness in literature searches for work before 1907. See the latter part of Chapter 8 for indexes that are independent of any single publication and the notes for information about them. Unfortunately, the Royal Society's *Catalogue of Scientific Papers* lacks a subject index for chemistry, so that it is most useful if one wishes to see if a given worker published papers that were not covered by the abstract journals of that period. The *International Catalogue of Scientific Literature* is very valuable for the period 1901–1914; the subject indexing has been thoroughly done, but pure chemistry is given greater attention than applied chemistry in this index. A particularly valuable publication for industrial chemistry and technology for the period 1823–1909 is the *Repertorium der technischen Journal-Literatur,* which includes many papers not mentioned by the abstract journals of that time.

(7) The final touches on the literature search may include a number of points.

In some searches it is necessary to go through the files of one or more periodicals that specialize in the field of the search to obtain information that cannot be located through the abstract journals either because (*a*) it is a type which they do not abstract, (*b*) it may have been missed by abstractor, indexer, or index user, or (*c*) it may be a type almost impossible to designate exactly for indexing. Business information and prices of chemicals are examples of (*a*). Unnamed chemical reactions are examples of (*b*) and laboratory techniques are examples of (*c*).

Although a number of organic reactions are known by the names of the chemists who originate them, as the Grignard reaction, many are unnamed or do not have any commonly recognized names. Sometimes, instead of examples, one wants to know how generally applicable a given reaction is and what are the variations in conditions for it. Lack of a system for naming chemical reactions is a serious defect in our chemical nomenclature. Methods of preparing chemical compounds by means of generally applicable reactions present a special problem in literature searching for this reason. The problem is not entirely nomenclature; it is partly the question of identification of a reaction as a specific example of a general one by the author of the paper and by the abstractor. Laboratory techniques are very difficult to abstract and index adequately. The same is true for certain procedures and methods of handling materials in the manufacture of chemicals.

There are **other reasons for examining files of periodicals** that specialize in a given field of chemistry. Such examination sometimes gives one a better idea of the way in which a subject developed and was influenced by other developments in the field than it is possible to get by reading isolated papers. One gets a picture of the intellectual climate, so to speak, that may be very useful in some cases.

A better idea of the development of a field of chemistry in a given country may also be gained.

If possible the searcher should not stop quite yet. Is there not some other way of getting at the matter? Is the feeling of completeness possibly due to a fixed state of mind into which the investigator has fallen, rather than to the actual state of the search? Perhaps it will pay to "browse about" a little and look at almost anything that might have a bearing. This seems a haphazard way of finishing a systematic search, but experienced workers testify to its value. Finding more that way may not be entirely a matter of luck. There may be a drawing, by some subconscious mechanism, on all of one's previous experience with the literature and on one's whole store of information. If this is true the scientific reading that one does in various lines, merely on account of general interest and without trying to remember what is read, may prove unexpectedly of use.

Perhaps, too, the searcher prefers at this point to arrange his material and work it roughly into shape, whereupon he discovers certain gaps to be filled in; or as a result of considering all of his data he develops certain definite ideas or raises certain questions that necessitate further examination of the literature. In these cases, the final touches on the search may go hand in hand with recording it in finished form. Completeness is a relative term as applied to literature searching; it is necessary to learn to recognize the point beyond which it is not reasonable to go because of the improbability of finding something of sufficient value to compensate for the time, effort, and expense of proceeding further.

SEARCHES IN INDUSTRIAL CHEMISTRY

These literature searches involve certain problems that could not be outlined while considering the general principles of a systematic literature search.

Some systematic industrial searches are very comprehensive and exhaustive and cover every available source of chemical information, including patents. The most exhaustive and comprehensive of all of these is the **validity search** that is made when it is necessary to determine the strength of an existing patent. In a validity search, every conceivable source (including patents) and every reference must be examined to find a fact or facts in print, no matter where they may be, before a certain date.

A **state-of-the-art search** is a full survey of all publications, including patents, to discover the present state of development of a subject or a field or even an industry without reference to ancient history; it is the same type of search an investigator in pure science makes when he surveys the literature, but more attention must be paid to patents and trade literature. **Patentability searches** include the examination of all sources of chemical information, including patents, to establish the fact that there is no published material on the subject which has been available to the public for more than two years. Of course the subject must be within the definition of patentability according to patent law. These patentability searches in fields where many patents exist must be very exhaustive to avoid infringement suits if a patent is granted.

It is evident from these brief comments that literature searches in industrial chemistry frequently involve some knowledge of patent law. It is also clear that there are some phases of these searches that can be handled only by a specialist in patent law who is also versed in chemistry; this is especially true of patents as legal documents. The searching of patents is a special problem that will be discussed separately.

Another type of literature search required in industrial chemistry is that relating to chemical market research and to chemical development. These searches have been made for many years, but as the work has become more specialized they have been called "chemical market research."

Chemical Market Research

Literature searching in this field involves a large amount of non-chemical information of many kinds: business, statistical, financial, engineering (other than chemical engineering), sources of raw materials—both foreign and domestic—and export and import trade. Much of this nonchemical information is published in periodicals but is not covered by the abstract journals or indexing serials. The *Engineering Index* and the *Industrial Arts Index* cover part of it. The new German abstract journal called *Technisches Zentralblatt*, 1951–   , covers some aspects. Locating much of such nonchemical information depends on knowing exactly which periodicals, books, government publications and agencies, trade associations and their publications, etc., to consult. A number of sources of information for chemical market research are given in Chapter 2, section 13, industrial chemistry. The Chemical Market Research Association, The Commercial Chemical Development Association, The Manufacturing Chemists Association, and the Division of Chemical Marketing of the American Chemical Society are sources of much valuable information for this work.

Patent Searches

Two points need to be kept in mind in relation to chemical patents. Patents are both chemical publications and legal documents. The best procedure to follow in making patent searches varies considerably with the object and needs of the searcher. If the purpose is merely to seek chemical ideas and information, as in the case of the investigator in pure science who is not concerned with legal considerations, a much more restricted search is conducted in a different way than would be suitable if the purpose were to settle some legal point. And, of course, the nature of legal questions to be settled alters procedure; different problems are presented by such matters as the patentability of inventions, the filing and prosecution of applications for patents, the validity and scope of issued patents, property rights in patents, the rights and obligations of patentees, and the infringement of unexpired patents.

In making searches of **patents as a part of the chemical literature,** and not as legal documents, the abstract journals are particularly useful. The convenient segregation and classification of patent abstracts and the better indexing in abstract journals make patent searching by means of these journals a much simpler task than it is when other facilities are utilized. For comments on how thoroughly and comprehensively the abstract journals cover the chemical patent literature of the world, see Chapter 4 of this book. Abstracts of patents should not be depended upon for full chemical information. The full patent should be consulted with particular attention to the section that describes the specific examples; in all probability this contains the most exact chemical information. Patent abstracts are often too brief to be of much value except as an indication that useful chemical information may be found in the patent.

Patent searches that treat **patents both as legal documents and as sources of chemical information** should be made only by a specialist in patent searches—one who is trained in both patent law and chemistry and has considerable experience. The average chemist cannot afford to attempt this work for himself; the legal aspect is beyond his realm of competence. In patent searches concerned with the legal aspect, it is necessary to turn to the full patent. The abstract journals cannot be expected to report legal aspects of patents; a fortune may hang on the wording of a single sentence.

A patent search of United States patents that requires that classes and subclasses be examined can be carried out in a number of places in the United States. However, searching in a place other than the United States Patent Office takes more time and there is more possibility of omissions. Libraries outside of Washington maintain patent files in which the patents are bound in numerical order as issued; they do not have duplicate files in which the patents are arranged by classes and subclasses. It is possible to obtain the numbers of the patents in a class or subclass from the Patent Commissioner. Then these patents can be read in a library where a complete numerical file is maintained. Copies of all patents in a class may also be purchased from the Patent Office. But the system of classification is not entirely satisfactory from the chemical point of view, and the Patent Office has several aids that help to avoid omissions.

The only place where a thorough search of foreign patents can be made is in the United States Patent Office. There are cases in which a reliable patent attorney resident in the foreign country must be retained for work in a foreign patent office.

For a discussion of patents, sources of information about them, where to obtain them, and other questions, see Chapter 4 of this book.

NOTES ON PATENT SEARCHES

Since patent searching from the legal standpoint at the Patent Office in Washington is considered to be a task to be referred in almost all circumstances to a competent patent attorney, no effort will be made to describe in detail the procedure considered best in such searches. A reasonably full description of the patent literature and of the facilities for the various kinds of searches are given in Chapter 4. It is well to have general information on the matter. For this reason, in addition to the discussion in Chapter 4, some of the important points to keep in mind in Patent Office searches are given in the form of notes.

(1) The same general considerations apply to a patent search as to a systematic literature search in which patents are among the other sources covered. These general considerations are a preliminary study of the subject (the preliminary search), a plan for the search, a decision on how complete the search should be, knowledge of the history of the field, and, perhaps, consultation with someone of practical experience along the line involved.

(2) In some industries patents have been resorted to frequently,

as in the petroleum industry, which produces both petroleum products and chemicals that are manufactured from petroleum products;
in other industries very little patent literature may exist. The trained
searcher learns to recognize these variations according to industries.

(3) Unless there is some special reason for departing from usual
practice, it is advisable to begin the search with U. S. patents. It is
rare that a search need be extended beyond the patents of the
countries of western Europe, Canada, and Japan. After the U. S.
patents, in order of preference in a search, come the British and then
the German patents. The order for the rest matters less. Many
inventions made elsewhere are patented in England and in the
United States.

(4) The patent classification systems that must be used in these
searches have their shortcomings and limitations. There is a good
deal of scattering of like patents owing to different points of view.
In most cases a number of classes and subclasses must be examined
and it is a problem to decide which ones should be selected. Facility
in the use of the classification systems depends on experience with
them and on learning numerous little "tricks of the trade" to locate
classes and subclasses to be examined. The index to the system is
often useful in locating classes and subclasses. Knowledge of the
existence of one or more patents on the subject or on a closely related
subject is usually very helpful in determining which classes and subclasses to search. These patents are usually located by use of the
abstract journals, but they may be found in the preliminary search
in a book or treatises.

(5) When a patent of interest has been found, the use of the indexes of patentees of the same and other countries is often an easier
way to find further patents of interest than any other method. In
many countries patents may be issued to companies, but in the United
States they are issued only to individuals. A U. S. patent issued to
A. B. Jones, for example, may correspond, therefore, to one taken
out in some other country by company X for which he works.

(6) In the actual examination of chemical patents to determine
which ones in the selected subclasses are of interest it is seldom necessary to read the whole patent. It is often sufficient to read the
first and last claims and examine the drawings, if any are included.

(7) For each subclass revised by the Classification Division of the
United States Patent Office, there is a "search card" on which is
found a definition of the subclass and references to all other classes
and subclasses which may contain relevant material.

(8) Foreign patents can best be examined in the Scientific Library of the Patent Office. This library has duplicate sets of patents for most countries—one set bound in numerical order, the other arranged according to the classification system of the country. The next best place is in the examiners' foreign files. If special care is desirable, it is well to examine the patents in both places because different classifications are likely to take cognizance of different features in a patent. This prevents omissions. The patent examiners' foreign files are arranged according to the United States system of classification.

(9) The final steps in a patent search usually include examination of (a) application files of issued U. S. patents of particular interest and (b) records of interferences, if any. The author indexes of the abstract journals are used to find papers on the same subjects as the patents or on related subjects.

(10) It is possible to consult the examiners at the U. S. Patent Office when advice is needed and they, as well as other Patent Office employees, are courteous and obliging.

MECHANICAL AIDS

Mechanical aids for literature searching are receiving much attention at the present time. The store of information is so large and is growing so rapidly that efforts are being made to develop methods of doing part of the searching mechanically. Chemical information can be recorded on punched cards, microfilm, and magnetic tape, to mention some of the devices that are being used or investigated. Then the information can be selected as it is needed from these records by inserting them in a suitable machine. Punched or notched cards are receiving the most attention at present because cards and equipment for sorting them or selecting information from them had been developed previously for business use. These are being used for working with scientific literature, but are not suitable for many aspects of it (see page 272). Equipment is being designed that is better for literature searching, and some of it is beginning to appear on the market.

The development of these mechanized tools for searching chemical literature involves the solution of difficult indexing and coding problems. It is not entirely a matter of the designing of better machines by engineers by any means.

How rapidly these mechanical aids will develop is difficult to estimate. Some chemical manufacturers are building up punched-card files of information for their own use. So far the mechanical handling of broad fields or subjects such as the whole field of chemistry has not been successfully managed.

These mechanical aids will save much time in literature searches, but they cannot be expected to carry out the phases that require thought, evaluation, imagination, and the creative mind of a human being.

There are several sources of information on mechanical aids in literature searching and on automation in the library. The following sources are among the most useful ones.

The American Chemical Society had a Committee on Scientific Aids for Literature Searching from 1947 to 1955. In 1956 the Society's Division of Chemical Literature established a Standing Committee on Aids to Chemical Documentation to continue the study of the documentation needs of the members of the American Chemical Society and to investigate and to evaluate new and improved documentation techniques. The committee reports are published in *Chemical and Engineering News* and in *Chemical Literature,* the Society's and the Division's respective publications, and give quite detailed information.

The National Research Council of the National Academy of Sciences of the United States has a Committee on Codification, Ciphering and Punched-Card Techniques. Copies of the reports of this committee can be obtained from the Council, Washington, D. C.

There is considerable information on machine literature searching in the sciences and some of the most useful publications are:

Apler, A., and Norton, T. R., "New Speed to Structural Searches," *Chem. Eng. News* **34**, 2812–2816 (1956).

Berry, M. M., Casey, R. S., and Perry, J. W., *Punched Cards. Their Applications to Science and Industry,* 2nd ed., New York, Reinhold, 1957, about 500 pp.

Berry, M. M., Kent, A., and Perry, J. W., *Machine Literature Searching,* New York, Interscience Publishers, 1956, 200 pp.

Levin, P., *Tools and Methods of Searching the Chemical Literature; a Selective Bibliography.* Philadelphia, Drexel Institute of Technology (M.S. Thesis), 1955, 41 pp.

Loftus, H. E., and Kent, Allen, "Automation in the Library—An Annotated Bibliography," *American Documentation* **7**, 110–127 (1956).

McGaw, H. F., *Marginal Punched Cards in College and Research Libraries,* Washington, D. C., Scarecrow Press, 1952, 218 pp.

RECORD KEEPING

A literature search of any magnitude requires that a systematic record be kept from the very beginning. Otherwise time is lost through useless repetition and, what is more serious, a large quantity of work may be done to no purpose because certain parts or phases of the literature search were omitted or their significance lost in the confusion. There is not much point to a carefully thought out plan for a literature search unless the method of recording both positive and negative results in looking for information is selected while planning the search and then carefully adhered to throughout the search. It is also necessary to record changes that are made in the plan of the search while it is in progress if any are necessary. Exactly the kind of record that is made depends upon the nature of the search and the kind of information that is sought. So, no specific method can be said to be better than all others. However, some generally useful techniques can be outlined.

This record keeping is concerned with three general areas: (1) check lists, (2) work sheets, and (3) notes. The comments that follow are intended to assist inexperienced literature searchers. Before these are considered, the question of the physical form of the records will be discussed briefly.

Physical Form

The physical form of the record depends very largely on how extensive the search is, whether the record is for the worker's personal use or will be used by others, and how long the record will be preserved. A search that is not too extensive can be recorded in bound notebooks of convenient size, but it is usually easier to work with looseleaf ones. Some workers prefer to use only filing cards of suitable size for all phases of a literature search that is not too comprehensive. However, a combination of looseleaf notebooks and filing cards is usually the most practical. Looseleaf notebooks are particularly good for check lists and work sheets, whereas cards are usually better for notes. Three kinds of cards may be used for notes.

Cards. Ordinary filing cards are familiar to all, but the punched or edge-notched cards for note taking are a recent development. The punched or notched cards have certain advantages if a large body of information is to be collected; they do not require classification and indexing by subject, author, formula, etc. They are sorted mechanically or manually by the use of a simple tool, a long needle. The cards are notched or punched according to a code so that the machine can be adjusted to sort out the ones that record desired information. In sorting manually, the needle catches and lifts out of the tray all cards except those wanted for certain information; these drop back into the card tray. The practical difficulty in using punched or notched cards is the code; it must be worked out before the search begins, and every kind of information to be obtained from the notes on the cards must be anticipated. It has been pointed out that in a search of any magnitude adjustments and modifications in terminology, names, etc., are necessary as the search progresses. If a code is made, it must allow for growth, the addition of new items. Any mechanical system produces exactly what is predetermined and put into the system, no more. For more information on punched and notched cards see the books and papers listed on page 314.

Check Lists

A list of items (names, subjects, formulas, etc.) is prepared in the preliminary literature search to use in looking up and locating information in the systematic search. It is seldom possible to use the entire list as a check list while working with indexes of *Chemical Abstracts* or other abstract journals. This is also true when the indexing serials, *Engineering Index*, etc., are being used. The list often needs to be subdivided and different parts or combinations of parts used with various indexes. To get the best results in the least time with an index requires: (1) knowledge of what general subject matter an abstract journal covers and what kinds of indexes it has, (2) knowledge of what general subject matter an independent index, such as the *Engineering Index*, covers and what kind of an index it is— subjects or authors, or both, etc., (3) knowledge of the coverage of other publications to be used in the search and of their indexes, (4) thought and planning to make a check list that is suited to each index to be used, and (5) skill in the use of indexes.

A discussion of the coverage of the various abstract journals will be found in Chapter 3, and indexes of all kinds are considered in Chapter 8.

The preparation of a check list to be used with a certain index is worth the time and thought it requires. A lot of time can be wasted looking in an index for things that it does not cover because they are outside its range of subject matter or for types of entries that it does not use—such as formulas, patent numbers, authors, and names of manufacturers.

The check lists used for the various indexes in a search should allow space for additions as the search progresses. A new line of thought may produce additional items. Names and terminology change. The period of time covered by items added during the search should be clearly indicated and they should be marked to distinguish them from the items with which the search started. In searches that cover a long period of time, items on the original check list may not apply to searching indexes to locate the older literature because of changes in theories or terminology, and because of discovery of facts on dates subsequent to the time of publication of the older literature. As soon as this is clear the item should be marked to show why it was not used with the older literature.

If the literature search has been made for another chemist, these check lists should be a part of the final report in certain cases.

The check lists need to be kept systematically throughout the search. An example for the subject index of *Chemical Abstracts* is given below. This is enough to indicate the general idea, to show

	1954	1953	D.I. 4	D.I. 3	D.I. 2	D.I. 1
Antibiotics	+	+	+	+	Term introduced about 1930	
Chemotherapy	+	+	+	+	+	+
Erlich, Paul *	0	0	0	0	0	+
Merck & Co., Inc.	−	−	+	−	−	−
Penicillin	+	+	+	+	Discovered 1929	
Salvarsan	+	−	+	+	+	Discovered 1909

that references were found (+), or no references were found (−), that Paul Erlich's name (*) was not on the original list, that several terms would be of no value in checking indexes before a certain date, and that an item was not checked (0) for a certain period. Paul Erlich died in 1915; he discovered salvarsan in 1909. D.I. 4, etc., is an abbreviation for decennial index for *Chemical Abstracts*.

The arrangement of the check lists varies. If a list is made for trade literature, it is usually best to make the list of manufacturers first and then check their trade literature against this.

A check list of all books used during a complete search, including all books and reference works used during the preliminary search, should be kept. This list should show which ones provided information or no information and the topics checked.

Work Sheets

Work sheets should be used when locating information in using abstract journals to avoid omissions and repetition, and kept until the search is finished. The sheets can be prepared in such a way that a typist can help with certain stages of the note taking. If the page

numbers for each volume are recorded in numerical order while checking the indexes, a record can be kept of which references were of value
and which were not. If the page (column) numbers are recorded in
order, this saves a lot of time in looking up the abstracts, too. When
new topics must be added during a search, these sheets show which
abstracts have been read and prevent repetition. They also show
which references were found valuable and noted, whether or not the
abstract was copied in full, or whether a portion of the abstract was
copied. Again an example for *Chemical Abstracts* illustrates the
general idea.

Chemical Abstracts, Vol. 48, 1954

11855e	Ubbelohde	√	12057	(X)	
11903d	Bowen (S)	√	12372d	Levi	√
1954a	Piganiol	√	1246c	Brit 707,647	√

As the chemist works through the indexes, the page numbers are noted
first; then when he reads the abstract he adds the name of the author
or the number of the patent if the reference and the abstract are to be
copied. A symbol which follows shows whether the abstract should
be copied only in part (S). An (X) after a number shows that the
abstract did not indicate pertinent information and the reference
should not be copied. If a typist then copies the references and the
abstracts, a portion of an abstract can be indicated by book markers
made from strips of heavy paper that are cut so the slit grips the
edge of the page. A √ after the number indicates that the reference
and abstract were copied by the typist. It is often better to have
photographic copies made of the abstracts. There are many types
of photographic equipment that are available at present, the cheapest
of which is the Contoura camera (manufactured by L. G. Ludwig
Associates, Pease Road, Woodbridge, Conn.).

Work sheets can save repetition and omissions when working with
large reference works, such as Beilstein's *Handbuch der organischen
Chemie,* if a lot of information must be collected.

Notes

The notes of information collected from all sources must be kept
accurately and systematically or a considerable quantity of time and
work will be wasted. Also, information may be "lost in the notes"
because the notes are too vague or are not classified and filed correctly, and when the search is finished, existing information will be
omitted from the report. If a subject has a number of subdivisions,

it is best to classify and index the information as much as possible while it is being collected. This not only saves time because the cards are read and handled only once, but also it enables one to see very quickly how much information has been obtained on the various phases of the subject as the search progresses. This practice is also useful in evaluating the information as one works. If punched or notched cards are used, they will need to be sorted at intervals to see how the search is progressing. If one is collecting data on physical constants and the physical properties of substances, he must be very careful in taking notes.

References from Abstract Journals. Notes on a paper in a periodical or on another source abstracted should include both the reference to the abstract journal and to the original publication. There are several reasons for this. This procedure shows whether most or little of the subject is covered by abstract journals. If errors are made in copying citations and the original reference cannot be located, it can be checked very quickly in the abstract journal. Unless the entire abstract is copied, it may be necessary to refer to it again because the original publication is not available. In some cases a copy of the publication cannot be obtained by photoprint, microfilm, or other methods, and the abstract must be relied upon exclusively.

References Obtained from Indexes. References obtained from the *Engineering Index* and other indexes that are independent of any specific publication should also indicate the index as well as the original publication. If an error is made in copying a reference it is often easier to check the Index again than to locate the trouble by internal evidence, such as a table that synchronizes the volume with the year of the periodical or examining the index of the periodical. Again the practice shows what proportion and which phases of the subject are covered by these Indexes, and whether they should be examined more thoroughly.

References Obtained from Catalogs and Indexes of Government Publications. Any reference located through sources of these kinds should also carry a note of the catalog or index. Again it is not just a question of checking in case of error in copying, but it may be useful in deciding whether or not to look at these indexes and catalogs more thoroughly or over a longer period of time.

References from Bibliographies. A reference obtained from a separate bibliography or from one found in a paper, a book, or other publication should also carry a note of where the reference was found. A reference that is cited in several places may be a particularly good one or it may just be copied from place to place. If errors occur in the copying, the context of the publication may be helpful in locating the original reference.

The **notes on a paper in a periodical** should always include: the full name of the author (at least the initials for all given names), the title of the paper, the name of the periodical in which it was published with volume, page, and year, the reference to the abstract journal or other publication through which the paper was located, and where the work was done. The card should also carry a nota-. tion as to whether or not the original paper was read. Then an abstract or annotation should follow. Exactly how this information is arranged on the card may vary, but a form must be adopted and used for all records or there will be omissions. For example:

Billman, John H., and Cash, R. V. . . . . OR
  "Alkylation by the Gabriel Synthesis"
  Proc. Indiana Acad. Sci. **62,** 158–159 (1952)
  C.A. **48,** 12038c (1954). Indiana University.
  Abstract and/or annotations.

In this case OR in the top right corner means that the original was read and any necessary additions made to the abstract. The *Chemical Abstracts* (*C.A.*) reference may give just the year or volume and page. *Engineering Index, Chemisches Zentralblatt,* and others may be abbreviated too. If a copy of the full paper is needed, the card should show where the photoprint is filed.

The **notes on a patent** should include the name of the patentee or inventor, the name of the company to which the patent is assigned, the number of the patent, the title, *Chemical Abstracts* reference, abstract or annotation, a note of whether or not the full patent was read, and, if a photocopy was obtained, where it is filed. In the case of a patent number, the date on which it was issued or published and its classification should also be recorded if given. Both *Chemical Abstracts* and *Chemisches Zentralblatt* often give all numbers when equivalent patents have been issued in two or more different countries; this should be noted too. For example:

Burney, D. B., and Cerveny, Wm. J.
  (to Standard Oil Co., Indiana)
  U. S. Patent 2,658,083, Nov. 3, 1953 . . . . OR
  Brit. Patent 703,100, Jan. 27, 1954
  C.A. **48,** 1216a (1954)
  "Selective hydrogenation of oxo-process aldehydes." (Abstract or annotations, including place where copy of full patent is filed if one was obtained.)

The **notes on a pamphlet** should be made as shown in the following example:

Gibson, K. S. .... OR
"Spectrophotometry"
U. S. Dept. of Commerce, Natl. Bureau of Standards
Circ. **484,** Sept. 15, 1949
Dec. index to Monthly Cat. Govern. Pub. (1941–1950)
(Abstract or annotation. Note if copy is in file.)

The **notes on books, dissertations,** etc., should also carry complete bibliographic information.

A lot of time can be saved if the bibliographic information is entered in exactly the same form on the card with the notes as will be used later when assembling a bibliography from the notes or using them to cite references. If this is done carefully, a typist can copy from the cards used for notes and it is not necessary to spend time rearranging and copying references before another person can use them.

There are many other details that could be mentioned. Enough has been said to make it clear that a definite system must be adopted for taking notes, and that this must be followed exactly and systematically to obtain the best results and the most valuable notes.

FOREIGN LANGUAGES

A chemist needs to have a good working knowledge of several languages in addition to English. The languages needed most frequently are English, German, Russian, and French. The Japanese do a large amount of scientific work, but much of it is published in English, French, or German. Dutch and Scandinavian chemists frequently publish in English, French, or German. The amount of chemical research done in Spain, Mexico, and South America is growing rapidly so that Spanish is more useful in scientific reading than it used to be.

A considerable quantity of work is being done on developing machines to translate material from one language into another. *Mechanical Translation* (Vol. 1, 1954) published by the Massachusetts Institute of Technology includes an annotated bibliography in each number in addition to papers on mechanical translation. The machines are still in the experimental stage of development, but some of them may prove to be useful tools in dealing with the numerous languages used in chemical publications.

When translations are needed, there are several other ways of obtaining them. See page 153.

There are a large number of dictionaries that are useful for translating from various languages into English and for reference while reading. Only a few of them are given here. For others see:

Collison, R. L., *Dictionaries of Foreign Languages*, London, Hafner, 1955, 230 pp. This work is an annotated bibliography of over 1,400 dictionaries in 255 different languages and includes both general and technical dictionaries.

Foreign Language-English Dictionaries, 2nd ed., 2 vols., Washington, D. C., The Library of Congress Card Division, 1955. Volume 1 of this work is devoted to special-subject dictionaries with special emphasis on science and technology. Volume 2 is devoted to general-language dictionaries. The emphasis is on dictionaries published since 1940.

UNESCO Bibliography of Interlingual Scientific and Technical Dictionaries, 3rd ed., New York, Columbia Univ. Press, 1954.

Winchell's Guide to Reference Books, 7th ed., Chicago, American Library Association, 1951 and supplements.

FRENCH–ENGLISH

Patterson, A. M., *A French–English Dictionary for Chemists*, 2nd ed., New York, Wiley, 1954, 476 pp.

DeVries, Louis, *French–English Science Dictionary*, 2nd ed., New York, McGraw-Hill, 1951.

GERMAN–ENGLISH

Leibiger, O. W., and Leibiger, I. S., *German–English and English–German Dictionary for Scientists*, Ann Arbor, Mich., Edwards Bros., 1950.

Patterson, A. M., *A German–English Dictionary for Chemists*, 3rd ed., New York, Wiley, 1950.

DeVries, Louis, *German–English Technical and Engineering Dictionary*, New York, McGraw-Hill, 1950.

Webel, A., *A German–English Dictionary of Technical, Scientific, and General Terms*, 4th ed., New York, Dutton, 1953.

ITALIAN–ENGLISH

Denti, R., *Italian–English and English–Italian Technical Dictionary*, 2nd ed., Milan, U. Hoepli, 1951.

Marolli, G., *Dizionario technico. Inglese–italiano, italiano–inglese*, 2nd ed., New York, W. S. Heinman, 1949.

JAPANESE

Ishihara, Jun, Inoue, Toshi, and Tamamushi, Bunichi, *Japanese Dictionary of Physics and Chemistry*, rev. and enlarged ed., Ann Arbor, Mich., G. Wahr, 1942.

SPANISH–ENGLISH

Goldberg, Morris, *Spanish–English Chemical and Medical Dictionary*, New York, McGraw-Hill, 1952.
Koster, T. A., *Technical Dictionary, English–Spanish*, New York, Steckert-Hafner, 1951.
Sell, Lewis L., *Spanish–English Comprehensive Technical Dictionary*, 2 vols., New York, McGraw-Hill, 1943–1944.

RUSSIAN–ENGLISH

Bray, Alexander, *Russian–English Scientific–Technical Dictionary*, New York, International Univ. Press, 1945.
Callaham, Ludmilla I., *Russian–English Technical and Chemical Dictionary*, New York, Wiley, 1947.
Gertsfeld, K. M., *English–Russian Chemical–Technological Dictionary*, 2nd ed., Moscow, Gosudarst. Izdatel'sto Tech-Theoret. Lit., 1953, 706 pp.

POLYGLOT

Hoyer-Kreuter Technical Dictionary: Engineering, Industry and Their Scientific Foundations, edited by A. Schlomann, German–English–French, 6th ed., New York, F. Unger Pub. Co., 3 vols., 1944.
Langford, R. A., and Aeberhard, R. W., *Technical and Commercial Dictionary, English–French–German*, New York, Chem. Pub. Co., 1952.
Menshutkin, B. N., and Block, M. A., *Chemical–technical Dictionary* (German–English–French–Russian), New York, Chem. Pub. Co., 1942.
Schlomann, Alfred (ed.), *Illustrated Technical Dictionary* (in six languages: English, German, French, Russian, Italian, Spanish), 17 vols., New York, McGraw-Hill, 1906–1932. A new edition was started in 1938 under the title *Illustrierte technische Wörterbucher*, Berlin, V. D. Iverlag, but only a few volumes have appeared.
Slater, *Pitman's Technical Dictionary of Engineering and Industrial Sciences* (English, French, Spanish, Portuguese, Italian, Russian, and German), 5 vols., London, Isaac Pitman, 1928–1932. Vol. 5 is the index.
Veillon, E. (ed.), *Medical Dictionary, German–English–French*, New York, Grune and Stratton, 1953.

THE WRITTEN RECORD OF THE SEARCH

The nature of the final record of a literature search will vary greatly with circumstances. If a research worker has been consulting the literature in connection with his own problem to see what has already been done by others, he may not need to recast his original records at all.

If, on the other hand, he is expected to make a report, or is preparing a monograph or a review, the writing-up process is important. Many organizations require the reports of literature searches to be prepared in a standard way for distribution and filing.

In any case, the final record should be of such a nature that it is clear and will enable the user to avail himself readily at any time of whatever has been noted, and to refer to the original sources as far as he desires.

Critical versus Noncritical Compilations. There are many noncritical compilations from the literature. Numerous books and reviews, as well as minor reports, are exactly this, and they have their place. If they are clearly written, they say to the user, "Here is what the literature says—draw whatever conclusions you wish." Indeed, a searcher who is not a competent specialist on the subject in question can scarcely do more. When one reflects, however, on the great differences in quality of chemical articles and the satisfaction it is to find a presentation in which each piece of work is considered critically and given its due weight, he can hardly avoid concluding that the reporter should use his critical faculty to the extent that his training and ability permit. It is possible to do this without warping the statement of facts or coloring the statements of authors with one's own ideas. A critical compilation when well done is always more valuable than a noncritical one. No reviewer, however, is infallible in his judgment and some important discoveries are not recognized as such for years.

Scientists are constantly being reproached for their sins of expression. It is a fact that many scientific writings are less pleasant reading than they should be, or convey wrong impressions because of poor style. Those interested in technical composition, report writing, details of preparing bibliographies, methods of citing the literature, and similar matters may obtain information from the following:

Crouch, W. G., and Zetler, R. L., *A Guide to Technical Writing*, 2nd ed., New York, Ronald Press, 1954.
Hawley, G. G., *Hawley's Technical Speller*, New York., Reinhold, 1955, 160 pp.
Joughin, G. L., *Basic Reference Forms*, New York, Crofts, 1941.
Kerekes, F., and Winfrey, R., *Report Preparation*, 2nd ed., Ames, Iowa, Iowa State College Press, 1950.
Manual of Style, The Univ. of Chicago Press.
Mills, G. H., and Walter, J. A., *Technical Writing*, New York, Rinehart, 1954.
Nelson, J. R., *Writing the Technical Report*, 3rd ed., New York, McGraw-Hill, 1952.
Rose, L. A., Bennett, B. B., and Heater, E. F., *Engineering Reports*, New York, Harper, 1950.
Style Manual, United States Government Printing Office, Washington, D. C.
Trealease, S. F., *The Scientific Paper*, Baltimore, Md., Williams & Wilkins, 1947.

Weil, B. H. (ed.), *The Technical Report,* New York, Reinhold, 1954.
Williams, G. E., *Technical Literature; Its Preparation and Presentation,* London, Allen & Unwin, 1948.

The book edited by B. H. Weil is probably the most comprehensive; it covers illustration, printing, filing, and distribution as well as writing the report and the preparation of bibliographies and literature summaries.

CHRONOLOGICAL TABLE

The following table of some of the more important serials publishing abstracts and summaries gives the dates of the periods during which they have appeared and the fields covered. The dates that follow the titles refer to collective indexes. By this arrangement one can tell at a glance which publications are available for any period back to 1779 that he may wish to cover. At the same time, from the field covered, he can judge whether or not a given publication is at all likely to yield the particular information wanted.

1778–1781.	General.	Crell's *Chemisches Journal.*
1781–1786.	General.	Crell's *Die Neuesten Entdeckungen in der Chemie.*
1784–1803.	General.	Crell's *Chemische Annalen.*
1785–1787.	Pharmacy.	*Magazin für Apotheker* (Elwert).
1789–1870.	General.	*Annales de chimie et de physique.*
1790–1796.	General.	*Repertorium für Chemie* (Elwert).
1795–1840.	Pharmacy.	*Berlinisches Jahrbuch für Pharmacie* (annual).
1803–1818.	Agriculture.	*Archiv der Agrikultur-chemie* (Hermbstaedt).
1807–1950.	Mineralogy, etc.	*Neues Jahrbuch für Mineralogie, Geologie und Paläontologie.* Ten-year indexes 1830–1879, 5-year indexes 1880–1950.
1811–1833.	General.	*Jahrbuch der Chemie und Physik.*
1815–1876.	Pharmacy.	*Repertorium für die Pharmacie (Gehlen).* 1815–1848.
1820–1931.	Industrial.	*Dingler's Polytechnisches Journal.* 1820–1840, 1841–1850, 1851–1860, 1861–1870.
1822–1847.	General.	*Berzelius' Jahresberichte der Chemie.* Annual. For continuation see 1847–1915, Liebig and Kopp.
1830– .	General.	*Chemisches Zentralblatt.* See pages 133–135.
1847–1915.	General.	Liebig and Kopp's *Jahresbericht über die Fortschritte der Chemie und verwandter Teile anderer Wissenschaften.* Annual. Continuation of Berzelius' *Jahresbericht.* Collective indexes 1847–1906 at 10-year intervals.
1855– .	Industrial.	Wagner's *Jahresbericht über die Leistungen der chemischen Technologie.* Index at 10-year intervals 1855–1904
1858–1947.	General.	*Bulletin de la société chimique de France.* See page 137.

1862-1935. Analysis. *Zeitschrift für analytische Chemie.* Collective indexes at 10-year intervals. 1862-1935.

1868-1896. General. *Berichte der deutschen chemischen Gesellschaft.* Collective indexes at 10-year intervals.

1869- . Ferrous metals. *Journal of the Iron and Steel Institute.*

1871-1925. General. *Journal of the Chemical Society* (London). See page 136.

1872-1936. Agriculture. *Zentralblatt für Agrikulturchemie* (Biedermann). 1872-1896, 1897-1906.

1877-1919. Physical science. *Bleiblätter zu den Annalen der Physik.*

1877- . Analysis. *The Analyst.* Collective indexes 1877 through 1935 at 10-year intervals.

1877- . General. *Chemiker-Zeitung.*

1882-1925. Industrial. *Journal of the Society of Chemical Industry* (London). Ten-year indexes. See page 137.

1884- . Dyes, etc. *Journal of the Society of Dyers and Colourists.*

1887-1918. Industrial. *Zeitschrift für angewandte Chemie.* 1887-1907.

1889-1946. Agriculture. *Experiment Station Record.* See page 146.

1890-1930. Gas. *American Gas Association Bulletin of Abstracts.*

1891-1918. General. *Jahrbuch der Chemie* (Meyer). Annual. (*Bericht über die Wichtigsten Fortschritte der reinen und angewandten Chemie.*)

1892-1941. Minerals, metals, etc. *Mineral Industry* (McGraw-Hill).

1895-1906. General. *Review of American Chemical Research.* In *Technology Quarterly* during 1895-1901 and in *Journal of American Chemical Society* 1897-1906.

1898- . Physical science. *Science Abstracts.*

1899-1918. General. *Repertoire générale de chimie pure et appliquée.*

1902- . Biochemistry. *Berichte über die gesamte Physiologie und experimentelle Pharmacologie.*

1904- . General. *Annual Reports of the Chemical Society* (London).

1904-1919. Radioactivity. *Le radium.*

1904- . Metals. *Revue de métallurgie.*

1906- . Colloids. *Kolloid Zeitschrift.*

1906- . Leather. *Journal of the American Leather Chemists Association.* 1906-1915.

1907- . General. *Chemical Abstracts.* See page 129.

1908- . Ceramics. *Transactions of the Ceramic Society* (London).

1908- . Sugar. *International Sugar Journal.*

1909- . Nonferrous Metals. *Journal of the Institute of Metals.*

1910- . Textiles, etc. *Journal of the Textile Institute.*

1911- . Metals. *Zeitschrift für Metallkunde.*

1912-1944. Leather. *Collegium.*

1914- . Petroleum. *Journal of the Institute of Petroleum,* 1914-1923.

1915- . Internal secretions. *Endocrinology.*

1915- . Photography. *Eastman Kodak Co. Monthly Abstract Bulletin.*

1916-1926. *Abstracts of Bacteriology.*

1916-1937. Biochemistry. *Physiological Abstracts.*

1916- . *Reports on the Progress of Applied Chemistry.* Annual.

1917–	.	Glass. *Journal of the Society of Glass Technology.*
1917–	.	Leather. *Journal of the Society of Leather Trades' Chemists.*
1918–	.	Ceramics. *Journal of the American Ceramic Society.*
1918–	.	Industrial. *Chimie et industrie.*
1919–1926.		Plant chemistry. *Botanical Abstracts.*
1919–1949.		Sanitation. *Journal of Industrial Hygiene and Toxicology.*
1919–	.	Water. *Journal of the American Water-Works Association.*
1920–1939.		Fuels. *Brennstoff-Chemie.*
1920–	.	*Mineralogical Abstracts* in *Mineralogical Magazine.*
1920–	.	Physical science. *Physikalische Berichte.*
1921–	.	*Photographic Abstracts.*
1926–	.	Biochemistry. *Biological Abstracts.*
1926–1953.		General. *British Abstracts.* See page 135.
1927–	.	General. *Complete Abstracts of Japanese Chemical Literature (Nippon Kagaku Soran).*
1928–	.	Metals. *Metals Review.*
1929–	.	*Food Science Abstracts.*
1930–	.	*Bulletin of the Institute of Paper Chemistry.*
1931–	.	*Nutrition Abstracts and Reviews.*
1935–	.	General. *La Chimica e L'industria.*
1944–	.	*British Plastics Federation Abstracts.*
1945–	.	*Gas Abstracts.*
1945–	.	*Fuel Abstracts.*
1948–	.	Biochemistry. *Excerpta Medica.*
1948–	.	*Electroplating and Metal Finishing.*
1948–	.	*Nuclear Science Abstracts.*
1950–	.	*Geophysical Abstracts.*
1950–	.	*Archives of Industrial Hygiene and Occupational Medicine.*
1954–	.	Industrial. *Journal of Applied Chemistry.*
1954–	.	Analytical Chemistry. *Analytic Abstracts.*

LITERATURE RELATING
TO CHEMICAL LITERATURE

‖‖

THE DOCUMENTATION OF CHEMISTRY

There is an extensive literature devoted to the production, distribution, and use of the chemical literature that is recorded in a variety of chemical publications. Papers on chemical literature in chemical periodicals can be located by the use of *Chemical Abstracts,* which reports briefly and indexes such papers. Most of the books on the subject are included in the following list:

American Chemical Society, *Advances in Chemistry Series,* no. 4, *Searching the Literature of Chemistry,* 1951; no. 10, *Literature Resources for Chemical Process Industries,* 1954. Both of these books are collections of papers presented at meetings of the American Chemical Society by its Division of Chemical Literature. No. 4 is being revised.

Boni, A., *Guide to the Literature of Photography and Allied Subjects,* New York, Morgan and Lester, 1944.

Crane, E. J., and Patterson, A. M., *A Guide to the Literature of Chemistry,* New York, Wiley, 1927, 438 pp. The first edition contains some material that deals with the older chemical literature that had to be omitted from the second edition for lack of space.

Cornubert, R., *La literature chimique mondiale,* Paris, Dunod, 1943, 74 pp.

Dyson, G. M., *A Short Guide to Chemical Literature,* London, Longmans, Green, 1951, 152 pp. Revised 1957.

Jackson, Lucile, *A Guide to Minerals Industries Literature,* State College, Pa., Pennsylvania State College, Library Studies no. 2, 1941.

Levin, P., *Tools and Methods for Searching the Chemical Literature: a Selective Bibliography,* Philadelphia, Drexel Institute of Technology (M.S. thesis), 1955, 41 pp.

Mason, F. A., *An Introduction to the Literature of Chemistry,* London, Oxford Univ. Press, 1924, 42 pp.

Mellon, M. G., *Chemical Publications, Their Nature and Use,* 2nd ed., New York, McGraw-Hill, 1940, 271 pp. Third edition is in preparation.

Milek, J. T., *Guide to Foreign Sources of Metallurgical Literature*, Pittsburgh, Richard Rimbach Associates, 1951, 95 pp.

Ostwald, Wi., *Die chemische Literatur und die Organisation der Wissenschaft*, Berlin, Akademie Verlag, 1919. (Vol. 1 of *Handbuch der allgemeinen Chemie*, edited by Ostwald and Drucker.)

Reid, E. E., *Introduction to Organic Research*, New York, Van Nostrand, 1924, 351 pp. Contains five chapters on chemical literature.

Rimbach, Richard, *How to Find Metallurgical Information*, Pittsburgh, Richard Rimbach Associates, 1936, 32 pp.

Serrallach, M., *Bibliografia quimica; documentacion cientifico-industrial*, Barcelona, Jose Bosch, 1946, 358 pp.

Soule, B. A., *Library Guide for the Chemist*, New York, McGraw-Hill, 1938, 302 pp.

Valuable information that can be applied to the documentation of chemistry frequently appears in publications devoted to the other sciences. Much of the information is covered by *Chemical Abstracts*, which examines many periodicals devoted to the other sciences for papers of interest to chemists. For a list of books on the other sciences, see page 223.

Two annotated bibliographies published in each number of two scientific periodicals are of great value, namely: (1) *Chemical Literature*, a quarterly news bulletin distributed to the members of the Division of Chemical Literature of the American Society and (2) *La Ricerca Scientifica*, published by the Italian National Research Council. Many items are listed in these bibliographies which do not appear elsewhere.

However, one who is concerned with the complete documentation of chemistry cannot rely solely on publications devoted to chemistry and the other sciences for information on the documentation of chemistry. Pertinent and valuable information is published frequently in periodicals devoted to library science or to documentation in general. The keys to the library and general documentation literature are:

Library Literature, 1921– , New York, Wilson Co. This index is published quarterly and covers the more important periodicals and books of the world devoted to library science and to documentation. *Library Literature* is more than an index; annotations or abstracts accompany entries for publications in languages other than English.

Library Science Abstract, 1950– , London, The Library Association. These abstracts are published quarterly and cover the more important periodicals and books of the world devoted to library science. Some information on documentation is abstracted. The two fields, library science and documentation, overlap in some areas.

A few journals devoted to library science or to documentation publish information that is of value for the documentation of chemistry with sufficient frequency to make it worth while to read them regularly, namely:

American Documentation, published by the American Documentation Institute. In addition to papers, an excellent annotated bibliography covering the more important documentation literature of the world is included in each number.

College and Research Libraries (U. S.). Semi-annual lists of new reference works and periodicals are included.
Journal of Documentation (England).
Journal of the Special Libraries Association (U. S.).
Library of Congress Information Bulletin (U. S.).
Revue de la documentation (Brussels). A journal published by the International Federation for Documentation includes an excellent classified and annotated bibliography on documentation in each number.
UNESCO Bulletin for Libraries.

Aside from publications, several organizations are sources of much information that is useful in the documentation of chemistry, namely:

The Division of Chemical Literature of the American Chemical Society, a unique organization in its field. The Division is actively engaged in improving the documentation of chemistry, has sponsored the publication of several useful books, and presents valuable papers (most of which are published) at the meetings of the American Chemical Society.

The National Research Council of the National Academy of Sciences of the United States, Washington, D. C.

The National Science Foundation, Washington, D. C.

The International Federation for Documentation, The Hague, The Netherlands.

UNESCO. New York and Paris. An excellent summary of UNESCO's program and an annotated list of its principal publications are given in V. W. Clapp's paper in *American Documentation* **7**, 127–135 (1956).

SYMBOLS, ABBREVIATIONS, AND STANDARDS USED IN CHEMICAL LITERATURE

▌▌

A great variety of symbols and abbreviations are used in chemical literature. Unfortunately, standardization is limited and in cases where a standard does exist it may not be in general use. A book, a reference work, or a journal frequently gives a list of abbreviations and symbols used in it. Abstracting journals, as *Chemical Abstracts* and *Chemisches Zentralblatt*, give lists (except abbreviations for titles of journals) in the annual index. Other periodicals often give a list with each volume. Large reference works may give a list in the first volume or repeat it in each volume.

The abbreviations for the names of scientific journals that are used by *Chemical Abstracts* are given in the *List of Periodicals Abstracted by Chemical Abstracts;* this is published at intervals of about five years, the latest having appeared in 1956.

Abbreviations for journal names that are used by *Chemisches Zentralblatt* vary somewhat from those used by *Chemical Abstracts* and are given in its list, *Periodica Chimica*, 2nd ed., 1952, edited by M. Pfluecke and A. Hawele, and published by Akademie-Verlag, Berlin.

Abbreviations used in the *World List of Scientific Periodicals* (3rd ed., 1952, New York, Academic Press, or London, Butterworth) vary in some cases from those used in the two chemical abstracting journals mentioned above.

For a discussion of the methods of abbreviating journal names, see page 153.

A paper on *Technical Abbreviations and Contractions* in English by Charlotte Schaler [*J. Chem. Educ.* **32**, 114–117 (1955)] contains a bibliography of 100 items and provides much useful information.

The most extensive compilation in book form is *Scientific and Technical Signs and Symbols* by O. T. Zimmerman and I. Lavine, Dover, New Hampshire, Industrial Research Service, 2nd ed., 1949. This book is devoted largely to American usage and includes abbreviations used in chemistry and chemical engineering.

Standards have been adopted by various organizations and by various countries. Standards are in existence for many things—petroleum products, textiles, laboratory glassware, and the determination of viscosity, to name a few. Information is needed frequently about standards by chemists. The American Standards Association Inc., 70 East 45th Street, New York 17, N. Y., is the best source of information in the United States. The Association's Library of Standards is a clearing house for information on standards from every source that is of national or international importance. The Library of Standards (ASA) sells copies of standards and photostats of standards, both foreign and domestic. The Association is a member of the International Organization for Standardization.

The International Organization for Standardization, 39, route de Malagnou, Geneva, Switzerland, has accepted 18 standards and copies are available for distribution. The Organization's Technical Committees are considering the drafts of about 100 standards. See the *IOS Journal* for more information about the Organization's activities.

LIST OF SYMBOLS AND ABBREVIATIONS USED IN THE OLDER CHEMICAL LITERATURE

In the following list unclassified symbols come first, then letters of the Greek alphabet in order, and finally Roman letters and abbreviations. The list includes many abbreviations for words that occur frequently in the titles of journals, as *Am.* and *Amer.* for American, *Ann.* for Annales, Annalen, etc., and *Soc.* for Society, Société, etc. By making use of these one can often decipher the title of a journal from its shortened form. The complete abbreviations adopted by the International Union of Pure and Applied Chemistry for journal titles are not included; they will be found in the List of Periodicals Abstracted by *Chemical Abstracts*.

The abbreviations in the present list are from various languages, but it has not been thought necessary to use the labels "German," "French," etc. English translations have been given in cases where the meanings of foreign words are not readily apparent.

=	gives, forms; is equal to, equals.
→	gives, passes over to, leads to.
⇄	forms and is formed from (reversible reaction).
⇌	is equivalent to.
>	is greater than; above.
<	is less than; below.
+	plus, and, reacting with.
−	minus, less.
*	asterisk, star (used to mark asymmetric carbon atoms).
′	prime; feet, ft.
″	second; inches, in.
(+)	in Gegenwart von (in presence of).
°	degree(s); vo (as, 8° or 8vo, octavo).
%	per cent.
%ig.	prozentig (per cent).
%₀ig.	promillig (per mille, per thousand).

Ж *Journal of the Russian Physical-Chemical Society.*

α (alpha) degree of dissociation; angle of optical rotation; coefficient of linear or cubical expansion.

$[\alpha]$ specific rotatory power.

α- alpha- (1st in order or position).

β- beta- (2d in order).

γ (gamma) surface tension; ratio of specific heats; ionization; Newtonian gravitational constant.

γ- gamma- (3d in order).

Δ (delta) diffusion coefficient.

δ (delta) density.

δ- delta- (4th in order).

ϵ (epsilon) dielectric constant; electrode potential.

ϵ- epsilon- (5th in order).

ζ- zeta- (6th in order).

η (eta) viscosity.

η- eta- (7th in order).

θ (theta) angle (plane); temperature Centigrade.

θ- theta- (8th in order).

ι- iota- (9th in order).

κ (kappa) electrical (volume) conductivity; magnetic susceptibility.

κ- kappa- (10th in order).

Λ (lambda) equivalent conductivity.

λ (lambda) wave length.

λ- lambda- (11th in order).

μ (mu) micron (one millionth of a meter); molecular conductivity; magnetic permeability.

μ- mu- (12th in order).

μμ micromicron (one millionth of a micron).

ν (nu) frequency.

ν- nu- (13th in order).

ξ- xi- (14th in order).

ο- omicron- (15th in order).

π (pi) ratio of circumference to diameter; osmotic pressure.

π- pi- (16th in order).

ρ (rho) refractive power.

ρ- rho- (17th in order).

Σ (sigma) summation.

σ (sigma) Stefan's constant; surface tension; thousandth of a second.

σ- sigma- (18th in order).

τ- tau- (19th in order).

υ- upsilon- (20th in order).

φ (phi) fluidity; angle; aryl radical, specif. phenyl.

φ- phi- (21st in order).

χ- chi- (22d in order).

ψ- pseudo-; psi- (23d in order).

ω- omega- (denoting end or last, or side-chain position).

[ω] specific magnetic rotatory power.

A atomic weight; maximum work; abaissement (lowering).

α- asymmetric.

A argon.

A. Annalen der Chemie (Liebig's); Annales; Abstracts in the Journal of the (London) Chemical Society or part A of British Chemical Abstracts; Alkohol; Analyse (analysis).

Ä. Äther (ether).

Å. Ångström unit(s).

a. asymmetrisch (asymmetric).

A. A. L. Atti della reale accademia nazionale dei Lincei.

a. a. O. an anderen Orten (elsewhere); an angeführten, or angegebenen, Orte (in the place cited).

Abd. Rk. Abderhaldensche Reaktion (Abderhalden's reaction).

Abh., Abhandl. Abhandlungen (papers, transactions).

abs., absol. absolut, absolute.

abst., abstr. abstract.

Ac actinium; acetyl.

Ac. Academy, Académie.

ac. acide (acid).

a. c. alternating current.

Acad. Academy, Académie.

Accad. Accademia (Academy).

acct. account.

Ac-Em actinium emanation, actinon.

A. ch. Annales de chimie (et de physique).

Act actinium.

addn. addition

ad. lib. (ad libitum) at pleasure, as desired.

Å. E. Ångströmeinheit (Ångström unit).

Ae Aether (ether).

A. G. Atomgewicht (atomic weight); Aktiengesellschaft (joint-stock company).

Ag silver.

Agr., Agri., Agric. Agricultural; Agriculture.

aig. aiguilles (needles).

Ak., Akad. Akademie (academy).

akt. aktiv (active).

Akt.-Ges. Aktiengesellschaft (joint-stock company).

Al aluminum.

alc. alcohol, alcool.

ald. aldéhyde, aldehyde.

Alk. Alkohol.

alk. alkali, alkaline.

alkal. alkalisch (alkaline).

alkoh. alkoholisch (alcoholic).

alky. alkalinity.

allg. allgemein (general).

a. m. forenoon.

Am amyl.

Am. American; American Chemical Journal.

Amer. American.

amp. ampere(s).

amp.-hr. ampere hour(s).

Am. Soc. Journal of the American Chemical Society.

Amst. Proceedings of the Royal Academy of Sciences of Amsterdam.

amt. amount.

amts. amounts.

An. Anales (annals); Anmerkung (remark).

an. anorganisch(e).

Anal. Analyse (analysis).

anal. analytical, analytique, analytisch(e); anales (annals).

ang., angew. angewandt, -e (applied).

anh. anhydride; anhydrous.

anhyd. anhydrous.

Anm. Anmerkung (note, remark).

Ann. Annalen, Annales, Annali, Annals; specif., Annalen der Chemie (Liebig's); Annual, Annuaire.

anom. anomal (anomalous).

anorg. anorganisch, -e (inorganic).

Anw. Anwendung (employment, use).

Anz. Anzeiger.

A. P.   Amerikanisches Patent; Austrian Patent.
Ap.   Apotheker (druggist).
A. Ph.   *Annales de physique.*
App.   Apparat (apparatus).
app.   apparatus.
appl.   applicata, appliqué (applied).
approx.   approximate, approximately.
A. Pth.   *Archiv für experimentelle Pathologie und Pharmakologie.*
Aq, aq   water, H_2O.
aq.   aqueous; water.
aq. dest.   aqua destillata (distilled water).
Ar.   *Archiv der Pharmazie.*
Arb.   Arbeiten (works, pieces of work).
Arch.   Archief, Archiv, Archives, Archivio.
'Arch. Gen.   *Archives des sciences physiques et naturelles.* Genève.
Arch. Néerl.   *Archives néerlandaises des sciences exactes et naturelles.*
as-   asymmetric.
A. S.   Ampère-Stunde (ampere hour).
As   arsenic.
Asoc.   Asociación (association).
Assn.   Association.
asym.   asymmetric, asymétrique, asymmetrisch.
asymm.   asymmetric, asymmetrisch.
At.   Atom (atom); Atmosphäre (atmosphere).
at.   atomic.
At.-%   Atomprozent (atomic per cent).
At.-Gew.   Atomgewicht (atomic weight).
äth., äther.   ätherisch (ethereal).
atm.   atmosphere(s), atmospheric.
Atomgew.   Atomgewicht (atomic weight).
at. wt.   atomic weight.
Au   gold.
a. u. a.   auch unter andern (also among others).
Aufl.   Auflage (edition).
ausg.   ausgegeben (produced, edited, etc.).
Aust. P.   Australisches Patent (Australian patent).
av.   average; avoirdupois.
ä. W.   äussere weite (outside diameter).
AZ.   Acetylzahl (acetyl number).
Az   azote (nitrogen).
B   boron.
B.   Bildung (formation); *Berichte der deutschen chemischen Gesellschaft;* Baumé.
b.   boils at, boiling at.
B. A.   balneum arenae (sand bath).
Ba   barium.
Bact.   Bacteriology.
bacteriol.   bacteriological.
B. & S.   Brown & Sharpe (wire gage).
Bastand.   Barometerstand (height of barometer).
B. A. U.   British Association unit.
bbl.   barrel, barrels.
Bd.   Board; Band (volume).
Bde.   Bände (volumes).
Be   beryllium.

Beibl.   Beiblätter (supplements).
Beih.   Beihefte (supplements).
Beitr.   Beiträge (contributions); Beitrag (contribution).
Belg.   Belgian, Belgisch; Belgium, Belgique.
Ber.   Berichte (reports); specif., *Berichte der deutschen chemischen Gesellschaft.*
ber.   berechnet (calculated).
Berl. Ber.   Berliner Berichte (*Berichte der deutschen chemischen Gesellschaft*).
Best., Bestimm.   Bestimmung (determination).
betr.   betreffend (concerning).
bez., bezw.   beziehungsweise (respectively, or).
Bg.   Balling.
b.h.p., b.hp., B.H.P.   brake horse power.
Bi   bismuth.
bibl.   bibliothèque (library); bibliography.
Bild., Bildg.   Bildung (formation).
Bioch., Biochem.   Biochemical, Biochemische.
Biol., biol.   biological, biologisch(e); biology.
Bio. Z.   *Biochemische Zeitschrift.*
Bl.   Bulletin; specif., *Bulletin de la société chimique de France.*
Bl. Belg.   *Bulletin de la société chimique de Belgique.*
blf.   blätterförmig (in leaflets or flakes).
Blg. P.   Belgisches Patent (Belgian Patent).
Blt.   Blättchen (leaflets, lamellas).
B.-M.   bain-marie (water bath).
Boll   Bolletino (bulletin).
B. O. T.   Board of Trade.
Bot.   Botanisch, Botanical; Botany.
B. P.   British Pharmacopeia.
b. p.   boiling point(s).
B. Ph.   British Pharmacopeia.
B. Ph. P.   *Beiträge zur chemischen Physiologie und Pathologie.*
Br   bromine.
Brit.   British.
Bros.   Brothers.
B.th.u.   British thermal unit(s).
B.T.U., B.t.u.   British thermal unit(s); Board of Trade unit.
Bu   butyl.
bu.   bushel, bushels.
Bul.   Buletinul (bulletin); Bulletin.
Bulet.   Buletinul (bulletin).
Bull.   Bulletin.
Bur.   Bureau.
B.W.G.   Birmingham wire gage.
Bz   benzoyl.
Bz.   Benzol (benzene).
bzgl.   bezüglich (respecting).
Bzl.   Benzol (benzene).
Bzn.   Benzin (benzine).
bzw.   beziehungsweise (respectively, or).
C concentration; molecular heat; capacity.
c specific heat; velocity of light in free space.
c_p specific heat at constant pressure.
c_v specific heat at constant volume.
C   carbon.

C.   Zentralblatt, Centralblatt; specif., *Chemisches Zentralblatt;* Centigrade; cathode.

c.   centimètre, centimeter.

C. A.   *Chemical Abstracts;* coefficient d'abaissement (coefficient of freezing-point lowering).

Ca   calcium.

ca.   (circa) about, approximately.

c.-à-d.   c'est-à-dire (that is to say, that is, i. e.).

Cal.   (large, or kilogram) calorie(s); Calico.

cal.   calorie(s).

calc.   calculate.

calcd.   calculated.

calcg.   calculating.

calcn.   calculation.

Can.   Canadian.

Cb   columbium.

cbcm.   cubic centimeter(s).

cbm.   cubic meter(s), cu. m.

cc., c.c., c.cm.   cubic centimeter(s).

cca.   (circa) about.

Cd   cadmium.

c. d.   current density (or densities).

Ce   cerium.

Cel.   Celsius.

Cent.   Centigrade.

cent.   centième (hundredth); centime (1/100 franc).

cent. cub.   centimètre cube (cubic centimeter, c. c.).

Centr.   Centralblatt.

cf.   (confer) compare.

cg., cgm.   centigram(s).

C. G. S., cgs.   Centimeter-gram-second system.

Ch.   Chemistry, Chemie, Chimie; Chemical, Chemisch, Chimique.

ch.   chapitre, chapter.

chem.   chemical, chemisch.

Chem.   Chemical, Chemisch; Chemists, Chemiker.

Chem. N.   *Chemical News.*

Chem.-Ztg.   *Chemiker-Zeitung.*

Ch. I.   *Chemische Industrie.*

chim.   chimico, chimie, chimica, chimique (chemistry, chemical).

Ch. Ind.   *Chimie & industrie.*

Chlf.   Chloroform.

Ch. N.   *Chemical News.*

Ch. Z.   *Chemisches Zentralblatt; Chemiker-Zeitung.*

Cie., Cie Compagnie (Company, Co.).

Cim.   *Nuovo cimento.*

cir.   circular.

Circ.   Circular.

Cl   chlorine.

cm.   centimeter(s).

cm^q, cm^2 square centimeter(s).

cm^c, cm^3 cubic centimeter(s).

Co   cobalt.

Co.   Company.

coeff.   coefficient.

coeffs.   coefficients.

Col.   Color, Colour; Colorant, Coloring; Colorist.

Coll.   College.

com.   commercial.

comb.   combinaison (compound, combination).

compd.   compound.

compn.   composition.

Compt. rend.   Comptes rendus (reports); specif., *Comptes rendus hebdomadaires des séances de l'Académie des Sciences.*

conc.   concentrate; concentrated, concentré.

concd.   concentrated.

concn.   concentration.

cond.   conductivity.

condens.   condensation.

conf.   compare, see, cf.

const.   constant.

cont.   continued; continental.

contg.   containing.

cor.   corrected.

corr.   corrected, corrigé, corrigiert.

corresp.   correspondant (corresponding).

cos   cosine.

cosec   cosecant.

cosh   hyperbolic cosine.

cot   cotangent.

C. P.   chemically pure.

c. p., cp.   candle power.

Cp   cassiopeium (lutecium).

C. r., C. R., CR.   = *Compt. rend.,* above.

Cr   chromium.

crist.   cristaux (crystals).

cristall.   cristallisation (crystallization).

crit.   critical.

crys.   crystal.

cryst.   crystalline.

crystd.   crystallized.

crystn.   crystallization.

C. S.   current strength.

Cs   cesium.

Ct   celtium (hafnium).

Cu   copper.

cu.   cubic.

cu. ft.   cubic foot (feet).

cu. m.   cubic meter(s).

cwt.   hundredweight.

Cy   cyanogen, CN.

cycl.   cyclisch (cyclic).

C. Z.   *Chemisches Zentralblatt;* Cellulosezahl (cellulose number).

D   density.

d   diameter; total differential; density.

d_c critical density.

d-   dextro-, dextrorotatory.

D.   Dichte (density) Deutsch (German); *Dinglers polytechnisches Journal.*

d.   density; penny, pence; des, der (of the); der, die, das, den (the); etc.

dad. gek.   dadurch gekennzeichnet (distinguished, or characterized, by this).

dam.   decamètre, decameter.

Dän. P.   Dänisches Patent (Danish patent).

LIST OF SYMBOLS 337

Darst. Darstellung (preparation).
d. c. direct current.
dch. durch (through, by).
D. D. Dichten (densities).
DD. Dampfdichte (vapor density).
DE. Dielektrizitätskonstante (dielectric constant).
déc. décomposition.
decompn. decomposition.
deg. degree(s).
Denkschr. Denkschriften (memoirs).
Dep., Dept. Department.
depur. (depuratus, -a, -um) purified.
Der. Derivat (derivative).
dér. dérivé (derivative, derived).
deriv. derivative.
Deriv. Derivat (derivative).
des. desmotropic, desmotrop.
dest. destilliert, -e (distilled); destillieren (distil).
Dest., Destillat. Destillation (distillation).
det. determine.
detd. determined.
detg. determining.
detn. determination.
Deut. Deutsch (German).
dg. decigram(s).
dgl. dergleichen (the like).
d. h. das heisst (that is, i. e.).
Di didymium.
d. i. das ist (that is, i. e.).
diagr. diagram.
diam. diameter(s).
dil. dilute.
diln. dilution.
Dingl. Dinglers polytechnisches Journal.
Disp. Dispensatory.
Diss. Dissoziation (dissociation); Dissertation.
Dissert. Dissertation.
Dissoz. Dissoziation (dissociation).
dist. distillation.
distd. distilled.
distg. distilling.
distn. distillation.
d. J. dieses Jahr (of this year).
dl-, d,l- racemic.
dl. deciliter.
d. M. dieses Monats (of this month).
dm. decimeter(s).
dm^q, dm^2 square decimeter(s).
dm^c, dm^3 cubic decimeter(s).
D. P. = D. R. P.
D. Prior. Deutsches Priorität (German priority).
Dr Docteur (Doctor, Dr.).
Dr. Doctor.
dr. dram, drams.
drgl. dergleichen (the like).
D. R. P. Deutsches Reichs-Patent (Imperial German patent).
Dr. phil. doctor of philosophy, Ph.D.
Ds dysprosium.

dsgl. desgleichen (likewise, ditto).
Dy dysprosium.
DZ., dz. Doppelzentner (double centner, 100 kilograms).
E electromotive force; electrode potential; energy.
e electronic charge; base of natural logarithms.
E. Erstarrungspunkt (freezing point, solidification point); Eigenschaften (properties).
Eb. point d'ébullition (boiling point).
éb. ébouillit (boils).
ébull. ébullition (boiling).
effy. efficiency.
e. g. (exempli gratia) for example.
Eg. Eisessig (glacial acetic acid).
e. hp. electric horsepower.
Eig. Eigenschaft (property).
Eigg. Eigenschaften (properties).
Einfl. Einfluss (influence).
Einw. Einwirkung (action, effect).
E. K., EK. = E. M. K.
El. ch. Z. Elektrochemische Zeitschrift.
elec., elect. electric, electrical; electricity; electuary.
Elekt. Elektrizität (electricity).
elekt. elektrisch (electric).
Em radium emanation (radon).
E. M. F., e. m. f., emf. electromotive force.
E. M. K., EMK. Elektromotorische Kraft (electromotive force, e. m. f.).
Eng. Engineering; Engineer.
enth. enthaltend (containing).
entspr. entsprechend (corresponding).
Entsteh. Entstehung (origin).
Entw. Entwickelung (evolution).
E. P. Englisches Patent, English Patent.
equil., equilib. equilibrium, equilibria.
equiv. equivalent; specif., electrochemical equivalent.
Er erbium.
erh. erhitzt (heated).
Erh. Erhitzung (heating).
Erk. Erkennung (detection, recognition).
Erstarr.-Pkt., Erstp. Erstarrungspunkt (freezing point).
erw. erwärmt (warmed).
esc. escompte (discount).
Esp. Espagnole (Spanish).
est. estimate.
estd. estimated.
estg. estimating.
estn. estimation.
Et ethyl.
et seq. (et sequentes) and the following.
E. T. Z. Elektrotechnische Zeitschrift.
Eu europium.
ev. eventuell (eventual, in question, under consideration).
evap. evaporate.
evapd. evaporated.
evapg. evaporating.
evapn. evaporation.

event. eventuell (eventual, eventually).
ex. exemple, example.
examd. examined.
examg. examining.
examn. examination.
exp. experimentell, experimental.
exper. experimental.
expt. experiment; experimentell, experimental.
exptl. experimental.
ext. extract; external.
extd. extracted.
extg. extracting.
extn. extraction.
EZ. Esterzahl (ester number).
F Faraday's constant (number of coulombs per gram equivalent of an ion).
F fluorine; free energy.
F. Fusionspunkt (melting point); fusible; Fahrenheit.
f. für (for); fest (solid); fein (fine); fond (melts); franc.
Fahr. Fahrenheit.
falsif. falsification(s).
Farb. Farben (colors).
farm. farmaceutico (pharmaceutical).
Fe iron.
F. E. M. force électromotrice (electromotive force, e. m. f.).
F. f. Fortsetzung folgt (to be continued).
ff., f. f., fff. sehr fein (very fine); und folgende (and following, et seq.).
fi. fisica (physical).
F. i. D. Faden in Dampf (thread in vapor).
fig. figure.
fis. fisica (physical).
Fl. Flüssigkeit (liquid; fluid).
fl. fluid; flüssig (liquid, fluid); flüchtig (volatile).
fldr. fluidram(s).
Fll. Flüssigkeiten (liquids, fluids).
fl. oz. fluidounce(s).
flüss. flüssig (liquid, fluid).
Flüssigk. Flüssigkeit (liquid, fluid).
F. O. flamme oxydante (oxidizing flame, O. F.).
F. P. French Patent, Französisches Patent; foot-pound(s).
Fp. Fusionspunkt (melting point).
f. p. freezing point.
F. R. flamme réductrice (reducing flame, R. F.).
Fr. Fresenius' *Zeitschrift für analytische Chemie*.
fr. frei (free); franc.
frakt. fraktioniert (fractionated).
frbl. farblos (colorless).
Frdl. Friedländer's Fortschritte der Teerfarbenfabrikation.
ft. foot, feet.
ft.-lb. foot-pound(s).
fum., fumar. fumaroid.
Fys. Fysik (physics).
g,G,g gravitation constant.

G. *Gazzetta chimica italiana;* Gesellschaft (society, company).
g. gram, grams.
Ga gallium.
gal. gallon(s).
gasf. gasförmig (gaseous).
Gaz., Gazz. Gazzetta (Gazette); specif., *Gazzetta chimica italiana*.
Gd gadolinium.
Ge germanium.
gebd. gebunden (bound).
geg. gegen (toward, against, etc.).
Geh. Gehalt (content, contents).
gek. gekennzeichnet (distinguished, characterized).
gel. gelöst (dissolved).
gem- geminate (said of two like groups attached to the same atom).
gem. gemein (common).
Gen. Genève (Geneva).
gén. général.
Geol. Geological, Geology.
Ges. Gesellschaft (society; company).
ges. gesamt (whole, entire); gesättigt (saturated); gesetzlich (by law).
Ges.-Amt. Gesundheitsamt (health office, bureau or board).
gesätt. gesättigt (saturated).
ges. gesch. gesetzlich geschützt (protected by law, patented).
Gew. Gewicht (weight); Gewerbe (industry, trade).
gew., gewöhnl. gewöhnlich (usual, ordinary; usually).
Gew. T. Gewichtsteil (part by weight).
Geww. Gewichte (weights).
gg. gegen (toward, against, etc.).
Ggw. Gegenwart (presence).
Giorn. Giornale (Journal).
Gl glucinum, glucinium (beryllium).
GM. Goldmark(en), gold mark(s).
gm. gram.
G. m. b. H. Gesellschaft mit beschränkter Haftpflicht (limited company).
Gött. N. *Nachrichten von der Königlichen Gesellschaft der Wissenschaften zu Göttingen.*
G. P. German Patent.
gr. grain, grains; (in French) gramme (gram); (in German) Gramm (gram).
grm. gram, grams.
G. S. Geological Survey.
G. T. Gewichtsteil (part by weight).
gtt. (gutta, guttae) drop, drops.
GWF *Das Gas- und Wasserfach.*
h height; Planck's constant of action.
H hydrogen; heat content.
h Planck's constant of action.
H. Hoppe-Seylers *Zeitschrift für physiologische Chemie;* Härte (hardness); Höhe (altitude); Haben (credit); Hoheit (highness).
h. hour; horizontal; heiss (hot); hochschmelzend (high-melting); hoch (high).

ha. hectare(s).
Hal halogen.
He helium.
hect. hectoliter(s).
Helv. Helvetica (Swiss); *Helvetica chimica acta.*
Herst. Herstellung (preparation, production).
H.-F. high-frequency.
Hf hafnium.
Hg mercury.
hg. hectogram(s).
H.-ion, H-ion. hydrogen-ion.
Hl. Halbleder (half-leather).
hl. hectoliter(s).
Hlg. Halogen.
Ho holmium.
Holl. P. Holländisches Patent (Dutch patent)
h. p., hp., H. P. horsepower.
hp.-hr. horsepower-hour.
hr. hour.
hrs. hours.
h. s. l. heiss sehr löslich (very soluble hot).
ht. height.
h. w. l. heiss wenig löslich (not very soluble hot).
Hyg. Hygiene.
H. Z. Hydrolisierzahl (hydrolyzation number).
I Electric current; intensity of magnetization.
i- (optically) inactive; iso-.
I iodine.
i. in; im (in the); ist (is).
i. B. auf. in Berechnung auf (calculated on the basis of).
ibid. (ibidem) in the same place.
I. C. T. International Critical Tables.
i. D. im Dampf (in steam; in the form of vapor).
i. e. (id est.) that is.
i. h. p., i. hp., I. H. P. indicated horsepower.
i.hp.-hr. indicated horsepower-hour.
i. J. im Jahre (in the year).
Imp. Imperial.
In indium.
in. inch, inches.
inakt. inaktiv (inactive).
Inaug. Diss. inaugural dissertation.
Inc. Incorporated.
Ind. Industry, Industrie; Industrial, Industriel.
inorg. inorganic.
insol. insoluble.
insoly. insolubility.
Inst. Institute.
Instit. Institut, Institute.
Io ionium.
I. P. Italian Patent, italienisches Patent.
Ir iridium.
Istit. Istituto (Institute).
ital. italiana (italian).
It. P. italienisches Patent (Italian patent).
I. U. immunizing unit.

i. V. im Vakuum (in a vacuum).
i. W. innere Weite (inside diametrer).
J mechanical equivalent of heat; adiance.
J Jod (iodine).
J. Journal; (less often) Jahrbuch (yearbook), or Jahresbericht (annual report); specif., *Jahresbericht über die Fortschritte der Chemie.*
J. A. C. S. *Journal of the American Ceramic Society; Journal of the American Chemical Society.*
Jahrb. Jahrbuch (yearbook).
Jahresb., Jahresber. Jahresbericht(e); specif., *Jahresbericht über die Fortschritte der Chemie.*
Jahrg. Jahrgang (year).
Jb. Jahrbuch (yearbook).
Jber. Jahresberichte (annual reports).
J. C. S. *Journal of the Chemical Society* (London).
Jour., Journ. Journal.
J. pr. *Journal für praktische Chemie.*
J. S. C. I. *Journal of the Society of Chemical Industry.*
J. S. D. C. *Journal of the Society of Dyers and Colourists.*
J. Th. *Jahresbericht der Tierchemie.*
K constant; specif., chemical equilibrium constant; dielectric constant; electric dissociation constant.
k constant; specif., velocity coefficient of reaction; molecular gas constant.
K potassium; constant; Kelvin scale; karat.
k constant.
K. Kelvin (absolute centigrade) scale.
k. königlich, koninklijk (royal); kaiserlich (imperial); kalt (cold); kathode.
ka. kathode.
Kap. Kapitel (chapter).
Kem. Kemi (chemistry).
kg. kilogram(s).
kgl. königlich (royal).
kg.-m. kilogram-meter(s).
K. K., k. k. kaiserlich-königlich (imperial-royal).
k. Kal. kleine Kalorie (small calorie).
kl. kiloliter(s); kaum löslich (scarcely soluble).
klin. klinisch (clinical).
km. kilometer(s).
Koeff., Koeffz. Koeffizient (coefficient).
Koll. Z., Koll. Zeits. *Kolloid Zeitschrift.*
kompr. komprimiert (compressed).
Konst. Konstitution (constitution).
Konz. Konzentration (concentration).
konz. konzentriert (concentrated).
kor., korr. korrigiert (corrected).
Kp. Kochpunkt (boiling point).
Kr krypton.
Kr. Krystallographie (crystallography).
Krist. Kristallographie (crystallography); Kristall(e) (crystal(s)); Kristallisation (crystallization).

krist. kristallisiert (crystallized); kristallinisch (crystalline).
Kristfm. Kristallform (crystal form).
Kryst. Krystallographie (crystallography).
k. s. l. kalt sehr löslich (very soluble cold).
kva. kilovolt-ampere(s).
kw., K. W. kilowatt(s).
kw.-an. kilowatt-an (kilowatt-year).
kw.-hr. kilowatt-hour(s).
k. w. l. kalt wenig löslich (not very soluble cold).
Kwst. Kilowattstunde (kilowatt hour).
KW-stoff. Kohlenwasserstoff (carbohydrate).
L latent heat per mole; conductance.
l length; latent heat per gram.
l- levo-, levorotatory.
L latent heat.
l. liter, liters; löslich (soluble); lies (read).
La lanthanum.
lab. laboratory; labil, labile.
Landw. Landwirtschaft (agriculture); land wirtschaftlich (agricultural).
L. B. Landolt-Börnstein Tabellen.
lb. pound(s).
L. B. V. Landolt-Börnstein Tabellen, 5th edtion.
L. C. Library of Congress.
Leg. Legierung (alloy; alloying).
Legg. Legierungen (alloys).
leichtl. leichtlöslich (easily soluble).
L.-F. low-frequency.
lfd. laufend (running, current, consecutive).
Lfg. Lieferung (issue, number, part).
Lg. Ligroin.
Li lithium.
lin. linear.
liq. liquor.
ll. leicht löslich (readily soluble).
log logarithm.
Lösl. Löslichkeit (solubility).
lösl. löslich (soluble).
Lösungsm. Lösungsmittel (solvent).
Lsg. Lösung (solution).
Lsgg. Lösungen (solutions).
Lsgs.-Mittel. Lösungsmittel (solvent).
Ltd. Limited.
Lu lutecium.
L. V. St. Landwirtschaftliche Versuchsstationen (agricultural experiment stations).
l. W. lichte Weite (internal diameter).
M molecular weight.
$M[\alpha]$ molecular rotatory power.
$M[\omega]$ molecular magnetic rotatory power.
m mass.
m- meta-.
M Mark, Marken (mark, marks); metal (in formulas.
m^2 square meter(s).
m^3 cubic meter(s).
M. Masse (mass); Monat (month); Mittelsorte (medium grade); *Monatshefte für Chemie;* Moniteur; Monsieur (Mr., Sir); Majesté, Majesty.

m. meter(s); melts at, melting at; minute(s); (meridies) noon; mit (with); mein, meine, meines (my, of my); mon (my); midi (south).
Ma masurium.
Mach. Machinery.
Mag. Magazine, Magazin.
mal., malein. maleinoid.
m. amp. milliampere(s).
manuf. manufacture.
manufd. manufactured.
mat. matières (matters).
max. maximum.
m. E. meines Erachtens (in my opinion).
Me methyl; Metall (metal).
mech. mechanical.
Med. Medical; Medicine.
med. medizinisch (medical, medicinal).
Mem. Memoirs, Memorias, Memorie.
Mém. Mémoires; *Mémorial des poudres et salpêtres.*
m. e. p. mean effective pressure.
Met. Metallurgical; Metals; Metallurgie, Metallurgy.
Mét. Métallurgie (Metallurgy).
Metallk. Metallkunde (science of metals).
Meth. Methode (method).
mfg. manufacturing.
mfr. manufacturer.
M. G. Molekulargewicht (molecular weight).
Mg magnesium.
m. G. mit Goldschnitt (with gold edges).
mg. milligram(s).
Min. Mineralogical, Mineralogie, Mineralogy; Mining; Minute (minute).
min. minimum; minute(s).
Mitt. Mitteilung, ungen (communication, -s).
mitt. mittels (by means of).
mixt. mixture.
Mk. Mark, Marken (mark, marks).
mk. mikroskopisch (microscopic).
m.-kg. meter-kilogram.
mkr. mikroskopisch (microscopic).
ml. milliliter(s).
mm. millimeter(s).
m. m. f. magnetomagnetic force(s); magnetomotive force.
Mn manganese.
Mo molybdenum.
mol. molecule; molecular.
Mol.-%. Molprozent (molar per cent).
Mol.-Dispers. Molekulardispersion.
Mol.-Gew. Molekulargewicht (molecular weight).
Mol.-Refr., Mol.-Refrakt. Molekularrefraktion.
mol. wt. molecular weight.
Mon. Moniteur (monitor); Monographie (monograph).
Monatsh. Monatshefte ("monthly numbers"); specif., *Monatshefte für Chemie und verwandte Teile anderer Wissenschaften.*
Monit. Moniteur (monitor).

m. p. melting point.
m. p. h. miles per hour.
M. S. *Moniteur scientifique.*
ms- meso-.
Ms-Th mesothorium.
mv., m. v. millivolt(s).
N normal; Avogadro's number.
N- united to nitrogen.
n refractive index; Loschmidt's number; variable number (as in C_nH_{2n+2}).
n- normal.
n_a transport number of anion.
n_k transport number of cation.
N nitrogen.
N. nachmittags (afternoon, p. m.); nachts (at night); Nord, Norden (north).
N°. numéro (number).
n. normal; nördlich (northern); netto (net).
Na sodium.
Nachf. Nachfolger (successor, successors).
nasz. naszierend (nascent).
nat. naturel (natural).
Nb niobium (columbium).
Nd neodymium.
Nd. Niederschlag (precipitate).
Ndd. Niederschläge (precipitates).
Ne neon.
néerl. néerlandais (of the Netherlands, Dutch).
n. F. neue Folge (new series).
Ni nickel.
N. J. Neues Jahrbuch (new yearbook).
Nk. Normalkerze (standard candle).
nl. nicht löslich (not soluble).
No. Number, Nummer.
no. number.
norm. normal.
N. P. Norwegisches Patent (Norwegian patent).
Nr., Nro. Numero (number).
N. T. normal temperature.
Nt niton (radon).
Ntf. Naturforscher (scientific investigator).
n. t. p. normal temperature and pressure.
O- united to oxygen.
o- ortho-.
O oxygen.
O. Ost (east); ouest (west).
o. oder (or); oben (above); ohne (without).
o. drgl. oder dergleichen (or the like).
Oe. P. Oesterreichisches Patent (Austrian patent).
Oesterr. Oesterreichisch (Austrian).
O. F. oxidizing flame.
of. official.
Off. Official.
ol. (oleum) oil.
ol. res. oleoresin.
Ö. P. Oesterreichisches Patent (Austrian patent).
opt. optical.
opt.-akt. optisch aktiv (optically active).
org. organic.

Os osmium.
Öst. Österreichisch (Austrian).
Ö.U.P. Österreich-ungarisches patent (Austro-Hungarian patent).
oz. ounce, ounces.
o. Zers. ohne Zersetzung (without decomposition).
P, p pressure.
P- united to phosphorus.
p- para-.
P phosphorus.
P. Proceedings, specif., *Proceedings of the Chemical Society;* Patent.
p. point; page(s); parties (parts); pouvoir (power); pour (per).
p. 100 pour cent (per cent).
P.A. poids atomique (atomic weight).
Pa protoctinium.
P. AE. (partes aequales) equal parts.
PAe. Petroleumäther (petroleum ether).
par. paragraph.
Pat. Patent, Patent Office.
Path. Pathologie, Pathology.
pathol. pathological.
P.-B. Pays-Bas (Netherlands).
Pb lead.
p. c. c. pour copie conforme (true copy).
P. C. H. *Pharmazeutische Zentralhalle.*
P. Ch. S. *Proceedings of the Chemical Society.*
P. C. N. "physique, chimie, naturelle" (certificate given on completion of studies in physics, chemistry and natural history).
pctig. procentig (per cent).
Pd palladium.
p. d. potential difference.
P. E. parties égales (equal parts); point d'ébullition (boiling point).
p. ex. par exemple (for example, e. g.).
Pf. Pfund (pound).
Pfg. Pfennig (pfennig, 1/100 mark).
P. G. German Pharmacopeia.
Ph Phenyl.
Ph. Pharmacie, Pharmacy; Physique; Physikalisch.
ph. physical, physique; philosophical.
Phar. Pharmacopeia.
Pharm. Pharmacy, Pharmacie, Pharmazie; Pharmacopeia.
pharmacol. pharmacological.
Ph. Ch. *Zeitschrift für physikalische Chemie.*
Phil. Philosophical.
Ph. Mag. *Philosophical Magazine.*
Phot. Photographic.
Photog. Photography.
Ph. Rev. *Physical Review.*
phys. physical, physikalisch: Physics, Physik.
phys.-ch. physikalisch-chemisch (physico-chemical).
physik., physikal. physikalisch (physical).
physiol. physiological, physiologisch.
Ph.Z. *Physikalische Zeitschrift.*
Pkt. Punkt (point).
P. M. poids moléculaire (molecular weight).

p. m. afternoon.
Po polonium.
Pol. Polytechnisch.
powd. powdered.
pp. pages.
ppd. precipitated.
p. p. m. parts per million.
ppn. precipitation.
ppt. precipitate; (in pharmacy) prepared.
pptation. précipitation.
pptd. precipitated.
ppté. précipité (precipitate, precipitated).
pptg. precipitating.
pptn. precipitation.
Pr praseodymium; propyl.
Pr. Proceedings.
pr. praktisch (practical, applied); précédent (preceding).
prakt. praktisch (practical, applied).
préc. précédent (preceding).
prep. prepare.
prép. préparer (prepare), préparation.
prepd. prepared.
prepg. preparing.
prepn. preparation.
prim.- primär, primary.
Prior. Priorität (priority); specif., Unionspriorität.
pro anal. for analysis.
Proc. Proceedings.
Prod. Product, Produit, Produkt.
Prodd. Produkte (products).
proport. proportional, proportionnel.
propr. propriété (property).
p. rot. pouvoir rotatoire (rotatory power).
Proz. Prozent (per cent).
ps- pseudo-.
P. S., PS., Pst. Pferdestärke (horsepower, h. p.).
p. suiv. page suivante (following page).
Pt platinum.
pt. point; pint.
P. T. O. please turn over.
pulv. (pulvis) powder.
Q quantity; heat absorbed.
q quintal.
q. quadrat (square); quintal.
qcm. Quadratcentimeter (square centimeter).
qdm. Quadratdecimeter (square decimeter).
q. m. quintal métrique (metric quintal, 100 kg.).
qmm. Quadratmillimeter (square millimeter).
q.s. (quantum sufficit) a sufficient quantity.
qt. quart.
qual. qualitative.
quant. quantitative.
qui., quim. quimica (chemical).
q. v. (quod vide) which see.
R gas constant per mole of ideal gas; electrical resistance.
r radius.
r_g specific refractivity (Gladstone and Dale).

r_L specific refraction (Lorentz and Lorenz).
R radical.
R- ring, cyclic, cyclo-.
R. Reale, Royal; Recueil, specif., *Recueil des travaux chimiques des Pays-Bas;* Réaumur; Russe, Russian; Referat (abstract, review).
Ra radium.
Ra-Ac radioactinium.
rac., racem. racemic, racemisch.
Rad. Radioactivity, Radioaktivität; Radium.
Ra-Em radium emanation (radon).
R. A. L. *Rendiconti della Accademia dei Lincei.*
Ra-Th radiothorium.
Rb rubidium.
Re rhenium.
Rec. Recueil (compilation); Records.
recryst. recrystallize.
recrystd. recrystallized.
recrystn. recrystallization.
Red. Reduktion (reduction).
Rend. Rendiconto (report).
Rep. Report, Reports.
Repert. Repertorium (compendium).
Répert. Répertoire (compilation).
Res. Research.
resp. respectively; respektive (respectively, or rather, or).
Rev. Review, Revista, Revue; specif., *Revue générale de chimie pure et appliquée.*
rez. reziprok (reciprocal; reciprocally).
R. F. reducing flame.
Rh rhodium.
Riv. Rivista (Review).
Rk. Reaktion (reaction).
Rkk. Reaktionen (reactions).
R. M. réfraction moléculaire (molecular refraction).
RM., Rm. Rentenmark; Reichsmark.
r. m. s. square root of mean square.
Rn radon.
Roy. Royal.
R-P. Reichs-Patent (imperial patent).
r. p. m. revolutions per minute.
r. p. s. revolutions per second.
R. R. Railroad.
R^t. rendement (yield).
Ru ruthenium.
Russ. Russisch, Russian.
Ry. Railway.
S, S entropy; point de solidification (freezing point).
S- united to sulfur.
s time of outflow.
s- symmetric.
S sulfur.
S. Society; Seite (page); Säure (acid); Sankt (Saint, St.).
s. shilling(s); stere (cubic meter); siehe (see); symmetrisch (symmetric); son, sa (his, her, its); sauf (save, except).
Sa samarium.
s. a. siehe auch (see also).

LIST OF SYMBOLS 343

sapon. saponification.
sapond. saponified.
sapong. saponifying.
sat. saturate; saturated.
satd. saturated.
satg. saturating.
satn. saturation.
Sb antimony.
Sc scandium.
Sc. Science.
Sch. School.
schm. schmelzend (melting); schmilzt (melts).
Schmelzp., Schmp., Schmpt. Schmelzpunkt (melting point).
Schw. Schweizerisch (Swiss).
Schwed. P. Schwedisches Patent (Swedish patent).
Schweiz. Schweizerisch (Swiss).
schwerl. schwerlöslich (difficultly soluble).
Schwz. P. Schweizerisches Patent (Swiss patent).
Sci., Scien. Science, Scientific, Scientifique.
scr. scruple.
s. d. siehe dies (see this, which see, q. v.).
Sd. Siedepunkt (boiling point).
sd. siedend (boiling); siedet (boils).
Sdp. Siedepunkt (boiling point, b. p.).
Se selenium.
sec secant.
sec- secondary.
sec. second(s).
sek.- sekundär (secondary).
Sek. Sekunde (second).
sep. separate.
sepd. separated.
sepg. separating.
sepn. separation.
S. F. sans frais (without charges).
s. G. spezifisches Gewicht (specific gravity, sp. gr.).
s. g. sogenannt (so-called).
S. G. D. G. sans garantie du gouvernement (not guaranteed by the government).
s. hp. shaft horsepower.
Si- united to silicon.
Si silicon.
sied. siedend (boiling).
sin sine.
sinh hyperbolic sine.
Sitz., Sitz. Ber., Sitzber. Sitzungsberichte (Proceedings).
sl. slightly.
sll. sehr leicht löslich (very readily soluble).
S. M. Seine Majestät (His, or Her, Majesty).
Sm samarium.
Sm. Smithsonian Institution; Schmelzpunkt (melting point).
Sn tin.
s. o. siehe oben (see above).
Soc. Société, Society; *Journal of the Chemical Society* (of London).
sogen. sogenannt (so-called).

sol. soluble; solution.
sol. alcool. solution alcoolique (alcoholic solution).
sol. aq. solution aqueuse (aqueous solution).
soln. solution.
solns. solutions.
soly. solubility.
So. Z. Sodazahl (soda number or value).
S. P. Swiss Patent.
sp. specific.
spec. specific, specifisch.
spektr. spektroskopisch (spectroscopic, -ically).
spez. spezifisch (specific).
spez. Gew., sp. G. spezifisches Gewicht (specific gravity, sp. gr.).
sp. gr. specific gravity.
sp. ht. specific heat.
Spl. Supplement.
spt. spirit.
sq. square.
sq. cm. square centimeter(s).
sq. ft. square foot.
sq. m. square meter(s).
Sr strontium.
Sr. Senior; Seiner (His).
S. S. Schwefelwasserstoffsäure (hydrosulfuric acid, H₂S).
SS. Säuren (acids).
s. S. siehe Seite (see page).
St. Saint, Sankt; Stunde (hour).
stab. stabil (stable).
Std. Stunde, Stunden (hour, hours).
std. stündig (-hour, -hours).
Stde. Stunde (hour).
stdg. stündig (-hour, -hours).
Stdn. Stunden (hours).
s. u. siehe unten (see below).
Subst. Substanz (substance).
supers. supersaturated.
s. W. spezifische Wärme (specific heat).
swl. sehr wenig löslich (very slightly soluble).
s. w. u. siehe weiter unten (see below).
sym., sym- symmetric, symmetrisch, symétrique.
symm. symmetrisch (symmetric).
SZ., S. Z. Säurezahl (acid number).
s. Z. seiner Zeit (in his, or its, time, at that time).
T absolute temperature.
T_c critical temperature (on the absolute scale).
t time; temperature centigrade.
t_c critical temperature centigrade.
T temperature.
T. Teil (part).
t. ton, tons; tome (volume); transcrivez (copy, transcribe).
Ta tantalum.
tan tangent.
Tb terbium.
Te tellurium.
tech. technical, technisch.

techn. technisch (technical).
Temp. Temperatur (temperature).
temp. temperature.
temps. temperatures.
Text. Textile.
Tfl. Tafel (table).
Th thorium.
Th-Em thorium emanation, thoron.
Thl. Theil (part).
Thle. Theile (parts).
Thln. Theilen (parts).
Ti titanium.
Tids. Tidsskrift.
tinct. tincture.
Tl thallium.
Tl. Teil, Teile (part, parts).
Tle., Tln. Teile, Teilen (parts).
Tm thulium.
Tr. Transactions; Travaux (works, researches).
tr. tincture.
Trans. Transactions.
transf. transformation.
trav. travaux (works).
Tu thulium.
T. W. Teile(n) Wasser (parts of water).
U uranium; (ionic) mobility; internal energy.
U. University, Universität, Université; unit.
u. und (and).
u. a. unter anderen (among others).
u. a. a. O. und an anderen Orten (and elsewhere).
u. a. m. und andere mehr (and others); und anderes mehr (and so forth, and so on).
u. ä. m. und ähnliches mehr (and the like).
u. a. O. und andere Orte (and elsewhere); unter anderen Orten (among other places).
üb. über (over).
Überf. Überführung (conversion).
übert. an. übertragen an (assignor to).
Übf. Überführung (conversion).
u. d. f. unde die folgende (and those following).
u. dgl. und dergleichen (and the like).
u. dgl. m. und dergleichen mehr (and such like).
u. e. a. und einige andere (and some others).
u. Mk. unter dem Mikroskop (under the microscope).
Umwandl. Umwandlung (transformation, conversion).
unges. ungesättigt (unsaturated).
Univ. University, Universität, Université.
unk. unkorrigiert (uncorrected).
unl., unlösl. unlöslich (insoluble).
uns. unsymmetrisch (unsymmetric).
unt. unter (under, during, with).
Unters. Untersuchung (investigation, examination).
unv. unveröffentlicht (unpublished).
U. S. United States.
u. s. f. und so fort (and so on).

U. S. P. United States Pharmacopeia; United States Patent.
u. s. w., usw. und so weiter (and so forth, and so on, etc.).
Uwp. Umwandlungspunkt (transformation point, transition point).
U X uranium X.
U Y uranium Y.
u. Z., u. Zers. unter Zersetzung (with decomposition).
V volume; potential.
v volume.
v- vicinal, neighboring.
V vanadium.
V. Vorkommen (occurrence, presence); Verein (union, society); vormittags (in the forenoon, a. m.).
v. volume(s); volt(s); velocity; vicinal; (vide) see; von (of, from, etc.); vormals (formerly); votre (your).
va. volt-ampere(s).
Vak. Vakuum (vacuum).
var. variable; variant.
Vb. Verbindung (compound).
Vbb. Verbindungen (compounds).
v. Chr. vor Christo (before Christ, B. C.).
V. D. I. Zeitschrift des Vereines deutscher Ingenieure.
v. d. L. vor dem Lötrohr (before the blowpipe, B. B.).
Ver. Verein (union, society).
Verb. Verbindung (compound; combination).
verb. verbessert (improved, revised).
Verbb. Verbindungen (compounds).
verbr. verbraucht (consumed, used).
Verd. Verdünnung (dilution).
verd. verdünnt (diluted, dilute).
Verf. Verfahren (process); Verfasser (author).
Verfahr. Verfahren (process).
Vergl. Vergleich (comparison).
vergl. vergleiche (compare, cf.).
Verh. Verhalten (behavior); Verhältnis (proportion, ratio); = Verhandl., below.
Verhandl. Verhandlungen (transactions, proceedings).
verm. vermehrt (enlarged); vermindert (diminished, reduced).
Veröff. Veröffentlichungen (publications).
Vers. Versuch (experiment; test); Versammlung (convention, congress).
Verss. Versuche (experiments; tests).
Vf. Verfasser (author).
Vff. Verfasser (authors).
vgl. vergleiche (compare, see, cf.).
vgl. a. vergleiche auch (see also).
v. H. vom Hundert (per cent).
Vhdl. Verhandlungen (Transactions).
vic. vicinal.
viz. namely, to wit.
v. J. vorigen Jahres (of last year); vom Jahre (of the year).
V. M. voltmeter.

v. M. vorigen Monats (last month).
v. o. von oben (from above, from the top).
Vol. Volumen (volume).
vol. volume.
Vol. T. Volumenteil (part by volume).
vor. vorig (former, preceding).
Vork. Vorkommen (occurrence).
vorm. vormals (formerly).
Vorr. Vorrichtung (device, arrangement; preparation).
V. S. volumetric solution.
vs. versus, against.
V. St. Vereinigte Staaten (United States).
V. T. Volumenteil (part by volume).
v. u. von unten (from below, from beneath, from the bottom).
VZ. Verseifungszahl (saponification number).
W electrical resistance (Widerstand).
W tungsten, wolfram; work.
W. Wasser (water); *Annalen der Physik* (Wiedemann-Drude).
w. watt, watts; warm.
Wa. Rk. Wassermannsche Reaktion (Wassermann reaction).
wasserl. wasserlöslich (water-soluble).
wässr. wässerig (aqueous).
W. E., WE. Wärmeeinheit (heat unit).
Wet. Wetenschappen (Sciences).
w.-hr. watt-hour(s).
Wied. Ann. *Wiedemanns Annalen.*
Wirk. Wirkung (action; effect).
wiss. wissenschaftlich (scientific).
w. l. wave length.
wl. wenig löslich (slightly, or difficultly soluble).
wlösl. wasserlöslich (soluble in water).
w. o. weiter oben (above).
Woch. Wochenschrift (weekly).
Wochenschr. Wochenschrift (weekly).
w. p. c. watts per candle.
Wrkg. Wirkung (action; effect).
Ws. Wasser (water).
wss. wässerig (aqueous, hydrous).
wt. weight.
x unknown number or quantity.

X univalent negative radical (in formulas); xenon.
X^{bre} décembre (December).
Xe xenon.
Y yttrium.
Yb ytterbium.
yd. yard(s).
yr. year(s).
Yt yttrium.
Z atomic number.
Z. Zeitschrift, specif., *Zeitschrift für Chemie;* Zeile (line); Zeit (time); Zoll (inch).
z. zu (at, for, by); zum, zur (at the, for the).
Z. a. Ch. *Zeitschrift für anorganische Chemie.*
Z. Ang. *Zeitschrift für angewandte Chemie.*
Z. B. *Zeitschrift für Biologie.*
z. B. zum Beispiel (for example).
Z. Ch. *Zeitschrift für Chemie.*
Zeit. Zeitung (News); Zeitschrift.
Zeitsch., Zeitschr. Zeitschrift.
Z. El. Ch. *Zeitschrift für Elektrochemie.*
Zentr. Zentralblatt.
zerfl. zerfliesslich (deliquescent).
Zers. Zersetzung (decompcsition).
zers. zersetzend (decomposing); zersetzt (decomposes); zersetzbar (decomposable).
Z. Instr. *Zeitschrift für Instrumentenkunde.*
Z. Kr. *Zeitschrift für Krystallographie und Mineralogie.*
zl. ziemlich löslich (fairly soluble).
Zn zinc.
Zp Zersetzungspunkt (decomposition point).
Zr zirconium.
z. T. zum Teil (in part).
Ztg. Zeitung (News).
z. Th. zum Theil (in part).
Ztschr. Zeitschrift (journal, periodical).
Zus. Zusammensetzung (composition); Zusatz (addition).
zw. zwischen (between).
zwl. ziemlich wenig löslich (rather difficultly soluble).
Z. w. Phot. *Zeitschrift für wissenschaftliche Photographie.*
z. Z. zur Zeit (at present; acting).

APPENDIX 3

LIBRARIES

IIIIIIIIIIIIIIIIIIIIIIIIIIIIIIIIIIIIIIIIIIIIIIIIIIIIIII

AMERICAN LIBRARIES OF INTEREST TO CHEMISTS

There are several library directories that are useful on occasion.

1. *Special Library Resources*, 4 vols., New York, Special Libraries Association, 1941–1947.
2. *American Library Directory*, New York, Bowker Co., 20th ed., 1954.
3. *Directory of Special Libraries*, New York, Special Libraries Association, 1953.

The following list of Canadian and United States libraries was made on the basis of all available information, with a view of selecting those most likely to be of value to chemists. The information presented about these libraries was compiled from a variety of sources. The following abbreviations are used to give part of the information.

A. Depository for research reports from U. S. Atomic Energy Commission.

H. Sets of chemical journals are above average in completeness.

J. Unusually complete sets of chemical journals.

I. Maintained by a manufacturer and arrangements must be made to consult it.

M. Microfilm copying done from material in its collection.

P. Photoprints from material in its collections.

T. Translating service provided.

U. United States patent files are complete.

For detailed information on the microfilming services of large libraries in the United States, see Muller's paper in *College and Research Libraries* **16**, 261–266 (1955).

UNITED STATES

Alabama

Birmingham

Birmingham Public Library.
Southern Research Institute Library.

California

Berkeley

University of California. A. J. M. P. A very large chemical collection.

Emeryville

Shell Development Co. Library. I. Petroleum and chemicals made from petroleum.

Los Angeles

Los Angeles Public Library. Chemistry is a specialty.

University of California at Los Angeles. A. H. M. P. A large chemical collection.

Pasadena

California Institute of Technology. H. M. P. Chemical technology.

Stanford

Leland Stanford University. J. P. A large chemical collection.

Colorado

Denver

Denver Public Library. A. P. U. This library is affiliated with the Denver Bibliographic Center for Research, which is maintained by a number of libraries in the Rocky Mountain region. The Center is housed in the Denver Public Library and has a union catalog of the holdings of 60 libraries in the region.

Great Western Sugar Co. Sugar chemistry and beet sugar technology.

Connecticut

New Haven

Yale University. A. J. P. M. A very large chemical collection.

Delaware

Wilmington

E. I. du Pont de Nemours & Co. maintains three large scientific and technical libraries and several small specialized ones; all of these are devoted, for the most part, to chemistry and chemical technology.

Scientists can make arrangements to use them. Address inquiries to the Technical Library in the Dupont Building.

District of Columbia (Washington)

U. S. Department of Agriculture. J. M. P. This library has a very large collection of chemical books and periodicals. In 1942 all of the libraries in the various bureaus of the department were consolidated in the main library. This is the largest agricultural library in the world and one of the most important research libraries in the United States.

U. S. Department of Commerce Library. This is of interest mostly for its collection of statistical material on chemicals, chemical industries, and manufacturers, for foreign and domestic commerce reports, and for similar matters.

The Bureau of Standards has a separate library which contains many books and periodicals on chemistry and chemical technology.

The Office of Technical Services also has a separate library that specializes in scientific reports that originate in research carried out under contract with government agencies.

The Patent Office has a separate library that has been described in the chapter on Patents.

U. S. Department of Defense. The various agencies have separate libraries. The Army Medical Library is one of the largest medical libraries, perhaps the largest in the world, and is of interest to chemists for biochemistry, pharmacology, and other fields related to medicine. The National War College Library contains a number of publications of interest to chemists. The Office of Chief of Ordnance has a technical library. The Quartermasters Corp has a library in Philadelphia.

U. S. Department of Interior. The various bureaus have separate libraries. The Geological Survey Library has an excellent collection on inorganic chemistry, geochemistry, mineralogy, etc. The Bureau of Mines Library has a good collection which covers the entire mineral industry including metallurgy and petroleum; a large branch is maintained in Pittsburgh.

Library of Congress. A. J. P. This is an important library for scientists. Although it does not specialize in sciences, it contains a very large amount of scientific material. A science division was established in 1950.

National Research Council Library. This is a scientific library of medium size that contains helpful bibliographic material.

Smithsonian Institution Library. This is a large library that contains a considerable number of chemical publications; there is a special collection on geochemistry.

Tariff Commission Library. This includes a good collection of books on chemistry, chemical technology, manufacturers, and trade journals.

Georgia

Atlanta

Georgia Institute of Technology. A. P. U. Chemical engineering, ceramics, and textiles are specialties.

Illinois

Chicago

Abbot Laboratories, North Chicago. P. I. Biochemistry and pharmaceuticals.

American Medical Association Library.

John Crerar Library. A. J. M. P. U. (Translations and literature searches for a fee.) One of the best scientific libraries in the United States. It has a very large chemical and chemical technology collection and receives a very large number of current periodicals.

Illinois Institute of Technology. M. P. T. Branches are maintained at the Armour Research Institute and at the Institute of Gas Technology.

Portland Cement Association Library. P. I.

University of Chicago. A. J. M. P. A very large chemical collection.

Evanston

Northwestern University Technical Institute. H. M. P.

Lemont

Argonne National Laboratory. Chemistry and chemical engineering in relation to nuclear energy.

Maywood

American Can Co. Library. I. Chemistry and technology of canning and preserving foods. Cans and containers.

Urbana

University of Illinois. A. J. M. P. A very large chemical collection.

Indiana

Bloomington

University of Indiana. H. M. P.

Gary

Gary Public Library. Metallurgy and steel production.

Indianapolis

Eli Lilly and Co. I. M. Biochemistry, pharmacology, and pharmaceuticals.

Lafayette

   Purdue University. H. T.

Iowa

Ames

   Iowa State College. A. J. M. P. T.   A large chemical collection.

Iowa City

   University of Iowa. J. M. P.   A large chemical collection.

Kansas

Lawrence

   University of Kansas. H. M. P.

Kentucky

Louisville

   Devoe Reynolds Co. I.   Paints, pigments, oils.

Louisiana

Baton Rouge

   Louisiana State University. A. H.   Cane sugar technology and petroleum.

Maryland

Baltimore

   Johns Hopkins University. J. P.   A large chemical collection.

Bethesda

   National Institutes of Health.

Massachusetts

Boston

   American Academy of Arts and Sciences.

   Boston Medical Library. P. T.

   Boston Public Library. M. P. U.

Cambridge

   Arthur D. Little, Inc.   An industrial consulting laboratory that has a good technical library (translations, bibliographies, and literature searches for a fee).

   Harvard University. A. J. M. P.   A very large chemical collection.

Lever Brothers. I. Soap, edible oils, cosmetics, and detergents.

Massachusetts Institute of Technology. A. J. M. P. T. A very large collection on chemistry and chemical technology.

Lowell

Lowell Textile Institute. Dyes, textiles, leather, and paper.

Michigan

Ann Arbor

University of Michigan. A. J. M. P. A very large chemical collection.

Detroit

Detroit Public Library. A. H. P. U. A large technology division.

Parke, Davis & Co. I. Biochemistry and pharmaceuticals.

Wayne University. The Kresge-Hooker Scientific Library. M. P. T. This library has a very large chemical collection and receives a great many current periodicals.

Midland

Dow Chemical Company. I. M. P. A large chemical library with emphasis on technology.

Minnesota

Minneapolis

University of Minnesota. A. J. P. Large collection on chemistry and metallurgy.

Minneapolis Public Library. M. P. U.

Missouri

Kansas City

Linda Hall Library. A. M. P. U. An important library for science and technology. It receives a very large number of current periodicals of interest to chemists.

St. Louis

Mallinckrodt Chemical Works. I.

Monsanto Chemical Co. I.

Washington University. A. H. P.

Nebraska

Lincoln

University of Nebraska. H. M. P.

New Jersey

Hoboken

General Food Co. Central Research Laboratory. I. Food technology and chemistry.

New Brunswick

Rutgers University. H. P. There are special collections on ceramics and the chemical aspects of microbiology.

Phillipsburg

J. T. Baker Chemical Co. I. Inorganic chemistry and technology.

Princeton

Princeton University. A. J. M. A large collection on chemistry.

New York

Albany

New York State Library. H. M. P. U. Large collection of periodicals.

Buffalo

Grosvenor Library. U.

National Aniline Division of Allied Chemical and Dye Corporation. I. Organic chemistry and dyes.

Corning

Corning Glass Works. I. A large collection on the chemistry and technology of glass.

Ithaca

Cornell University. A. J. M. A large chemical collection.

New York

Chemists' Club Library. M. P. (Translations, bibliographies, and literature searches for a fee.) This is one of the largest chemical research libraries in the United States; journals on chemistry and related subjects make up about 75% of the collection. Many of the rare and hard-to-get journals received by *Chemical Abstracts* are eventually sent here.

Columbia University. A. J. M. P. A very large collection on chemistry and chemical technology.

Engineering Societies Library. M. P. T.

New York Academy of Medicine. M. P. T. A very large library.

New York Public Library. A. J. M. P. U. This is one of the most important libraries in the United States for chemists. It has a very large collection on chemistry and chemical technology. It receives a very large number of periodicals on chemistry and technology. Its patent collection is excelled only by that of the U. S. Patent Office Library.

Rochester

Eastman Kodak Co. Research Library. I. M. P. A large organic chemical collection and the largest collection on photography in the United States.

University of Rochester. H. P.

Syracuse

Solvay Process Division of Allied Chemical and Dye Corp. I. Chemistry and technology of alkalies.

Upton

Brookhaven National Laboratory. Chemistry in relation to nuclear energy.

North Carolina

Durham

Duke University. A. J. M. P. A large chemical collection.

Ohio

Akron

University of Akron. The Bierce Library has a very large collection on rubber and rubber technology, plastics, and resins. This library also has union lists of periodicals and books on these subjects for libraries in the Akron area and works in cooperation with the libraries of the rubber companies in that area (Firestone, Goodrich, Goodyear, General, and United States).

Cincinnati

University of Cincinnati. H. P.

Cleveland

Cleveland Public Library. A. H. M. P. T. U.

Columbus

Ohio State University. A. J. P. U. A large chemical collection and a very large number of journal sets.

Dayton

Monsanto Chemical Company Central Research Laboratory. I.

Oklahoma

Tulsa

Tulsa Public Library. M. P. T. Petroleum.

Pennsylvania

Marcus Hook

Sun Oil Company, Research and Development Department. I. Petroleum.

New Kensington

Aluminum Co. of America. I. Chemistry and metallurgy of aluminum, magnesium and light metals.

Philadelphia

Franklin Institute. P. U.

Philadelphia Textile Institute.

University of Pennsylvania. A. J. M. A large chemical collection. The Smith-Browne collection of rare chemical books is in this library.

Pittsburgh

Carnegie Library of Pittsburgh. A. H. P. T. U. Metallurgy, trade literature, and house organs are specialties.

Koppers Co. Inc. I. Coal tar products, synthetic resins, coke, gas.

Mellon Institute. P. Chemical technology.

U. S. Bureau of Mines. Metallurgy and mining.

State College

Pennsylvania State College. H. P. T. In addition to a good chemical collection, there is an extensive one on mineral industries which includes petroleum, metallurgy, natural gas, and geochemistry.

Rhode Island

Providence

Brown University.

Tennessee

Kingsport

Tennessee Eastman Corporation. I. Organic chemistry and polymers.

Nashville

Joint University Libraries. A. H. M. (Peabody College, Scarritt College, Vanderbilt University.)

Oak Ridge

Oak Ridge National Laboratory.

Oak Ridge Institute of Nuclear Studies.

Texas

Austin

University of Texas. A. J. M. P. A large chemical collection.

Baytown

Humble Oil Company. Petroleum.

Houston

Houston Public Library. Petroleum.

Rice Institute.

Virginia

Charlottesville

Institute of Textile Technology.

University of Virginia. H. M. P.

Washington

Seattle

University of Washington. A. H. M. P. A good collection in chemistry. A special collection on wood and pulp. The Pacific Northwest Bibliographic Center is here.

Wisconsin

Appleton

The Institute of Paper Chemistry.

Madison

The University of Wisconsin. A. J. M. P. A large chemical collection.

CANADA

Alberta

Edmonton

University of Alberta.

British Columbia

Vancouver

University of British Columbia.

Ontario

Kingston

Aluminum Laboratories Ltd.

Queens University.

356   LIBRARIES

Ottowa

Mines Branch, Dept. of Mines and Technical Surveys. Chemical technology, mineral industries, metallurgy, and ceramics are specialties.

National Research Council Library.

Toronto

University of Toronto. H. M. P.

Quebec

Montreal

McGill University. J. P. T.

OTHER LIBRARIES

The following reference works have international coverage and give considerable information about libraries in the various countries. If information about scientific and chemical libraries is not given for a country, it is usually possible to obtain this from a university library in that country.

Index Generalis, Paris, Masson. An annual publication.

World of Learning, London, Europa Pub. An annual publication. This British publication has somewhat different coverage than does *Index Generalis*.

UNESCO Guide to National Bibliographical Information Centers. The preliminary edition was published in the *UNESCO Bulletin for Libraries*, Vol. VII, no. 11–12 (Nov.–Dec. 1953, a special number of 68 pages). It is also available in French as no. 3 in the *UNESCO Bibliographical Handbook Series*, January 1954 (*Guide des Centres Nationaux d'Information Bibliographie*) from the Columbia Univ. Press, New York. This *Guide* gives at least one library for each country that provides scientific information from its own collections.

A BIBLIOGRAPHY OF
LISTS OF PERIODICALS

Only the most generally useful lists are given here. It is very difficult to keep these up to date, and many existing ones are too old to be of much value. Suggestions are given for methods of obtaining others.

In the United States one is frequently interested in the scientific periodicals that are available in a given library, city, or region of the United States. Some libraries publish lists of their holdings of periodicals and may be able to provide copies. A number of union lists of periodicals have been compiled that cover a city or a region; it is best to inquire about these from one of the largest libraries in the area. See Appendix 3 for directories that give the names and addresses of libraries.

Often one is interested in where scientific periodicals published in a given country are available. The Science Division of the Library of Congress, Washington, D. C., is the best source of such information in the United States. Raymund L. Zwemer, formerly of the Science Division of the Library of Congress, has stated that this Library collects journal lists from various countries and thus hopes to increase the Library's service to scientists (*Library of Congress Information Bulletin* **11**, 10–11, June 16, 1952).

The lists below are most frequently useful.

American Chemical Society, *List of Periodicals Abstracted by Chemical Abstracts*. Washington, D. C. American Chemical Society. This is issued at five-year intervals. The current list, 1956, has over 14,000 entries which cover current periodicals, discontinued ones, and changes in titles. See Appendix 6 for a fuller description.

Biological Sciences Serial Publications, a World List, 1950–1954. Philadelphia, Biological Abstracts, 1955, 277 pp.

Bolton, Henry C., *A Catalogue of Scientific and Technical Periodicals, 1665–1895, together with Chronological Tables and a Library Check-List.* Washington, D. C., Smithsonian Institution. 2nd ed., 1897, 1247 pp. This is valuable for old periodicals.

British Museum, *Catalog of Printed Books, Periodical Publications*. London,

The British Museum, 1899–1900. This covers all holdings of the Museum up to 1900. Useful for old periodicals.

British Union Catalogue of Periodicals, 4 vols., London, Butterworth, 1955– (in progress). Includes the periodicals of the world from the 17th century to the present day. Gives changes in names of journals.

Cobb, Ruth, *Periodical Bibliographies and Abstracts for Scientific and Technical Journals of the World*. Bulletin of the National Research Council (U. S.), **1**, Pt. 3, no. 3 (1920). Useful for old periodicals.

International Catalogue of Scientific Literature. List of journals, with name abbreviations, used in the catalogue as references. 1903, 312 pp.; supplement, 1904, 68 pp., London, The Royal Society.

New Serial Titles, 1953–   . This is a monthly journal issued by the Library of Congress, Washington, D. C., that covers periodicals that began publication after January 1, 1950, that are received by the Library of Congress and cooperating libraries. It serves as a continuing supplement to the *Union List of Serials in Libraries of United States and Canada* (see below).

Periodica Chimica. Edited by M. Pfluecke and A. Hawelek. Berlin, Akademie-Verlag. 2nd ed., 1952. This is the list of periodicals abstracted by *Chemisches Zentralblatt*.

Royal Society of London. *Catalogue of the periodical publications in the library of the Royal Society of London*. 1912, 455 pp. Useful for old periodicals.

Scientific and Technical Serial Publications, Soviet Union, 1945–1953. Washington, D. C. Science Division of the Library of Congress. This is a classified list of about 1,700 current titles issued by the Library in 1954; it gives publisher, place of publication, date of first issue, and a description of contents for each title.

Scientific and Technical Serial Publications, United States, 1950–1953. Washington, D. C., Science Division of the Library of Congress. This is a classified list of about 3,600 current titles. The same information is given for each title as in the Soviet list (see above).

Scudder, Samuel H. *Catalogue of Scientific Serials of All Countries, Including the Transactions of Learned Societies in the Natural, Physical and Mathematical Sciences, 1633–1876*, Cambridge, Mass., Harvard Univ. Press, 1879, 358 pp. (Library of Harvard Univ., Special Publication no. 1.) A very good source for old publications.

Ulrich's Periodical Directory, New York, R. R. Bowker & Co. 7th ed. edited by Eileen Graves, 1954. This is a classified directory.

Union List of Serials in Libraries of United States and Canada, 2nd ed., 1943; first supplement to 2nd ed., 1945; second supplement to 2nd ed., 1954. New York, Wilson Co. This covers library holdings through December 31, 1949. See *New Serial Titles*, above, for later information. This *Union List* is an indispensable reference work for libraries in the United States and Canada.

Union List of Technical Periodicals, 3rd ed., 1947, New York. Special Libraries Association. This covers a number of libraries maintained by industries or manufacturers of chemicals that are not covered by the *Union List of Serials* (above).

U. S. Department of Agriculture Library. List of serials currently received in the Library of the U. S. Department of Agriculture. Compiled by Katharine Jacobs. Washington, D. C., U. S. Government Printing Office, 1950, 349 pp.

World List of Scientific Periodicals, 3rd ed., 1100 pp. London, Butterworth Scientific Publications, 1952. (New York, Academic Press.) This gives full title, abbreviation of title, place of publication, date of first volume, and library location data in Great Britain for over 50,000 periodicals published in the years 1900–1950. Corrections and additions have been published in *Chemistry and Industry,* **1953,** 1013–1014; **1954,** 596–597; **1955,** 54–57.

For other lists of periodicals, see M. H. Gummer's paper on "Catalogues and Bibliographies of Periodicals" in the *Journal of Documentation* **12,** 24–38 (1956).

SCIENTIFIC AND TECHNICAL ORGANIZATIONS

Many academies, associations, institutes, societies, etc., publish journals, leaflets, and numerous bulletins of more or less interest to chemists. The trade associations collect various kinds of information which may be available to nonmembers under certain conditions. Occasionally one needs information about one of these organizations and its work, or its publications.

Some of these organizations are international. The most comprehensive source of information about these is: *UNESCO Directory of International Scientific Organizations*, 2nd ed., 1952, New York, Columbia Univ. Press.

Information about the most important scientific and technical organizations in each country is given in three reference works of international coverage; one is published in France, the other two in England. These usually give only the names of the periodicals that the organizations publish or sponsor.

1. *Index Generalis*, Paris, Masson (annual).
2. *The World of Learning*, London, Europa Pub. (annual).
3. Buttress, F. A., *World List of Abbreviations of Scientific, Technological, and Commercial Organizations*, London, Leonard Hill, 1955, 261 pp. This is limited to the name of the organization, its abbreviation, and the address.

Other sources are available. If supplementary information is needed, it is often best to write directly to the organization for it. A scientific organization may also be able to provide information about other organizations in the same country. There are guides, directories, or handbooks of scientific and technical organizations for a number of countries, but all of them are not up to date or available in all libraries. Libraries in the United States and in other countries that have large scientific collections usually own all of these specialized directories and may also have files of unpublished information from which they can answer questions about scientific organizations. See Appendix 3 for information about libraries.

Special sources are given only for the United States. A number for other countries are given in the *Guide to Reference Books* by Constance Winchell and its supplements (7th ed., Chicago, American Library Association, 1950–).

The most recent and generally useful sources are:

Bates, R. S., *Scientific Societies in the United States,* New York, Wiley, 1945, 246 pp.

Chemical Industry Facts Book, Washington, D. C., The Manufacturing Chemists Association, 1955. Chemical trade, scientific, and technical organizations are listed.

National Research Council, *Scientific and Technical Societies of the United States and Canada,* 6th ed., compiled by J. R. Kohr, Washington, D. C., National Research Council, 1955, 447 pp.

National Research Council, *Industrial Research Laboratories of the United States,* 10th ed., compiled by J. F. Mauk, Washington, D. C., National Research Council, 1956, 560 pp.

U. S. Department of Commerce, Office of Domestic Commerce, *National Associations of the United States,* compiled by Jay Judkins, Washington, D. C., U. S. Government Printing Office, 1949, 634 pp. This publication covers trade associations as well as scientific and technical organizations.

The name of a periodical often indicates which organization sponsors it. The *List of Periodicals Abstracted by Chemical Abstracts* provides the names and addresses of the publishers who can give information about the organizations if the publisher and the sponsoring organization are not identical.

APPENDIX 6

PERIODICALS OF CHEMICAL INTEREST

For other lists of periodicals see Appendix 4.

The most generally useful and probably the most complete list of periodicals of chemical interest is that published by the American Chemical Society, *List of Periodicals Abstracted by Chemical Abstracts*. This list is brought up to date every five years. The latest one appeared in 1956 and gives the following information. For each current periodical (about 7,000), the list gives the name and its official abbreviation, frequency of issue, volume number, name and address of publisher, and information as to which of almost 300 libraries in the United States and Canada receive it. For each periodical that has been discontinued since 1907, the list gives the name and its abbreviation, and the date on which it ceased publication. It also gives the changes in the names of periodicals that have occurred since 1907. This *List* appeared along with the December 10, 1956, number of *Chemical Abstracts;* reprints of the *List* (over 300 pages) can be obtained from the American Chemical Society, Special Publications Department, 1155 16th St. N. W., Washington 6, D. C.

A list of 93 chemical journals that were discontinued between 1800 and 1900, for the most part, is given in "Searching the Older Chemical Literature," a paper by G. M. Dyson which appeared in *Searching the Chemical Literature*, no. 4 in *Advances in Chemistry Series*, Washington, D. C., The American Chemical Society (1951). This list is also given as an appendix in Dyson's book, *A Short Guide to Chemical Literature*, New York, Longmans, Green, 1951. For each journal, this Dyson list gives the name of the editor, the place, and dates of publication. There are a few periodicals in this list that do not appear in the following one.

LIST OF PERIODICALS DISCONTINUED BEFORE 1910

These are periodicals of chemical interest that were discontinued before 1910. This list was compiled from various sources, the List of Technical Journals in Bolton's *Bibliography of Chemistry* being the main source of information. The names are arranged alphabetically as they appear on the cover, and the boldface type shows the common abbreviations. There may be omissions; only the more strictly chemical journals are listed.

A **plus sign** (+) following a date means that the journal, now discontinued, appeared later than the date given. The exact date of discontinuance could not be ascertained in some instances.

Actualités chimiques, Les. *Paris.* 1896.

Afhandlingar **i Fysik, Kemi** och **Mineralogi.** *Stockholm.* 1806–1818.

Agenda du **chim**iste. *Paris.* 1877–1892.

Alcool et le sucre. *Paris.* 1892+.

Allgemeine Chemiker-**Zeitung.** *Cöthen.* 1877–1878. Continued as **Chemiker-Zeitung.**

Allgemeine chemische **Bibliothek des neunzehn**ten **Jahrhunderts.** *Erfurt.* 1801–1805.

Allgemeines Journal *der* **Chem**ie. *Leipzig.* 1798–1803. Continued as **Neues allg**emeines Journal der **Chem**ie.

Allgemeine **Zeit**ung für die **gesamte Spir**itus-**Ind**ustrie. *Berlin.* 1890–1891.

Almanacco di **chim**ica **agri**cola. *Milan.* 1873–1878.

Almanach de la **chim**ie. *Rouen* and *Paris.* 1854–1861.

American Analyst. *New York.* 1885–1892+.

American Chemical Journal. *Baltimore.* 1879–1913. Combined with **J**ournal of the **American Chemical Society** in 1914.

American Chemical Review and **J**ournal for the **Spirit, Vinegar** and **Sugar Industry.** *Chicago.* 1882–1891+. Continuation of **Chemical Review** and **J**ournal for the **Spirit, Vinegar** and **Sugar Industry.**

American Chemist, The. *New York.* 1870–1877.

American Druggists' Circular and **Chemical Gazette.** *New York.* 1857–1865. Continued as **Druggists' Circular** and **Chemical Gazette.**

Americanische Annalen der Arzneikunde, Chemie und **Physik.** *Bremen.* 1802–1803.

American Laboratory, The. *Boston.* 1875.

Analysts' Annual **Note-Book,** The. *London.* 1875+.

Annalen der **Chem**ie und **Pharm**acie. *Heidelberg.* 1840–1873. Continuation of **Ann**alen der **Pharm**acie. Continued as **Ann**alen der **Chem**ie und **Pharm**acie, **Justus Liebigs.**

Annalen der **Chem**ie und **Pharm**acie, **Justus Liebigs.** *Leipzig* and *Heidelberg.* 1873–1874. Continuation of **Ann**alen der **Chem**ie und **Pharm**acie. Continued as **Ann**alen der **Chem**ie, **Justus Liebigs.**

Annalen der **chem**ischen **Literatur.** *Berlin.* 1802. Continuation of **Bibliothek** der **neuesten physisch-chem**ischen, met-

allurgischen, **techn**ologischen und **pharm**aceutischen **Literatur.**

Annalen der **Pharm**acie. *Lemgo* and *Heidelberg.* 1832–1839. Continued as **Ann**alen der **Chem**ie und **Pharm**acie.

Annalen der **Physik (Halle).** *Halle.* 1799–1818. Continuation of **Neues** Journal der **Physik.** Continued as **Ann**alen der **Physik** und der **physik**alischen **Chem**ie.

Annalen der **Physik** und **Chem**ie. *Berlin.* 1824–1877. *Leipzig.* 1877–1899. Continuation of **Ann**alen der **Physik** und der **physik**alischen **Chem**ie. Continued as **Ann**alen der **Physik.**

Annalen der **Physik** und der **physik**alischen **Chem**ie. *Halle.* 1819–1824. Continuation of **Ann**alen der **Physik.** Continued as **Ann**alen der **Physik** und **Chem**ie.

Annales de **chim**ie et de **phys**ique. *Paris.* 1817–1914. Separated into two journals, **Ann**ales de **chim**ie and **Ann**ales de **phys**ique.

Annales de la **soc**iété des **brasseurs** pour l'enseignement professionel. Combined with **Bul**letin de l'**association** des **anciens élèves** de l'**inst**itut supérieur des **ferm**entations de **Gand.**

Annali di **chim**ica **appl**icata alla **med**icina, cioè, alla **farm**acia, alla **toss**icologia, all'**ig**iene, alla **fis**iologia, alla **pat**ologia ed alla **terap**eutica. *Milan.* 1845–1884+. Continuation of **Bibl**ioteca di **farm**acia, **chim**ica, **fis**ica, **med**icina, **chir**urgia, **terap**eutica, **stor**ia naturale. Combined with **Riv**ista di **chim**ica **med**ica e **farm**aceutica and continued as **Ann**ali di **chim**ica **med**ico-**farm**aceutica e di **farm**acologia.

Annali di **chim**ica e di **farm**acologia. *Milan.* 1886–1890. Continuation of **Ann**ali di **chim**ica **med**ico-**farm**aceutica e di **farm**acologia.

Annali di **chim**ica e **stor**ia **nat**urale. *Pavia.* 1790–1802.

Annali di **chim**ica **med**ico-**farm**aceutica e di **farm**acologia. *Milan.* 1885. A combination of **Ann**ali di **chim**ica **appl**icata alla **med**icina, cioè, alla **farm**acia, alla **toss**icologia, all'**ig**iene, alla **fis**iologia, alla **pat**ologia ed alla **terap**eutica and **Riv**ista di **chim**ica **med**ica e **farm**aceutica, **toss**icologia, **farm**acologia e terapia. Continued as **Ann**ali di **chimica** e di **farmacologia.**

Annali di **fisica, chim**ica e **matematiche.** *Milan.* 1841-1847. Continued as **Ann**ali di **fisica, chim**ica e **sci**enze **affini.**

Annali di **fisica, chim**ica e **sci**enze **affini.** *Turin.* 1850. Continuation of **Ann**ali di **fisica, chim**ica e **matematiche.**

Annali di **fisica,** dell'Abbate F. C. Zantedeschi. *Padua.* 1849-1850. Continuation of **Raccolta fisico-chimica italiana.**

Annals of **Chem**ical **Med**icine. *London.* 1879-1881.

Annals of **Chem**ical **Philosophy,** etc., The. *London.* 1828-1829.

Annals of **Chem**istry, etc. (Translated from the French.) *London.* 1791.

Annals of **Chym**istry and **Pract**ical **Pharm**acy. *London.* 1843.

Annals of **Med**icine. Discontinued under this name but continued in new journal, **Ann**als of **Clin**ical **Med**icine.

Annales of **Pharm**acy and **Pract**ical **Chem**istry. *London.* 1852-1854.

Annals of **Philosophy** (or Magazine of **Chem**istry, Mineralogy, Mechanics, Natural History, Agriculture and the Arts). *London.* 1813-1820. New series, *London.* 1821-1826. United in 1827 with **Philo**sophical **Mag**azine and Journal.

Annuaire à l'usage du **chim**iste, du **méde**cin, du **pharm**acien. *Brussels.* 1843.

Annuaire de **chim**ie. *Paris.* 1845-1851.

Annuaire de la **chim**ie industrielle et de l'électrochimie. *Paris.* 1888-1890+.

Annuaire des **eaux minéral**es de **France.** *Paris.* 1830-1832.

Annuaire des **fabric**ants de **sucre,** distillateurs et **liquor**istes. *Douaé.* 1862.

Annuaire des **produits chim**iques, de la **drog**uerie et de l'**épicerie** en **gros.** *Paris.* 1874-1878.

Annuaire des **sciences chim**iques, ou Rapport sur les progrès des sciences naturelles, présenté à l'académie, Stockholm. *Paris.* 1837.

Annuario **almanacco** dei **chim**ici, **farm**acisti e **med**ici italiani. *Milan.* 1874-1879.

Annuario **chim**ico italiano dell'anno 1845. *Modena.* 1846.

Annuario del **lab**oratorio di **chimica gen**erale e **tech**nologica della r. accademia navale di **Livorno.** *Milan.* 1890-1891.

Annuario delle **sci**enze **chim**iche e **nat**urali. *Verona.* 1840.

Annuario delle **sci**enze **chim**iche, **farm**aceutiche e **medico-legali.** *Mantua.* 1841-1849. Continuation of **Ann**uario delle **sci**enze **chim**iche, **farm**aceutiche e **medico-legali** ad uso dei **farm**acisti e **med**ici.

Annuario delle **sci**enze **chim**iche, **farm**aceutiche e **medico-legali** ad uso dei **farm**acisti e **med**ici. *Mantua.* 1840. Continued as **Ann**uario delle **sci**enze **chim**iche, **farm**aceutiche e **medico-legali.**

Annuario di **chim**ica. *Turin.* 1885-1894.

Anuarul Laboratorului de **chim**ie **organica** pe anul bugetar 1888-1889. *Bucharest.* 1889.

Anzeiger für die **chem**ische **Ind**ustrie. *Charlottenburg.* 1893-1894.

Appendice alla **gazz**etta **chimica ital**iana. *Rome.* 1883-1887.

Archiv der **Agriculturchem**ie für denkende **Land**wirthe. *Berlin.* 1803-1818.

Archiv des **Apoth**eker-**Ver**eines im **nörd**lichen **Teutsch**land. 1822. Continued as **Ann**alen der **Pharm**acie.

Archiv für die **theoretische Chem**ie. *Jena* and *Berlin.* 1800-1802.

Archiv für die **thier**ische **Chem**ie. *Halle.* 1800-1801.

Archiv für **physio**logische und **patholog**ische **Chem**ie und **Mikroskop**ie in ihrer **Anwend**ung auf die **prakt**ische **Med**icin. *Vienna* and *Berlin.* 1844-1847. Continuation of **Beiträge** zur **physiologisch**en und **patholog**ischen **Chem**ie und **Mikroskop**ie in ihrer **Anwend**ung auf die **prakt**ische **Med**icin. Continued as **Arch**iv für **physio**logische und **patholog**ische **Chem**ie und **Mikroskop**ie mit besonderer Rücksicht auf die **med**icinische **Diagnostik** und **Therap**ie.

Archiv für **physio**logische und **patholog**ische **Chem**ie und **Mikroskop**ie mit besonderer Rücksicht auf die **medicin**ische **Diagnostik** und **Therap**ie. *Vienna.* 1852-1854. Continuation of **Arch**iv für **physio**logische und **patholog**ische **Chem**ie und **Mikroskop**ie in ihrer **Anwend**ung auf die **prakt**ische **Med**icin.

Archiv für **Wärmewirtschaft.** Name changed in 1926 to **Arch**iv für **Wärmewirtschaft** und Dampfkesselwesen.

Ärsberättelse om **Framstegen** i **Kemi** och **Mineral**ogi. *Stockholm.* 1841-1848. Continuation of **Arsberättelse** om **Framstegen** i **Physik** och **Kemi.** Continued as **Arsberättelse** om **Framstegen** i **Kemi** till **Kongl.** **Vetenskaps-Akad**emien.

Arsberättelse om **Framstegen** i **Kemi** till **Kongl.** **Vetenskaps-Akad**emien. *Stockholm.* 1849-1851. Continuation of **Arsberättelse** om **Framstegen** i **Kemi** och **Mineral**ogi.

Arsberättelse om **Framstegen** i **Physik** och **Kemi.** *Stockholm.* 1822-1841. Continued as **Arsberättelse** om **Framstegen** i **Kemi** och **Mineral**ogi.

Atti dell'**accad**emia **pont**ifica de **Nuovi Lincei.** *Rome.* 1847–1873. Continued as **Atti** della reale **accad**emia dei **Lincei.**

Atti ufficiali della **società** italiana dei **chim**ici **ana**lisi. *Pavia.* 1893.

Auswahl aller **eigenthüml**ichen **Abhandl**ungen und **Beobacht**ungen in der **Chem**ie, mit einigen Verbesserungen und Zusätzen. *Leipzig.* 1786–1787.

Auswahl vorzüglicher **Abhandl**ungen aus den sämmtlichen Bänden der französischen **Ann**alen der **Chem**ie zur vollständigen Benutzen derselben durch Ergänzung der von ihrem Anfange an den chemischen Annalen einverleibten Aufsätzen für deutsche Scheidekünstler von Lorenz von Crell. *Helmstedt.* 1801.

Beiblätter zu den **Ann**alen der **Physik.** *Leipzig.* 1877–1919. Merged in 1920 with **Physik**alische **Ber**ichte.

Beiträge zu den **chem**ischen Annalen von Lorenz **Crell.** *Leipzig* and *Dessau.* 1785–1799.

Beiträge zur **Chem**ie in **Ueberset**zung oder **vollständ**igen **Auszüg**en neuer **Chem**ischer **Abhandl**ungen, sammt einigen neuen Aufsätzen. *Vienna.* 1791.

Beiträge zur **chem**ischen **Physiol**ogie und **Path**ologie. Merged in 1908 with **Bio**chemische Zeitschrift.

Beiträge zur **physiol**ogischen und **pathol**ogischen **Chem**ie und **Mikro**skopie in ihrer **Anwen**dung auf die **prakt**ische **Med**icin. *Berlin.* 1843. Continued as **Archiv** für **physiol**ogische und **pathol**ogische **Chem**ie und **Mikro**skopie in ihrer **Anwen**dung auf die **prakt**ische **Med**icin.

Berichte der **deut**schen **chem**ischen **Gesellschaft** zu Berlin. *Berlin.* 1868–1877. Continued as **Ber**ichte der **deut**schen **chem**ischen **Gesellschaft.**

Berichte der **oesterr**eichischen **Gesellschaft** zur **Förderung** der **chem**ischen **Industrie.** *Prague.* ?–1896.

Berichte über die neuesten **Fortschritte** in der **chem**ischen und **physik**alischen **Techn**ik. *Carlsruhe.* 1865.

Berliner **klin**ische **Wochenschr**ift. Combined with **Therap**eutische **Halbmonats**hefte in 1922 to form **Klin**ische **Wochen**schrift.

Berlinisches **Jahrb**uch der **Pharmac**ie. *Berlin.* 1795. Continued as **Berlin**isches **Jahr**buch für die **Pharm**acie und für die damit **verbund**enen **Wissen**schaften.

Berlinisches **Jahr**buch für die **Pharmac**ie und für die damit **verbund**enen **Wissen**schaften. *Berlin.* 1796–1840. Continua-

tion of **Berlin**isches **Jahrb**uch der **Pharmac**ie.

Beyträge zur **Physk, Oecon**omie, **Chem**ie, **Techn**ologie, **Mineral**ogie und **Statistik,** besonders der russischen und angränzenden Länder. *Berlin.* 1786–1788.

Biblioteca di **farmacia, chimica, fisica, med**icina, **chirurgia, Terap**eutica, **storia natur**ale. *Milan.* 1834–1845. Continuation of **Giorn**ale di **farmacia, chimica** e **scienze accessorie.** Continued as **Ann**ali di **chimica applicata alla med**icina, cioè, alla **farmacia,** alla **tossic**ologia, **all'igiene,** alla **fisiol**ogia, alla **patol**ogia ed alla **terap**eutica.

Bibliothek der neuesten **physisch-chem**ischen, **metall**urgischen, **tech**nologischen und **pharmac**eutischen **Literatur.** *Berlin.* 1788–1795. Continued as **Ann**alen der **chem**ischen **Literatur.**

Biochemisches **Centra**lblatt. 1902–1909. Continued as **Zentra**lblatt für **Biochem**ie und **Biophysik.**

Boston Journal of **Chem**istry. *Boston.* 1866–1880. Continued as **Boston J**ournal of **Chem**istry and **Popular Science Review.**

Boston Journal of **Chem**istry and **Popular Science Rev**iew. *Boston.* 1881–1882. Continuation of **Boston J**ournal of **Chem**istry. Continued as **Popular Science News** and **Boston J**ournal of **Chem**istry.

Bulletin de l'**acad**émie des **sciences (Petro**grad). Name changed in 1917 to **Bulletin** de l'**acad**émie des **sciences** de **Russie.**

Bulletin de l'**associat**ion **belge** des **chim**istes. *Brussels.* 1886+.

Bulletin de l'**inst**itut provincial d'**hygiène** et de **bact**ériologie du **Hainaut** à **Mons.**

Bulletin de **pharmac**ie. 1809–1904. Continued as **Bulletin** de **pharmac**ie et des **sciences accessoires.**

Bulletin de **pharmac**ie et des **sciences accessoires.** *Paris.* 1814–1815. Continued as **Journal** de **pharmac**ie et des **sciences accessoires.**

Bulletin des **sciences mathém**atiques, **astron**omiques, **phys**iques et **chim**iques. *Paris.* 1824–1831.

Bulletin des **sciences phys**iques et **nat**urelles en **néerlande.** *Leyden, Rotterdam* and *Utrecht.* 1838–1840.

Bulletin du **lab**oratoire de **chim**ie du **Caire.** *Cairo.* 1882.

Bulletin of the **American Society** for **Testing Materials.** 1898–1902. Continued as **Proc**eedings of the **American Society** for **Testing Materials.**

366 DISCONTINUED PERIODICALS

Bulletin of the **Chemical Society** of **Washington.** *Washington, D. C.* 1886–1893+.

Časopis chemiků českých. *Prague.* 1869. Continued as **Časopis chemiků českých.** Spolu organ spolku cukrovárniků východnich Čech.

Časopis chemiků českých. Spolu organ spolku cukrovárniků východnich Čech. *Prague.* 1870–1874. Continuation of **Časopis chemiků českých.**

Časopis cukrovarnický. *Prague.* 1872–1874.

Časopis pro prumysl Chemický. *Prague.* 1891+.

Central-Anzeiger (**Augsburg**). *Augsburg.* 1891–1893. Continuation of **Centralblatt der gesammten chemischen Grossindustrie.** Continued as **Chemische Mittheilungen.**

Central-Anzeiger (**Leipzig**). *Leipzig.* 1884–1887. Continued as **Centralblatt der gesammten chemischen Grossindustrie.**

Centralblatt der gesammten chemischen Grossindustrie. *Augsburg.* 1888–1890. Continuation of **Central-Anzeiger (Leipzig).** Continued as **Central-Anzeiger (Augsburg).**

Centralblatt für Agricultur-chemie und nationellen Wirthschaftsbetrieb. *Leipzig.* 1872–1880. Continued as **Biedermann's Centralblatt.**

Centralblatt für Nahrungs- und Genussmittel Chemie, sowie **Hygiene.** *Görlitz.* 1895– .

Chemical Gazette, The, or Journal of Practical Chemistry in All Its Applications to Pharmacy, Arts and Manufactures. *London.* 1843–1859. Followed by **Chemical News, The.**

Chemical Journal. *St. Petersburg.* 1859–1860.

Chemical Review, The. *London.* 1871–1892.

Chemical Review and Journal for the **Spirit, Vinegar** and **Sugar Industry.** *Chicago.* 1881. Continued as **American Chemical Review** and Journal for the **Spirit, Vinegar** and **Sugar Industry.**

Chemical Trades Journal. *Manchester.* 1887–1890+.

Chemische Ackersmann, Der. *Leipzig.* 1855–1875.

Chemische Annalen für die Freunde der **Naturlehre.** *Helmstädt* and *Leipzig.* 1784–1803.

Chemische en physische oefeningen voor de **beminnaars** der **schei- en Natuurkunde.** *Amsterdam* and *Leyden.* 1788. Followed by **Nieuwe chemische en physische oefeningen.**

Chemische Mittheilungen. *Augsburg.* 1894– . Continuation of **Central-Anzeiger** (**Augsburg**).

Chemisches Archiv. *Leipzig.* 1783. Continued as **Neues chemisches Archiv.**

Chemisches Centralblatt. Name changed to **Chemisches Zentralblatt** in 1897.

Chemisches Journal für die **Freunde** der **Naturlehre, Arzneygelahrtheit, Haushaltungskunst** und **Manufakturen.** *Lemgo.* 1778–1781. Continued as **Entdeckungen in der Chemie, Die neuesten.**

Chemisch - pharmaceutisch Archief. *Schoonhoven.* 1840–1841.

Chemisch-pharmaceutisches Centralblatt. *Leipzig.* 1850–1855. Continuation of **Pharmaceutisches Centralblatt.** Continued as **Chemisches Centralblatt.**

Chemisch-technischen Mittheilungen der **neuesten Zeit,** die. *Berlin, Halle.* 1849–1886.

Chemisch-technischer Central-Anzeiger. *Leipzig.* 1883–1892+.

Chemisch-technisches Correspondenzblatt. *Vienna.* 1894.

Chemisch-technisches Repertorium. *Berlin.* 1863–1895.

Chemisch-technische Zeitung. *Leipzig.* 1883–1888.

Chemisk-techniske Fag- og **Handels-Tidende.** *Copenhagen.* 1881–1882.

Chemist, The. *London.* 1824–1825, 1840–1858.

Chemist (**The**) and **Meteorological** Journal. *Amherst, Mass.* 1826.

Chemists' Journal, The. *London.* 1880–1882.

Chicago Chemical Bulletin. Name changed in 1919 to The **Chemical Bulletin (Chicago).**

Chimica industriale, La. 1899–1902. Continued as **L'industria chimica.**

Chimiste, Le. *Brussels.* 1865–1914.

Comptes-rendus mensuels des **travaux chimiques** de l'**étranger** ainsi que les laboratoires de **Bordeaux** et de **Montpellier,** *Montpellier.* 1845–1851.

Correspondenzblatt des **Vereines analytischer Chemiker.** *Magdeburg.* 1878–1880.

Crell's Chemical Journal. (English edition of Chemische Annalen für die Freunde der Naturleihre.) *London.* 1791–1793.

Deutsche Chemiker-Zeitung. *Berlin.* 1886–1892+.

Druggist and **Chemist, The.** *Philadelphia.* 1878–1879.

Druggists' Circular and **Chemical Gazette.** *New York.* 1866–1892+. Continuation of **American Druggists' Circular** and **Chemical Gazette.**

DISCONTINUED PERIODICALS 367

Dublin Journal of Medical and Chemical
Science. *Dublin.* 1832–1845. Continued
as Dublin Quarterly Journal of Medical
Science [exclusively medical].

Edinburgh Journal of Science, The.
Edinburgh. 1824–1832.

Electrochemical Industry. 1902–1904. Continued as Electrochemical & Metallurgical Industry.

Electrochemical & Metallurgical Industry.
Continuation of Electrochemical Indus-
try. Continued as Metallurgical and
Chemical Engineering.

Électrochimie, L'. *Paris.* 1895+.

Elektrochemische Zeitschrift. *Berlin.*
1893–1922.

Engineering & Cement World. Name
changed to Engineering World.

Entdeckungen in der Chemie, Die
neuesten. *Leipzig.* 1781–1786. Continuation of Chemisches Journal für die
Freunde der Naturlehre, Arzneygelahrtheit, Haushaltungskunst und
Manufakturen.

Fach-Zeitschrift für die chemische Seite
der Textil-Industrie. *Vienna.* 1883.

Fortschritte auf dem Gebiete der technischen Chemie, Die. *Leipzig.* 1877.

Fortschritte auf dem Gebiete der theoretischen Chemie, Die. *Leipzig.* 1874.

Fortschritte der Chemie. *Cologne.* 1879–
1885.

Franklin Journal, The. *Philadelphia.*
1826–1828. Continued as Journal of the
Franklin Institute.

Gazzetta di farmacia e di chimica che da
prima publicavasi in Este. *Venice.* 1855–
1857.

Gazzetta eclettica di chemica, farmaceutica, medica, tecnologica e di
respettiva letteratura e commentario
della conversazione chimico-farmaceutica.
Verona. 1835–1839.

Gazzetta eclettica di chimica tecnologica.
Verona. 1833–1834. Combined with
Gazzetta eclettica di farmacia e chimica
medica and continued as Gazzetta
eclettica di chimica, farmaceutica,
medica, tecnologica e di respettiva
letteratura e commentario della conversazione chimico-farmaceutica.

Gazzetta eclettica di farmacia e chimica
medica. *Verona.* 1831–1834. Combined
with Gazzetta eclettica di chimico tecnologica and continued as Gazzetta eclettica
di chimica, farmaceutica, medica, tecnologica e di respettiva letteratura e
commentario della conversazione chimico-
farmaceutica.

Giornale di farmacia, chimica e materia
medica applicata anche alla veterinaria.
Ancona. 1861–1862.

Giornale di farmacia, chimica e scienze
accessorie. *Milan.* 1824–1834. Continued as Biblioteca di farmacia,
chimica, fisica, medicina, chirurgia,
terapeutica, storia naturale.

Giornale di fisica, chimica ed arti. *Milan.*
1839.

Giornale di fisica, chimica e storia naturale. *Pavia.* 1808–1817. Continued as
Giornale di fisica, chimica, storia
naturale, medicina ed arti.

Giornale di fisica, chimica, storia naturale,
medicina ed arti. *Pavia.* 1818–1827.
Continuation of Giornale di fisica, chimica e storia naturale.

Giornale fisico-chimica italiano. *Venice.*
1846–1848 [–1851(?)].

Glashütte und Keramik. *Dresden* and
Leipzig. 1871–1886.

Industria chimica, L'. 1903–1914. Continuation of La chimica industriale.
Continued as Industria chimica min-
eraria e metallurgica.

Iron & Steel Magazine. Merged in
1906 with Electrochemical and Metallurgical Industry.

Jahrbuch für mineralogie, Geognosie,
Geologie und Petrefaktenkunde. 1830–
1833? Continuation of Zeitschrift für
Mineralogie. Continued as Neues Jahrbuch für Mineralogie, Geognosie, Geologie und Petrefaktenkunde.

Jahresbericht über die Fortschritte der
Chemie und Mineralogie. *Tübingen.*
1842–1851. Continuation of Jahresbericht
über die Fortschritte der physischen
Wissenschaften.

Jahresbericht über die Fortschritte der
Chemie und verwandter Theile anderer
Wissenschaften. *Giessen* (from 1886
Braunschweig) 1858– . Continuation of
Jahresbericht über die Fortschritte
der reinen, pharmaceutischen und tech-
nischen Chemie, Physik, Mineralogie
und Geologie.

Jahresbericht über die Fortschritte der
physischen Wissenschaften. *Tübingen.*
1822–1841. Continued as Jahresbericht
über die Fortschritte der Chemie
und Mineralogie.

Jahresbericht über die Fortschritte der
reinen, pharmaceutischen und technischen Chemie, Physik, Mineralogie und
Geologie. *Giessen.* 1849–1857. Continued as Jahresbericht über die Fortschritte der Chemie und verwandter
Theile anderer Wissenschaften.

Jahres-Rundschau. *Leipzig.* 1804.

Journal de **chimie** et de **physique**. *Brussels.* 1801–1804.

Journal de **chimie médicale**, de **pharmacie**, de **toxicologie** et revue des nouvelles scientifiques nationales et étrangères. *Paris.* 1845–1876. Continuation of Journal de **chimie médicale**, de **pharmacie** et de **toxicologie**. Combined in 1876 with **Répertoire** de **pharmacie** and continued as **Répertoire** de **pharmacie** et Journal de chimie médicale réunis.

Journal de **chimie médicale**, de **pharmacie** et de **toxicologie**. *Paris.* 1825–1844. Continued as Journal de **chimie médicale**, de **pharmacie**, de **toxicologie** et revue des nouvelles scientifiques nationales et étrangères.

Journal de **chimie** pour servir de complement aux Annales de chimie et d'autres ouvrages périodiques français de cette science. *Brussels.* 1792–1804.

Journal de **pharmacie** et des **sciences accessoires**. *Paris.* 1815–1841. Continuation of **Bulletin** de **pharmacie** et des **sciences accessoires**. Continued as Journal de **pharmacie** et de **chimie**.

Journal de **physique**, de **chimie**, d'**histoire naturelle** et des **arts**. *Paris.* 1794–1822.

Journal de physique pure et appliquée. *Paris.* 1872–   . Continued as Journal de **physique**, théorique et appliquée.

Journal der **Physik**. *Halle* and *Leipzig.* 1790–1794. Continued as **Neues** Journal der **Physik**.

Journal für **chemie** und **Physik**. *Nuremberg.* 1811–1833. Continuation of Journal für die **Chemie**, **Physik** und **Mineralogie**.

Journal für die **Chemie**, **Physik** und **Mineralogie**. *Berlin.* 1806–1810. Continuation of **Neues allgemeines** Journal der **Chemie**. Continued as Journal für **Chemie** und **Physik**.

Journal für **Physik** und **physikalische Chemie** des **Auslandes**. *Berlin.* 1851.

Journal für **technische** und **ökonomische Chemie**. *Leipzig.* 1828–1833. Continued as Journal für **praktische Chemie**.

Journal of **Analytical** and **Applied Chemistry**, The. *Easton, Pa.* 1891–1893. Continuation of The Journal of **Analytical Chemistry**. Incorporated with Journal of the American Chemical Society in 1893.

Journal of **Analytical Chemistry**, The. *Easton, Pa.* 1887–1890. Continued as The Journal of **Analytical** and **Applied Chemistry**.

Journal of **Applied Chemistry**, The. *New York, Philadelphia* and *Boston.* 1866–1875.

Journal of **Medicinal Chemistry** and

Pharmacy (St. Petersburg). *St. Petersburg.* 1892–1894.

Journal of **Natural Philosophy**, **Chemistry** and the **Arts**, A. *London.* 1797–1813. Combined in 1814 with The **Philosophical Magazine**.

Kemiska Notiser. *Stockholm.* 1887–1888. Continued as **Svensk Kemisk Tidskrift**.

Kleine physikalisch-chemische Abhandlungen. *Leipzig.* 1785–1797.

Kritische Zeitschrift für Chemie, Physik, Mathematik und die **verwandten Wissenschaften** und **disciplinen**. *Erlangen.* 1859. Continuation of **Kritische Zeitschrift für Chemie, Physik** und **Mathematik**. Continued as **Zeitschrift für Chemie** und **Pharmacie**.

Kritische Zeitschrift für Chemie, Physik und **Mathematik**. *Erlangen.* 1858. Continued as **Kritische Zeitschrift für Chemie, Physik, Mathematik** und die **verwandten Wissenschaften** und **Disciplinen**.

Laboratorium, Das. *Weimar.* 1825–1840.

Laboratory (**Boston**), The. (A monthly journal of the progress of chemistry, pharmacy, medicine, recreative science and useful arts.) *Boston.* 1874–1876.

Laboratory (**London**), The. Apr. to Oct., 1867.

Laboratory Yearbook, The. *Providence.* 1883–1892.

Listy Chemieké. *Prague.* 1875–1891+.

Magazin für Apotheker, Chemisten und **Materialisten**. *Nuremberg.* 1785–1787. Continued as **Repertorium für Chemie, Pharmacie** und **Arzneimittelkunde**.

Magazin für die höhere Naturwissenschaft und **Chemie**. *Tübingen.* 1784–1787.

Manufacturing Chemist, The. *London.* 1892–1894.

Mechanic and **Chemist**. *London.* 1836–1842.

Mélanges physiques et **chimiques** tirés du Bulletin physico-mathématique de l'académie impériale de sciences de St. Petersbourg. *St. Petersburg.* 1854–1891+.

Memoirs and **Proceedings** of the **Chemical Society** (London). *London.* 1843–1847. Continuation of **Proceedings** of the **Chemical Society** of London. Continued as **Quarterly Journal** of the **Chemical Society** (London).

Memoirs of the **Columbian Chemical Society** of **Philadelphia**. *Philadelphia.* 1813.

Mémorial pratique de **chimie manufacturière**. *Paris.* 1824.

Mitteilungen aus den königlichen **technischen Versuchsanstalten** zu **Berlin**. Published under this title from 1883 to 1903.

In 1904 it was changed to **Mitteilungen aus dem königlichen Materialprüfungsamt zu Gross-Lichterfelde West.**
Mittheilungen aus dem chemischen Laboratorium der Universität Innsbruck. *Vienna.* 1867–1873.
Mittheilungen aus dem Gebiete der reinen und angewandten Chemie. *Vienna.* 1865–1866.
Moniteur scientifique, Le. (Journal des sciences pures et appliquées.) *Paris.* 1864–1870. Continuation of Le **Moniteur scientifique du chimiste et du manufacturier.** Continued as **Moniteur scientifique du Docteur Quesneville.**
Moniteur scientifique du chimiste et du manufacturier. *Paris.* 1857–1863. Continuation of **Revue scientifique et industrielle des faits les plus utiles et les plus curieux observés dans la médecine, l'hygiène, la physique, la chimie, la pharmacie, l'économie rurale et domestique, l'industrie nationale et étrangère.** Continued as **Moniteur scientifique, Le.** (Journal des sciences pures et appliquées.)
Monthly Magazine of Pharmacy, Chemistry, Medicine, etc., The. *London.* 1876–1880.
Neues allgemeines Journal der Chemie. *Leipzig.* 1803–1806. Continuation of **Allgemeines Journal der Chemie.** Continued as **Journal für die Chemie, Physik und Mineralogie.**
Neues chemisches Archiv. *Leipzig.* 1784–1791. Continuation of **Chemisches Archiv.** Followed by **Neuestes chemisches Archiv.**
Neues Jahrbuch für Mineralogie, Geognosie, Geologie und Petrefaktenkunde. *Heidelberg.* 1833–1862. Continuation of **Jahrbuch für Mineralogie, Geognosie, Geologie und Petrefaktenkunde.** Continued as **Neues Jahrbuch für Mineralogie, Geologie und Paläontologie.**
Neues Journal der Pharmacie für Aerzte, Apotheker und Chemiker. Merged in 1834 with **Annalen der Pharmacie.**
Neues Journal der Physik. *Halle* and *Leipzig.* 1795–1797. Continuation of **Journal der Physik.** Continued as **Annalen der Physik.**
Neuestes chemisches Archiv. *Weimar.* 1798. Continuation of **Neues chemisches Archiv.**
New York Analyst, The. *New York.* 1885. (Successor to an American reprint of the Analyst published in London; hence it was styled "New Series.") Continued as **American Analyst.**
Nieuwe chemische en physische Oefeningen. 1797. Continuation of **Chemische en physische Oefeningen voor de**

Beminnaars der Schei- en Natuurkunde.
Nieuwe Scheikundige Bibliotheek. *Amsterdam.* 1799–1802. Continuation of **Scheikundige Bibliotheek.**
Nouvelle répertoire de chimie, pharmacie, matière pharmaceutique et de chimie industrielle. *Louvain.* 1831. Continuation of **Répertoire de chimie, pharmacie, matière pharmaceutique et de chimie industrielle.**
Pharmaceutisches Centralblatt. *Leipzig.* 1830–1849. Continued as **Chemisch-pharmaceutisches Centralblatt.**
Pharmacist, The. *Chicago.* 1873–1878. Continuation of **The Pharmacist and Chemical Record.** Continued as The **Pharmacist and Chemist.** Changed back to The **Pharmacist** in 1885. Merged in The **Western Druggist** in 1886.
Pharmacist and Chemical Record, The. *Chicago.* 1868–1872. Continued as The **Pharmacist.**
Pharmacist and Chemist, The. *Chicago.* 1879–1884. Continuation of The **Pharmacist.** Continued as The **Pharmacist.**
Philosophical Journal. *London.* 1797–1814. Combined with **Philosophical Magazine** and continued as **Philosophical Magazine and Journal.**
Philosophical Magazine. *London.* 1798–1814. Combined with **Philosophical Journal** and continued as **Philosophical Magazine and Journal.**
Philosophical Magazine and Journal. *London.* 1814–1827. Continuation of **Philosophical Magazine and Philosophical Journal.** Continued as **Philosophical Magazine or Annals of Chemistry, Mathematics, Astronomy, Natural History and General Science.**
Philosophical Magazine and Journal of Science, The London and Edinburgh. *London.* 1832–1840. Continuation of The **Philosophical Magazine or Annals of Chemistry, Mathematics, Astronomy, Natural History and General Science.** Continued as The London, Edinburgh and Dublin **Philosophical Magazine and Journal of Science.**
Philosophical Magazine or Annals of Chemistry, Mathematics, Astronomy, Natural History and General Science. *London.* 1827–1832. Continuation of **Philosophical Magazine and Journal.** Continued as The London and Edinburgh **Philosophical Magazine and Journal of Science.**
Physikalisch-chemisches Magazin für Aerzte, Chemisten und Künstler. *Berlin.* 1780.
Physikalisch - chemisches Zentralblatt. *Leipzig.* 1903–1909. Continued as **Fort-**

370 DISCONTINUED PERIODICALS

schritte der **Chemie, Physik** und **physikalischen Chem**ie.

Popular Science News and **Boston** Journal of **Chem**istry. *Boston.* 1883–1892+. Continuation of **Boston** Journal of **Chem**istry and **Popular Science Review.**

Proceedings of the **Am**erican **Chemical Society.** *New York.* 1877. Continued in the **Journal** of the **American Chemical Society.**

Proceedings of the **Association** of **Official Agri**cultural **Chem**ists. *Washington.* 1884–1893.

Proceedings of the **Chemical Society** of London. *London.* 1841–1843. Continued as **Mem**oirs and **Proceedings** of the **Chem**ical **Society** of London.

Proceedings of the **First General** Meeting of the **Society** of **Chemical Ind**ustry. *London.* 1881. Continued as **Journal** of the **Society** of **Chemical Industry.**

Proceedings of the **Society** of **Public Analysts.** 1876–1877(?). Followed by The **Analyst.**

Quarterly **Journal** of the **Chemical Society (London).** *London.* 1847–1861. Continuation of **Mem**oirs and **Proceedings** of the **Chem**ical **Society** of London. Continued as **Journal** of the **Chem**ical **Society** (London).

Raccolta fisico-**chimica italiana.** *Venice.* 1846–1848. Followed by **annali** di **fisica,** dell'Abbate F. C. Žantedeschi.

Rapport ann**uel** sur les **progrès** de la **chim**ie, présenté à l'académie royale des sciences de Stockholm. *Paris.* 1845–1846. Continuation of **Rapport annuel** sur les **progrès** des **sci**ences **phys**iques et **chim**iques présenté à l'académie royale des sciences de Stockholm.

Rapport ann**uel** sur les **progrès** des **sciences phys**iques et **chim**iques présenté à l'académie royale des sciences de Stockholm. *Paris.* 1841–1844. Continued as **Rapport annuel** sur les **progrès** de la **chim**ie, présenté à l'académie royale des sciences de Stockholm.

Recherches physico- **chim**iques. *Amsterdam.* 1792–1794.

Recueil des **mém**oires les plus **intéressants** de **chim**ie et d'histoire naturelle contenus dans les actes de l'académie d'Upsal et dans ceux de l'académie royale des sciences de Stockholm. *Paris.* 1764.

Recueil des **travaux chim**iques des Pays-Bas et de la Belgique. 1897–1919. Continued as **Recueil** des **travaux chim**iques des Pays-Bas.

Répertoire de **chim**ie. *Paris.* 1839. Continuation of **Répert**oire de **chim**ie **Scientifique** et **ind**ustrielle.

Répertoire de **chim**ie, de **phys**ique, et d'**applic**ations aux **arts.** *Paris.* 1837. Continued as **Répert**oire de **chim**ie **sci**entifique et **ind**ustrielle.

Répertoire de **chim**ie, **pharmacie, mat**ière **pharm**aceutique et de **chim**ie **indus**trielle. *Louvain.* 1828–1830. Continued as **Nouvelle répert**oire de **chim**ie, **pharm**acie, **mat**ière **pharm**aceutique et de **chim**ie **ind**ustrielle.

Répertoire de **chim**ie **sci**entifique et **ind**ustrielle. *Paris.* 1837–1838. Continuation of **Répert**oire de **chim**ie, de **phys**ique et d'**applic**ations aux **arts.** Continued as **Répert**oire de **chim**ie.

Répertoire de **pharm**acie, de **chim**ie, de **phys**ique, d'**hyg**iène **pub**lique, de la **méd**ecine **lég**ale et de **thérap**eutique. *Brussels.* 1842.

Repertorio italiano di **chim**ica e di **farm**acia. *Florence.* 1865.

Repertorium der **analy**tischen **Chem**ie für **Handel, Gewerbe** und **öffentl**iche **Gesundheitspflege.** *Hannover* (later *Hamburg*). 1881–1887. Incorporated with **Zeitschrift** für die **chemische Ind**ustrie and continued as **Zeitschrift** für an**gewandte Chem**ie.

Repertorium der **Chem**ie und **Pharm**acie. *St. Petersburg.* 1837+.

Repertorium der **neuen Entdeck**ungen in der **org**anischen **Chem**ie. *Leipzig.* 1829–1833. Continuation of **Repert**orium der **organischen Chem**ie.

Repertorium der **neuen Entdeck**ungen in der **unor**ganischen **Chem**ie. *Leipzig.* 1826–1827.

Repertorium der **org**anische **Chem**ie **(Leipzig).** *Leipzig.* 1826–1828. Continued as **Repert**orium der **neuen Entdeck**ungen in der **org**anischen **Chem**ie.

Repertorium der **Pharm**acie. 1815–1876.

Repertorium für **Chem**ie, **Pharm**acie und **Arzneimittelk**unde. *Hildesheim.* 1790. (Second edition in 1796.) Continuation of **Mag**azin für **Apoth**eker, **Chem**isten und **Material**isten.

Repertorium für **org**anische **Chem**ie **(Zürich).** *Zurich.* 1841–1843.

Repertorium für **Pharm**acie und **prak**tische **Chem**ie in **Russ**land. *St. Petersburg.* 1842.

Reports of the **Roy**al **Coll**ege of **Chem**istry. *London.* 1849.

Review of **American Chemical Research.** Abstracts published in **Tech**nology **Quart**erly, 1895–1901, and in **Journal** of the **American Chemical Society,** 1897–1906.

Revista quimico-farmacéutica de **Madrid.** *Madrid.* 1851.

Revue de chimie analytique. *Paris.* 1893+.

Revue de physique et de chimie et de leurs applications industrielles. *Paris.* 1896+.

Revue des industries chimiques et agricoles. *Paris.* 1878–1891+.

Revue des industries et des sciences chimiques et agricoles. *Paris.* 1873–1882.

Revue hebdomadaire de chimie scientifique et industrielle. *Paris.* 1869–1875.

Revue scientifique et industrielle des faits les plus utiles et les plus curieux observés dans la médecine, l'hygiène, la physique, la chimie, la pharmacie, l'économie rurale et domestique, l'industrie nationale et étrangère. *Paris.* 1840–1852. Followed by Moniteur scientifique du chimiste et du manufacturier, Le.

Riforma chimica, La. *Naples.* 1897+.

Rivista di chimica, medica e farmaceutica, tossicologia, farmacologia e terapia. *Torino.* 1883–1885. Combined with Annali di chimica applicata alla medicina, cioè, alla farmacia, alla tossicologia, all'igiene, alla fisiologia, alla patologia ed alla terapeutica and continued as Annali di chimica medico-farmaceutica e di farmacologia.

Rundschau für die Interessen der Pharmacie, Chemie und der verwandten Fächer. *Leitmeritz.* 1875–1855. *Prague.* 1886–1892+.

Russisches Jahrbuch der Pharmacie. *Riga.* 1803–1808. Continued as Russisches Jahrbuch für die Chemie und Pharmacie.

Russisches Jahrbuch für die Chemie und Pharmacie. *Riga.* 1809–1810. Continuation of Russisches Jahrbuch der Pharmacie.

Savonnerie, La. *Zurich.* 1887–1892.

Scheikundige Bibliotheek. *Delft.* 1790–1798. Continued as Nieuwe Scheikundige Bibliotheek.

Scheikundige Bijdragen. *Amsterdam.* 1867.

School of Mines Quarterly.

Skandinaviens kemisk-tekniske Centralblad for Danmark, Sverige, Norge og Finland. *Copenhagen.* 1882–1891.

Sugar Beet, The. *Philadelphia.* 1880–1891+.

Sugar Cane, The *Manchester.* 1869–1890+.

Taschenbuch für die gesamte Mineralogie. 1807– . Continued as Zeitschrift für Mineralogie.

Technisch-chemisches Jahrbuch. *Berlin.* 1880–1891.

Technisches Centralblatt. *Halle.* 1884.

Technology Quarterly. *Boston.* 1887–1908.

Tekno-Kemisk Journal. *Stockholm.* 1847–1848.

Tidsskrift for anvendt Chemi, for Fabrikanter, Chemikere, Pharmaceuter og Handlende. *Copenhagen.* 1869–1870.

Tidsskrift for Physik og Chemi samt disse Videnskabers Anvendelse. *Copenhagen.* 1862–1870.

Tijdschrift voor schei- en artsenijhereidkunde. *Leyden.* 1844–1845.

Transactions of the Newcastle-upon-Tyne Chemical Society. *Newcastle.* 1868–1882.

Vermischte Abhandlungen der physisch-chemischen Warschauer Gesellschaft. *Warsaw* and *Dresden.* 1768.

Vierteljahresschrift der Chemie der Nahrungs- und Genussmittel. 1882–1886. Continued as Vierteljahresschrift über die Fortschritte auf dem Gebiete der Chemie der Nahrungs- und Genussmittel.

Vierteljahresschrift für technische Chemie. *Quedlinburg.* 1859–1869.

Vierteljahresschrift über die Fortschritte auf dem Gebiete der Chemie der Nahrungs- und Genussmittel, der Gebrauchsgegenstände, sowie der hierher gehörenden Industriezweige. *Berlin.* 1886–1897. Continued as Zeitschrift für Untersuchung der Nahrungs- und Genussmittel sowie der Gebrauchsgegenstände.

Western Druggist, The. *Chicago.* 1879–1892+.

Wissenschaftlich-praktische Forschungen auf dem Gebiete der Landwirtschaft. *Leipzig.* 1872–1876.

Zeitschrift für Chemie. *Göttingen.* 1865–1871. Continuation of Zeitschrift für Chemie und Pharmacie.

Zeitschrift für Chemie und Pharmacie. *Erlangen* (later *Heidelberg*). 1860–1864. Continuation of Kritische Zeitschrift für Chemie, Physik, Mathematik und die verwandten Wissenschaften und Disciplinen. Continued as Zeitschrift für Chemie.

Zeitschrift für das chemische Grossgewerbe. *Berlin.* 1876–1882.

Zeitschrift für die chemische Industrie. *Berlin.* 1887. Continued as Zeitschrift für angewandte Chemie.

Zeitschrift für Elektrochemie. Name changed in 1904 to Zeitschrift für Elektrochemie und angewandte physikalische Chemie.

Zeitschrift für Mineralogie. 1825–1830. Continuation of Taschenbuch für die gesamte Mineralogie. Continued as Jahrbuch für Mineralogie, Geognosie, Geologie und Petrefaktenkunde.

APPENDIX 7

DEALERS AND PUBLISHERS

|||||||||||||||||||||||||||||||||||||||||||||||||||||||||||||||||||||||||||||||||||||||||||||||||||||||||||||||||||||||||||||||||

I. DEALERS IN CHEMICAL BOOKS AND PERIODICALS

Many book stores in the United States keep some of the chemical books published in the United States in stock and they will order others for customers; but relatively few of these stores deal in foreign chemical and scientific books. The *American Book Trade Directory* (13th ed., 1955, New York, R. R. Bowker Co.) indicates the nature of each dealer's business; there is no grouping of chemical books, these being classified with technical ones; there is a separate listing for dealers in books in the various foreign languages.

Lists of dealers in scientific and technical books and in back files of scientific and technical periodicals are given in the book edited by Lucile Jackson, *Technical Libraries*, New York, Special Libraries Association, 1951. These lists include both foreign and domestic dealers.

Relatively few dealers in back files of periodicals specialize in scientific ones.

American libraries that have large scientific collections are usually happy to recommend dealers from whom they obtain books and periodicals.

Dealers in the United States

Brentano's, Inc., 586 Fifth Avenue, New York 19, N. Y., and 29 S. Wabash Ave., Chicago, Ill. General dealers in new books in all languages.

Canner, J. S., & Company, 909 Boylston Street, Boston, Mass. A large stock of back files of scientific periodicals. Do not sell books.

Falk, W. E., Co., 701 Main Street, Cincinnati, Ohio. Specializes in scientific books.

Feger, Franz C., 17 East 22nd Street, New York 10, N. Y. Specializes in books from all Spanish and Portuguese speaking countries.

Four Continent Book Corporation, 821 Broadway, New York 3, N. Y. Specializes in books and periodicals from the Soviet Union. Subscriptions to current Russian journals are handled and files of back issues are also sold.

Johnson, Walter J., Inc., 125 East 23rd Street, New York 10, N. Y. Specializes in scientific books and periodicals. This company imports books in many languages and deals in both new and second hand books. It has branches in foreign countries, handles subscriptions for foreign periodicals, and has a large stock of back files of periodicals.

372

PUBLISHERS OF CHEMICAL BOOKS 373

Kramer, Sidney, 1722 H Street, N.W., Washington, D. C. New scientific books, both foreign and domestic.

Maxwell, I. R., and Co., Inc., 122 East 55th Street, New York 22, N. Y. This is a branch of an English firm. The firm specializes in scientific books and periodicals in many languages. It deals in both new and second hand books, handles subscriptions to periodicals and has a large stock of back files of periodicals. The name of this firm was previously Lange, Maxwell and Springer.

Login, B., and Sons, Inc., 29 East 21st Street, New York 10, N. Y. A large stock of back issues of scientific journals.

Perkins, P. D. and Ione, P.O. Box 167, South Pasadena, Cal. Specialists in books from the Near East and the Orient.

Philadelphia Book Company, 22 North 9th Street, Philadelphia 7, Pa. Scientific and technical books are a specialty.

Stechert-Hafner, Inc., 31 East 10th Street, New York, N. Y. This company, which has branches in Europe, deals in scientific books in many languages and handles subscriptions for current scientific journals of various countries.

Schoenhofs Foreign Books, Inc., 1280 Mass. Ave., Cambridge 38, Mass. Deals in both books and back files of periodicals.

Technical Book Company, 407 Market Street, San Francisco 5, Cal.

Technical Books of America, 597 Fifth Avenue, New York 17, N. Y. Books from all American publishers.

Tuttle, Charles E., Co., 28 South Main Street, Rutland, Vt. Specializes in Japanese and Oriental books and periodicals.

Wilson, H. W., Co., 950 University Avenue, New York 52, N. Y. Back files of periodicals.

Foreign Dealers

Apollo Book Company, 42 Wellington Street, Hong Kong. Chinese publications.

Australian National Research Council, Science House, 157 Gloucester Street, Sydney, Australia. Books.

Blackwell, B. H., Ltd., 50–51 Broad Street, Oxford, England. New scientific books.

Carswell Co., Ltd., 145–149 Adelaide Street West, Toronto 1, Canada. Books.

Dawson, Wm., & Sons, Ltd., 102 Wigmore St., London W. 1, England. Files of scientific periodicals.

Heffer, W. and Sons, Ltd., 4 Petty Cury, Cambridge, England. Books and journals.

Horrassowitz, Otto, Friedrichstrasse 4, Wiesbaden, Germany. Books.

Librarie Hachette, 79 Boulevard St. Germain, Paris 6. Books.

Librarie Int'l Scientific & Technique, 87 Chansse de Tirlemont, Corbeek, Belgium. Books.

Hoepli, Ulrico, Corso G. Matteotii 12, Milan, Italy. Books.

Maxwell, I. R. & Co. Ltd., 4–5 Fitzroy Square, London W. 1, London, England. Branches in United States and Europe. See entry under United States for more information.

Maruzen Company, P.O. Box 605 Tokyo Central, Tokyo, Japan. Books and periodicals.

Munksgaard, Ejnar, Norregade 6, Copenhagen K, Denmark. Books.

Nijhoff, Martinus, 9 Lange Voorhout, The Hague, Holland. Books.

Presses Universitaires de France, Les, 108 Boul. St. Germain, Paris 6, France. Current French books.

Sotheran, Henry and Co. Ltd., 2–5 Sackville Street, London W. 1, England. New and old books, rare books, journal sets.

Stevens and Brown, Ltd., 77–79 Duke Street, London W. 1, England. Books.

Wepf and Company, Eisengasse 5, Basel, Switzerland. Books.

II. PUBLISHERS OF CHEMICAL BOOKS

Publishers of Russian books are not given in this list because it is very difficult to obtain books and catalogs from the state publishing houses of the Soviet Union. See the list of dealers for those that specialize in Russian publications.

For other scientific book publishers in the United States see Hawkins, R. D., *Scientific, Medical, and Technical Books Published in the United States of America,* supplements, New York, R. R. Bowker, 1946– . The publishers on the following list that publish many chemical books are marked with an asterisk, but each of the others publishes a considerable number.

*Academic Press, 125 East 23rd Street, New York 10, N. Y.

Addison-Wesley Press, Kendall Square Bldg., Cambridge 42, Mass.

Akademie Verlag, Schiffbauerdamm 19, Berlin N.W. 7.

*Akademische Verlagsgesellschaft. See Geest & Portig.

Allen, George & Unwin, Ltd., 40 Museum St., London W.C. 1.

American Chemical Society, 1155 Sixteenth St., N.W., Washington, D. C.

American Society for Testing Materials, 1916 Race St., Philadelphia, Pa.

Annual Reviews, Inc., Stanford, Cal.

Appleton-Century-Crofts, Inc., 35 West 32nd St., New York 1, N. Y.

*Arnold, Edward, & Co., 41 Maddox St., London, W. 1.

*Bailliere, J. B., et Fils, 19 Rue Hautefeuille, Paris, 6.

*Bailliere, Tindall & Cox, 7-8 Henrietta St., London W.C. 2.

*Barth, Johann Ambrosius, Solomonstrasse 18B, Leipzig C 1.

Bell, George, and Sons Ltd., 6 Portugal Street, London W.C. 2.

Benn, Ernest, Ltd., 154 Fleet St., London E.C. 4.

*Beranger, Ch., Libraire Polytechnique, 15 Rue des St. Pères, Paris 6.

Birkhauser Verlag, Elisabethstrasse 15, Basel.

Blackie & Son, Ltd., 16-18 William IV St., Charing Cross, London W.C. 2.

Blakiston Co., The, 1612 Walnut St., Philadelphia 5, Pa.

Butterworth Scientific Publications, Ltd., 4-6 Bell Yard, Temple Bar, London W.C. 2.

*Cambridge University Press, 200 Euston Road, London N.W. 11.

Carl, Hans, Verlag, Breite Grasse 58-60, Nuremberg-A.

*Chapman & Hall, Ltd., 37-39 Essex St., Strand, London W.C. 2.

Chemical Education Publications, Easton, Pa.

*Chemical Publishing Co., Inc., 212 Fifth Avenue, New York, N. Y.

Chemonomics Inc., 40 Madison Avenue, New York, N. Y.

*Churchill, J. & A., 104 Gloucester Place, London W. 1.

Clarendon Press. See the Oxford University Press.

Columbia University Press, 2960 Broadway, New York 27, N. Y.

Constable & Co., Ltd., 10 Orange St., London W.C. 2.

Cornell University Press, 124 Robert Place, Ithaca, N. Y.

Crosby, Lockwood & Sons, Ltd., 39 Thurloe St., London S.W. 7.

Crowell, Thomas Y., Co., 432 Fourth Avenue, New York 16, N. Y.

Dechma, Ulmenstrasse 10, Frankfurt/Main, Germany.

Deuticke, Franz, Verlag, Helferstorferstrasse 4, Vienna 1.

*Dieterich'sche Verlagsbuchhandlung, Martinstrasse 11, Wiesbaden, Germany.

*Doin, G. & Cie., 8 Place de l'Odéon, Paris 6.

Dossat, S. A., Editorial, Plaza Santa Ana 9, Apartado 47, Madrid.

*Dunod, 91 Rue Bonaparte, Paris 6.

Edwards, J. W., Ann Arbor, Michigan.

Einaudi, Giulio, Editore, Corso Umberto 5 bis, Turin, Italy.

*Elsevier Press, Inc., 2330 Holcombe Blvd., Houston 25, Texas. Spuistraat 118, Amsterdam C, The Netherlands.

*Enke, Ferdinand, Verlag, Hasembergsteige 3, Stuttgart-W.

Espasa Calpe, S.A., Rios Rosas 26, Madrid.

Fischer, Gustav, Verlagsbuchhandlung, Villengang 2, Jena.

Franckh'sche Verlagshandlung der Verlag Des Kosmas, Pfizerstrasse 5-7, Stuttgart-O.

*Gauthier-Villars, 55 Quai des Grands Augustins, Paris 6.

*Geest & Portig Akademische Verlagsgesellschaft, Sternwartenstrasse 8, Leipzig C. 1.

Ginn & Co., Statler Bldg., Park Square, Boston 17, Mass.

Giorgio, V., Libreria Tecnica Editrice, Via Accademia Albertina 23, Turin.

*Griffin, Charles, & Co., 42 Drury Lane, London W.C. 2.

Grune & Stratton, Inc., 381 Fourth Avenue, New York 16, N. Y.

*Gruyter, Walter de, and Co., Genthiner Strasse 13, Berlin W. 35.

Gurney and Jackson, 98 Great Russel St., London W.C. 1.

Hauser, Carl, Verlag, Leonhard-Eck-Strasse 7, Munich 27.

Harper & Brothers, 49 East 33rd Street, New York 16, N. Y.

Harvard University Press, Cambridge 38, Mass.

Heath, D. C., & Co., 285 Columbus Avenue, Boston 16, Mass.

Heffer, W., & Sons, Ltd., 4 Petty Cury, Cambridge, England.

*Hermann & Cie., 6 Rue de la Sorbonne, Paris 5.

*Hill, Leonard, 17 Stratford Place, London W. 1.

*Hirzel, S., Verlag, Claridenhof-Gotthardstrasse, Zurich.

H.M. Stationery Office, P.O. Box 569, London S.E. 1.

*Hoepli, Ulrico, Corso Matteotti 12, Milan.

Houghton Mifflin Co., 2 Park St., Boston 7, Mass.

Huthig, Alfred, Verlag, Haupstrasse 20, Heidelberg.

Institute of Paper Chemistry, Appleton, Wisconsin.

Institute of Petroleum, 26 Portland Place, London W. 1.

*Interscience Publishers, 250 Fifth Ave., New York 1, N. Y.

Karger, S., Holbeinstrasse 22, Basel.

*Knapp, Wilhelm, Verlag, Feldstrasse 30, Dusseldorf, Germany.

Lavagnolo, G., Editore, Coro Vittorio Emmanuele 123, Turin.

Lea & Febiger, 600 South Washington Square, Philadelphia, Pa.

Legrand, Amedée, 9 Boulevard St. Germain, Paris 6.

*Lippincott, J. B., Co., East Washington Square, Philadelphia 5, Pa.

*Longmans, Green & Co., 6–7 Clifford S., London W. 1. 55 Fifth Avenue, New York 3, N. Y.

*McGraw-Hill Book Co., Inc., 330 West 42nd St., New York 18, N. Y.

*Macmillan Company, 60 Fifth Avenue, New York 11, N. Y.

*Macmillan & Co., Ltd., 10 South Audley Street, London W. 1.

Malfasi, Rodolfo, Casa Editrice, Via Mantova 21, Milan.

Maloine, Librarie, 27 Rue de l'Ecole de Medicine, Paris 6.

*Masson et Cie., 120 Boulevard St. Germain, Paris 6.

Methuen & Co., Ltd., 36 Essex Street, London W.C. 2.

Mosby, C. V. Co., 3207 Washington Blvd., St. Louis 3, Mo.

Munksgaard, Ejnar, Norregade 6, Copenhagen K, Denmark.

*Oxford University Press, Amen House, Warwick Square, London E.C. 4. 114 Fifth Avenue, New York 11, N. Y.

Parey, Paul, Verlag, Linderstrasse 44–47, Berlin S.W. 68.

Patron, Riccardo, Via Zamboni 26, Bologna, Italy.

Prentice–Hall, Inc., 70 Fifth Ave., New York 11, N. Y.

Presses Universitaires de France, 108 Boulevard St. Germain, Paris 6.

Princeton University Press, 14 Prospect Ave., Princeton, N. J.

*Reinhold Publishing Corporation, 430 Park Avenue, New York 22, N. Y.

Ronald Press Co., 15 East 26th St., New York 10, N. Y.

*Saunders, W. B., Co., West Washington Square, Philadelphia 5, Pa.

Spon, E. & F. N., Ltd., 22 Henrietta St., London W.C. 2.

*Springer-Verlag, Berlin, Heidelberg, and Vienna. Agent: I. R. Maxwell & Co., Inc., 122 East 55th St., New York, N. Y.

*Steinkopff, Dietrich, Verlag, Holshofallee 35, Darmstadt, Germany.

Steinkopff, Theodor, Dresden and Leipzig. Combined with Dietrich Steinkopff, see above.

Technical Microcard Publishing Corp., 112 Liberty St., New York 6, N. Y.

Theime, Georg, Verlag, Diemershaldenstrasse 47, Stuttgart-O, Germany.

Thomas, C. C., 301–327 East Lawrence Ave., Springfield, Ill.

Towsley, Microcards, Inc., 41 East 42nd St., New York 17, N. Y.

United States Government Printing Office, Washington 25, D. C.

University Presses. (Those in the United States occasionally publish a book on chemistry; California, Chicago, Cornell, Columbia, Harvard, Princeton, Pennsylvania, and Wisconsin University presses are among the more active ones in this respect.)

Urban & Schwarzenberg, Branizer Platz 5, Vienna.

*Van Nostrand, D., Co., Inc., 120 Alexander Street, Princeton, N. J.

*Verlag Chemie G.m.b.H., Haupstrasse 127, Weinheim/Bergstrasse, Germany.

*Vieweg, F., & Sohn, Burgplatz 1, Braunschweig, Germany.

Wepf & Co., Verlag, Eisengasse 5, Basel, Switzerland.

*Wiley, John, & Sons, Inc., 440 Fourth Avenue, New York 16, N. Y.

*Williams & Wilkins Co., Mt. Royal & Gilford Aves., Baltimore 2, Md.

*Wissenschaftliche Verlagsgesellschaft m.b.H., Tubinger Strasse 53, Stuttgart-S, Germany.

INDEX

* The subjects indexed here apply to industrial chemistry as a whole.
† The subjects indexed here apply to chemistry as a whole.

Holland, abstract journal published in, 144
books published in, bibliography of, 59
journals published in, 78, 84, 87, 89, 92, 100, 105, 107, 110, 123
Hormones (*see also* Biological chemistry; Pharmaceutical chemistry)
abstracts on, 129, 135, 143, 144
journals on, 97, 98
reviews (annual) on, 208
House organs (*see* Trade publications)
Hungary, books published in, bibliography on, 59
journals published in, 84
patents and patent office publications of, 161, 163, 168
Hydrocarbons (*see* Gas; Organic chemistry; Tar; Petroleum)
Hygiene, industrial (*see also* Sanitation)
abstracts on, 129
book on, 44
journal on, 101

Indexes, alphabeting in, 235, 236, 247, 248
author, 232–240
errors in, 238
Japanese names in, 233
Russian names in, 232
Scandinavian names in, 235
use of, in searches, 231, 253, 312, 313
card, 271, 272
chapter on, 227
characteristics of good, 228–230, 248
collective, to journals, information on, 75, 156
completeness of, 229, 244–246
cross references in, 238, 248, 249
errors in, 229, 238, 244
formula, 255, 266–270
Hill system of arranging, 267, 268
Richter system of arranging, 16, 267, 268
use of, in searches, 231
independent (*see* Indexes, independent)

Indexes, introductions to, 230
kinds of, 228
on microfilm, 275
patent-number, 132, 135, 270
use of, in searches, 231
of patents, 169, 170, 171
punched-card, 272–274
chemical-biological, 272
of inorganic compounds, 274
limitations of, 272, 273, 316
of organic compounds, 274
of ring systems, 39, 270
subject, 240–266
of abstract journals as nomenclature guides, 262
accuracy in, 244
choice of heading to consult in, 249
classification in, 229
compounds in, 254–266
convenience in use of, 247
cross references in, 248, 249
in foreign languages, 264
fullness of, 244–246
of individual abstract journals, 275–279
limitations of, 240
nomenclature in relation to use of, 254–260
qualifications needed in users of, 241
resourcefulness in using, 249, 250, 253, 257, 260
scattering of entries in, 242
subjects (general vs. specific) in, 252, 257, 258
of titles, 244
use of words not in text in, 243
use of, 241, 249–254
of words, 241, 242
use of, in searches, 227–231, 241, 249–254, 312, 313
Indexes (independent), 279
information sources on, 3, 128, 129, 151
list of, 279–285
use of, in literature searches, 298
Indexing, bibliography on, 274, 275
exhaustiveness of, 227

Date Due